RAYNAUD'S & SCLERODERMA

A Journey of Discovery

Compiled and edited by
Anne H Mawdsley MBE

Published by
Raynaud's & Scleroderma Association

First published 2002

Further copies of this book can be obtained from:

Raynaud's & Scleroderma Association

112 Crewe Road, Alsager, Cheshire ST7 2JA

Telephone: 01270 872776

Email: webmaster@raynauds.demon.co.uk

Website: http://www.raynauds.demon.co.uk

Registered Charity No. 326306

© Copyright - Raynaud's & Scleroderma Association

ISBN 0 9538297 0 7

ACKNOWLEDGEMENTS

Thanks to all the contributors who have supplied information for Hot News over the twenty year period covered by this book. It has been impossible to include all the material and mention everyone involved with the Association and space has limited the number of events, photographs and personal stories which have been included. However, the contents should be of great interest to newly diagnosed patients as well as to those who have followed our progress since we began this journey in 1982.

The book takes you through each year of the Association and the progress which has been made in research. Funding for this has only been made possible by the generous donations from individuals, companies and charitable trusts, to whom we are indebted. Special thanks to the doctors, nurses, researchers and other health professionals who have helped to make a difference to the lives of people with Raynaud's and scleroderma. We have come a long way but there is still a great deal to achieve before the mystery behind Raynaud's and scleroderma is solved.

Contents

We're Getting There

Towards the Future

Research News 2002

This book is dedicated to everyone who has supported the Association over the past twenty years, many of whom are sadly no longer with us. I feel honoured to have known so many brave, caring people, who fought with tremendous courage, often against all the odds, but who never gave up hope. They were instrumental in getting our charity off the ground and became good friends. The memories we shared have enriched my life and given me the determination to carry on promoting and developing the work of the Raynaud's & Scleroderma Association.

Anne H. Mawdsley

Anne H Mawdsley MBE

Foreword

by Professor Carol Black CBE

I am delighted to write the forward for this book which covers the activities of the Association over the last 20 years. In some ways, the last 20 years appear to have gone in a flash for those involved in the care of patients with scleroderma but we all know that for the Association, it has been a time of hard work, persistence, growth, and achievements that are quite staggering. This growth in so many areas has at all times been driven by Anne Mawdsley, the Board of Trustees and many helpers throughout the U.K. As this publication demonstrates, they have been a tremendous force for good and constant encouragement for patients.

Twenty years ago there was no support for patients with these conditions. They were out in the "cold" and it was for this reason that Anne founded the Association. There was also little medical help. The Raynaud's & Scleroderma Association over the last 20 years has changed the face of these disorders. It has provided patients with individual and group support by phone, letters and visits, written and commissioned educational materials for patients and their families, and encouraged and helped to establish nurse-led clinics and helplines.

Finally, the Association has made a major contribution to medical research at both a scientific and a clinical level and some of the research they have supported has changed or is changing clinical practice. It is always easy to start something. The difficult thing is to sustain momentum, activity and enthusiasm and this, the Association has done in an unparalleled manner. The book and its contents provide a lively survey of the multiplicity of activities of the Association and formal testimony to 20 years of outstanding progress under Anne's directorship.

Carol Black

The Beginning

In July 1981 Anne Mawdsley, a Raynaud's sufferer for 7 years since 1975, listened to the BBC Radio 4 programme 'Medicine Now', in which doctors from a Raynaud's Research Unit at a London Hospital were being interviewed. She couldn't believe her ears as no doctor had been able to tell her if or where, research was being carried out in this country. She immediately contacted the hospital concerned and after a consultation involving several hours of tests, she was accepted as being suitable for treatment in the form of plasma exchange, a procedure which she had in December 1981. At this time Anne had not met anyone else with Raynaud's and following her treatment at King's College Hospital Medical School, she discovered that money was needed in order for the plasma exchange treatment and research into Raynaud's to continue. She was also informed that Mr Hamilton would not be replaced when he finished in April due to lack of money. She therefore felt motivated to try and raise money for research. Being a swimming teacher, Anne decided to organise a Sponsored Swim involving local school children which was a great success, raising £6,000 which donated to the Raynaud's Unit at King's College Hospital Medical School, at Dulwich Hospital. This enabled the Unit to re-open for research in May 1982, covering the expenses involved in plasma exchange procedures and complex immunological tests during the winter.

Anne with her two sons, Andrew aged 8 and Craig 9, preparing for the swim.

In 1982 she set out with two aims, to raise funds and to make contact with other sufferers. Following Anne's appearance on a television programme, 'Where There's Life' with Rob Buckman and Miriam Stoppard, she was contacted by hundreds of fellow sufferers and this proved to be the beginning of the communication, which led to the start of the Association.

In the first newsletter in June 1982, Anne wrote. "I felt that there was a need for an Association in order that Raynaud's sufferers could contact each other and discuss treatments which they had found to be helpful. In response to articles in the Press and on television, some people said they were anxious to help, while others welcomed any information. Many had been told by doctors that there was no cure and very little help was available. Raynaud's can be such a painful and distressing condition that one could easily become despondent but with support from others who share similar problems it may become easier to cope with".

June de Trafford (bottom left and Mr Alan Hamilton front centre) from the Raynaud's Unit, who took part in the swim supported by youngsters and The Mayor and Mayoress of Congleton.

Early in 1982 Anne was invited to London to hear a Hunterian Lecture given by Dr. Alan Hamilton, her consultant at Dulwich Hospital, in which he described the experience gained in managing over 250 patients in the Raynaud's Unit.

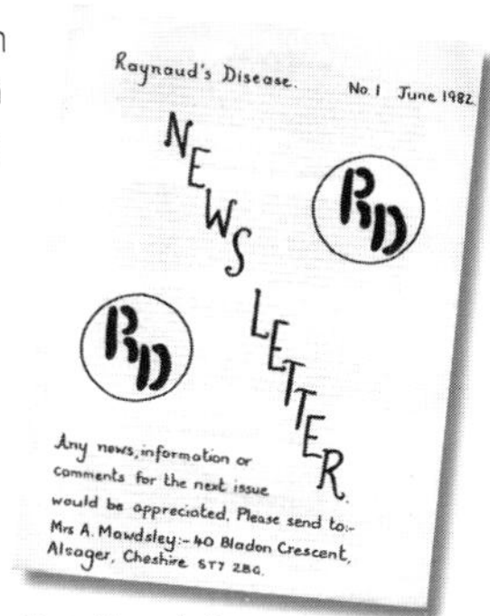
Raynaud's Disease. No. 1 June 1982.

NEWS LETTER

RD

RD

Any news, information or comments for the next issue would be appreciated. Please send to:- Mrs A. Mawdsley:- 40 Bladon Crescent, Alsager, Cheshire ST7 2BG.

First Newsletter

The following was taken from that lecture:

"Raynaud's phenomenon is a clinical condition in which cold causes a reduction in blood flow to the fingers with a characteristic numbness and, during an 'attack', the fingers feel clumsy with loss of normal function. In severe cases the blood flow is permanently reduced and may lead to finger ulceration and gangrene. In 1862 Dr. Maurice Raynaud postulated that an increased sympathetic drive produced arterial spasm and in 1929 Lewis suggested that the cause was a 'local fault' in the digital arteries. When Professor Jepson presented the last Hunterian Lecture on Raynaud's in 1951 the only treatment available was surgical sympathectomy. Since then many other modes of therapy have been suggested.

The physical property upon which flow is most dependent is its viscosity. In Raynaud's patients we have shown an elevated viscosity, a reduced red cell formability, enhanced platelet activity and evidence of an auto-immune disease. All these factors contribute to produce a local circulatory arrest by causing a mechanical blockage. We have also shown that using Doppler velocimeters we can record non-invasively these patencies at different thermal stresses and thus assess the severity of disease. In an attempt to improve blood flow, plasma exchange has been carried out on 68 patients. Following plasma exchange symptoms were relieved, ulcers healed, finger gangrene was prevented and there was an improvement in the digital artery patency. This was associated with a reduction in the viscosity, reduced platelet activity, an improvement in red cell deformability and a reduction in the humoral products of the immune response. In a few patients this auto immunity may have been reversed. Trials with two anti-platelet drugs, Ticlopidine and Prostacyclin, have not shown any lasting effect.

Our results would suggest that most patients with Raynaud's have altered blood rheology and that this is a major contributing factor in producing the cessation of blood flow that occurs during at 'attack'. Following plasma exchange there was an improvement in symptoms and digital artery patency, with more than two-thirds of patients obtaining relief of symptoms for more than a year. Plasma exchange clearly has a major role to play in the future and, if the altered environment could be maintained, the beneficial effects might be longer lasting".

Locally in Alsager, Anne's home town, many events were held to raise funds. These included a white elephant stall at a May Day market, a raffle, a disco, a musical production performed by the children in the primary school attended by Anne's children, a jumble sale and one child sold her gerbils to raise funds! A popmobility session was held, runners were sponsored in a marathon and one of Anne's sixth formers organised a sponsored train trip. Anne raised awareness by publicity on local radio, local and national newspapers and women's magazines as one of the main aims was to try and explain to people about the disease and how severe it can be. Unless people knew about the condition, it was difficult to ask for a donation.

Early members, Janet and Brian Roberts, from East Sussex, worked hard and with the help of friends, organised a sponsored slim, a coffee morning, a stall at a flower show and a variety show on two nights at their local Village Hall. As well as being a sell out and raising a lot of money, this event created much publicity with reporters from their local press attending and an article appearing in the paper. A Brownie Pack at Packmoor raised money with a Sponsored Matchbox Collection and one lady left books at her hairdresser's and asked for a small donation. Second hand book and toy sales were successful, especially near Christmas time, as were sales of plant cuttings and white elephant or bric à brac stalls. Several runners were sponsored in marathon events. Anne managed to get sponsorship for printed biros, balloons, badges and car stickers and a Christmas Draw was held. One of the very first donations of equipment to the Association was a filing cabinet from Twinlock Manufacturing Ltd. Within nine months, £13,000 had been raised for research, two newsletters had been published and the basis of a self help group was put into motion. Throughout the year the media still proved to be most interested in our cause with a mention in The Observer, attracting the notice of hundreds of fellow sufferers. Several newspapers and magazines gave our Association a mention as they obviously realised that there had been a lack of communication and there was a real need for this to be overcome. Yorkshire Television were amazed at the reaction to the 'Where There's Life' programme in April, and they made a short film of the work and aims of the Association, which was shown in October, again creating interest from fellow sufferers.

H.M.S.O.

An H.M.S.O. publication for the year September 1980 to September 1981, stated that there were 89,000 consultations for Raynaud's Disease in England and Wales and of those 70,000 patients were treated. So where were all these people?

Treatments

Interestingly, many of the early treatments are still in use today. In The Raynaud's Association Newsletter Issue 2, October 1982, the following were reported as having been tried or recommended:

Cervical Sympathectomy - Most people were disappointed with the results in that the effects wore off within a short time and several were left with side effects. A small minority, however, said that they had never looked back and would recommend the operation. In certain cases this operation prevented amputation of a finger although the effect on the general circulation did not last for long.

Lumbar Sympathectomy - This appeared to have had better results than the cervical one but was not successful in all cases.

Cervical and Lumbar Sympathectomies performed by injections of Ismelyn or Phenol - These have a similar effect to a surgical sympathectomy, but with only temporary relief. The general opinion was that they were useful for clearing up infections, but the effects tended to wear off more quickly.

Sympathetic Blocks - These are done by the injection of a drug into the hand with pressure on the upper arm, which is released after approximately fifteen minutes and the hand then flooded with blood.

Vasodilators - most patients had little or no relief from taking these, but some people found benefit from Opilon, Praxilene and Hexopal Forte.

Biofeedback Relaxation Techniques and Hypnosis - These may be beneficial but are very time consuming and need great concentration of body and mind. However, a small rise in temperature could be obtained by using these methods which are very relaxing, as is Yoga.

Plasma Exchange - This was one of the most successful treatments so far, with fifty five per cent of patients treated obtaining relief for more than a year.

Prostacyclin Drip - Two patients said they had obtained immediate relief from a 72 hour drip, whereas another two suffered side effects with no relief from their Raynaud's symptoms.

Connective Tissue Massage - This proved to be of help to some and others found acupuncture helped.

Vitamins - Several patients took Vitamin tablets, mainly E and C and one lady worked out a high dosage pattern of Vitamin B, E and C daily. She also took silica salts. Another lady recommended Pernivit tablets (Vitamins B and K), taking three a day from September to March, stepping up the dose in really cold weather.

A Hyperbaric Oxygen Tank - was used by one lady, breathing only pure oxygen. This helped to clear up an infection and others found certain antibiotics helped to heal ulcers.

Nicotine Acid Tablets were recommended, also one soluble Aspirin taken daily.

Efamol Evening Primrose tablets were also mentioned as being of help.

Intermittent Compression or Pneumotherapy proved to be effective in certain cases.

Cicatrin Powder (antibiotic) was effective in drying up ulcers.

An American physician, Dr. Donald McIntyre, tried a simple approach with two Raynaud's patients. He advised both patients to swing their affected arms briskly through an arc of 360 degrees. Both reported rapid benefit and one was able to reverse complete blanching of the fingers in about 90 seconds while the second needed to whirl the arm only six to eight times.

Tests were carried out using glyceryl trinitrate cream. A report stated that the rubbed-on trinitrate did have some systemic effects but a few patients experienced nitrate headache, hypotension and abnormal sensations in their untreated hand. However, only the treated hands improved, emphasising the ointment's local effect of improving blood supply.

Sad News

On 29th December 1982 we heard the sad news that Mr Alan Hamilton (pictured on page 2), Research Registrar and Anne's consultant during her plasma pheresis treatment at the Raynaud's Unit in Dulwich Hospital, had died suddenly. Mr Hamilton had encouraged the formation of the Association and will be remembered more as a friend than a doctor to his patients. His untimely death at the age of 38 was devastating for his wife Helen, and baby daughter Claire.

Early development of the Association

It was just a year since a self-help group was merely an idea and 1983 proved to be most successful in the development of The Raynaud's Association. Members appeared to be delighted that they were no longer alone and could communicate with fellow sufferers who understood their problems. Many were elderly, some housebound and others were not well enough to take an active part in the Association but it was important that they felt as much a part of our group as those who were able to put time and energy into fund raising and running the Association. Some members were already heavily committed to other charity work or had family involvements but other members requested that they would like to become actively involved. A few fellow sufferers volunteered to take responsibility for certain areas and this was a great help in spreading the work load and improving communications.

The first trustees meeting was held on the 8th February 1983 attended by Anne Mawdsley, Alan Golding and Robert Holmes. Alan Golding first contacted Anne after reading an article in the Observer, following which he wrote and offered his services as an accountant. Alan had both Raynaud's and scleroderma and was to remain a loyal Trustee until his retirement as Chairman in 2002. Membership of the Association was decided upon at £3 a year and postage was 12 1/2p. In 1983 it was decided to have a dedicated week, in which members could join in various activities and special efforts to raise funds and create awareness and so the first National Raynaud's Research Week, was held from 23rd-29th October 1983. We were proud to have the full support of a group of doctors who were prepared to act as medical and scientific advisers to the Association. They were - Dr. Jill Belch, Dr. Carol Black, Mr Leonard Cotton, Dr. Geoffrey Kempson and Mr Bruce Pardy.

The Duke of Westminster

Things were starting to happen and one of the most exciting developments was when the Duke of Westminster accepted our invitation to become a patron followed by Veronica, Lady Piercy, herself a Raynaud's sufferer, who also became a patron. In this same year, 1983, a Trust Deed was submitted to the Charity Commission, and we became registered charity number 326306. Membership reached 700 and was growing daily. Due to the tremendous amount of paperwork involved, it was felt that a computer system could save valuable time in the filing of information such as names and addresses, area lists and the printing of letters and several companies were approached with most generous results. We were on our way!

Veronica, Lady Piercy

How I became involved

Mr Kevin Lafferty

In the spring of 1982, I became involved with the problems of Raynaud's phenomenon. I had just been appointed as Research Registrar in the vascular laboratory at King's College Hospital, under the directorship of Mr. Leonard Cotton. My predecessor in the post was Mr. Alan Hamilton, who had just received a Hunterian Professorship from the Royal College of Surgeons for his research into the immunology of Raynaud's. Clearly he was going to be difficult to follow, so I asked for guidance from Mr. Cotton on what line of research I should adopt. "Just take a few weeks to familiarise yourself with what goes on and then we'll talk again," he said. So for a couple of weeks I peered over various shoulders, being introduced to the mysteries of rheology, computing, Dopplers, immunology, claudication and blood flow measurement, vessel imaging and thermal entrainment. The latter pair of shoulders belonged to a young lady called June De Trafford. June spoke like a machine gun and the verbal bullets contained incomprehensible terms such as normalised waveforms, Fourier transforms, entrainment factors and hertz. I nodded sagely and smiled sweetly, in the hope that she wouldn't realise I didn't understand a thing she was saying. After a time she paused to reload and I grabbed my chance. "What's it all for?" "Raynaud's of course", she said, "you see the blood flow variability in the acral regions shows abnormal patterns and . . ."

It was then that I resolved to steer well clear of Ms. De Trafford and Raynaud's phenomenon and find something easier and simpler with which to exercise my obviously inferior intellect. The next day I met Mr. Cotton in the hospital corridor as he was walking briskly in the opposite direction - I turned and tried to keep step. "How's the Raynaud's research going?" he inquired. "Oh, not bad', I heard myself say, "I had a long chat with June De Trafford yesterday". He stopped dead in his tracks. "That's good', he said, "come and see me at the end of the week and explain what she's doing". With that he turned and disappeared down the corridor leaving me standing. I was trapped and I'd talked myself into it!

That evening I met with June and she explained the fundamentals of thermal entrainment. Apparently, blood flow in the hands and feet (the acral regions) is very variable and simply measuring the flow from one moment to the next, even under resting and stable conditions, produces results which can differ by many hundreds of per cent. However, if one continually records the blood flow in one hand and simultaneously dips the opposite hand into hot and cold water at specific intervals, the blood flow in the measured hand gets locked on or entrained to the thermal stimulus. The pattern of this entrainment in patients with Raynaud's phenomenon is a reduction in blood flow when a cold stimulus is applied and an increase with a hot stimulus. Normal hands are more difficult to entrain in this manner and the blood flow hardly alters. Since the hand being measured is at rest and not directly challenged with a temperature stimulus, the patterns of blood flow measured must be the result of messages conducted via nerves between the stimulated hand and the measured hand. Assuming the nerves are normal, the interaction between the nerves and the hand blood vessels is different in normal people and those with Raynaud's phenomenon. Over the proceeding months I came to understand that June's previous gobbledygook was simply a mathematical way of measuring the degree of entrainment of blood flow. We constantly performed the thermal entrainment test on each other and on patients (to whom it became known as the hand dipping test), and I taught her what little physiology I knew whilst she taught me computing, physics, electronics, mathematics etc.

Whilst this one-sided flow of information was going on I met Anne Mawdsley who I understood was paying my wages via the Raynaud's Association. I was and remain extremely grateful to both Anne and the Trust for supporting my period of research but, as many of you will know, Anne is not the sort of person to give owt for nowt! Before long the Inaugural Conference of the Raynaud's Association was held at King's and she had me busy writing a Raynaud's book for patients.

To return to what thermal entrainment measures - June and I never did find out with certainty. Nevertheless, we had our ideas and theories involving the minute reactions between nerves, blood vessels and sex hormones which together could constitute a few thousand possibilities. But this is the nature of research and other workers with appropriate facilities have taken on our ideas and findings and continue to pursue them. A short review cannot cover the myriad research avenues opened and explored by the King's group; suffice to say that since 1982 the support of the Raynaud's & Scleroderma Association has helped to produce, directly and indirectly, a host of publications as well as PhD's, an MSc and my own MS thesis. Thank you.

Kevin Lafferty

On May 4th 1983 a cheque for £6,000 was presented to Mr Leonard Cotton - Dean of King's College Hospital Medical School - by Anne Mawdsley. This was the second £6,000 cheque to be handed over to the Raynaud's Research Unit and Mr Cotton expressed his sincere thanks to The Raynaud's Association.

Inaugural Conference

The Association's Inaugural Conference was held at King's College Hospital, London on Saturday 17th September 1983. Delegates travelled from all over the country to attend and several enjoyed a weekend break. It was attended by 200 members, their friends and relatives. One lady commented on how good it was to meet and talk with other fellow sufferers without having to hide her hands in embarrassment. Others said it was lovely to talk to people who suffered in a similar way and who understood the way they felt. Members found the Conference most helpful, informative and encouraging and pointed out that the number of people attending really underlined the fact that suffering from Raynaud's is more widespread that many of us thought. The reason for the meeting was to provide a means of direct communication between patients and the doctors and scientists researching into the disease. The speakers were chosen specifically to represent some of the many facets of current research and each was an expert in his or her own field. The conference consisted of presentations by leading researchers on Raynaud's Phenomenon. Speakers were Birgitta Arneklo-Nobin (Sweden), Dr. Jill Belch, Dr. Carol Black, Dr. Geoffrey Kempson, Mr Kevin Lafferty and Mr Bruce Pardy. This was the first time that these doctors with a special interest in Raynaud's had come together and as a result, a Raynaud's Study Group was formed. Mr Kevin Lafferty was asked to write a book on Raynaud's in layman's terms, based on the conference.

Research News

Research into Raynaud's phenomenon worldwide took off at a great pace. In particular a number of different drugs became available which may be of some use in the future. Such drugs included ketanserin, nifedipine and dazoxiben. One of the main drawbacks to research in the past has been a way of accurately measuring the severity of the problem in order to assess various treatments. Several centres had devised all sorts of ingenious ways of provoking an attack at the time of consultation but at King's College they developed a test which measured the degree of Raynaud's without the need to produce an attack. This test was called Thermal Entrainment and provided much information as to the basic defects in Raynaud's. It appeared that the controlling mechanism for hand blood flow is set incorrectly, causing the arteries to constrict at abnormally high temperatures. One way of 'fooling' the deranged control mechanism for hand blood flow is to keep the hands at an artificially high temperature. More and more interest developed in the microscopic vessels of the hands and some excellent work was done in Sweden, where the blood vessels were looked at directly under a microscope and the various effects of temperature noted. It seemed likely that in the future, research would be focussed in this direction in order to find the local blood flow control mechanism.

Much confusion reigned as to the correct terminology of Raynaud's. Names such as Raynaud's Disease, Raynaud's phenomenon and Raynaud's syndrome, all terms used to differentiate between Raynaud's which occurs spontaneously and Raynaud's occurring in association with other disorders such as scleroderma, SLE and rheumatoid arthritis. Doctors began to recognise the problem as a symptom rather than a disease entity in itself. In much the same way that a limp can be due to anything from an ingrown toenail to a fractured leg, so it seemed Raynaud's Phenomenon (the preferred term) could be produced by any number of conditions. Furthermore some people are naturally more sensitive to cold than others, just as some people have bandy legs or walk oddly, but neither have what could be described as a disease. One can now see where the confusion arose and why most people working in this field were content to call the condition Raynaud's Phenomenon, whilst at the same time checking for any underlying disease which may have caused it.

Dr. Carol Black seen here at the West Middlesex Hospital with the 'Little Sister' autoclave which was an essential piece of equipment in daily use in the laboratory, donated by the Association.

In the photograph, Dr. Mike Smith, (right), who recently became a patron of the Association, is seen with Anne Mawdsley and staff from Kings College Hospital Medical School, demonstrating the Laser Doppler Flowmeter, (a non-invasive technique used to measure blood flow in the skin of the fingers), donated by the Association.

£6,000 Raised at Sponsored Swim 1983

The second sponsored swim to be held at Alsager Leisure Centre, organised by Anne Mawdsley was held during Raynaud's Awareness Week. 450 swimmers of all ages entered this event completing distances ranging from one length to ten miles. The total distance completed was 530 miles which is the equivalent of 24 Channel crossings! Everyone must be congratulated on their tremendous effort, not only in swimming but also in collecting the enormous amount of sponsor money. Many thanks to all members who sent donations towards the swim which raised £6,000. BBC Radio Stoke covered the first morning of the swim live on their 'Here and Now' programme and we are most grateful to one of their engineers, Des Richards, who not only swam a mile but also managed to give several interviews while doing it! There was a 'phone-in' for sponsorship during his swim and we also acquired three new members from the broadcast. The appearance of First Division football players, Bruce Grobbelaar, Steve Coppell and Peter Fox boosted the sponsor money by over £400, and these celebrities taking part, helped to make the week even more successful. On 12th November a medal presentation was held for all who swam one mile or more with Alsager Round Table kindly donating medals to over 300 swimmers.

Stoke City Goalkeeper Peter Fox talks to helpers before his swim

In the photograph, Steve Coppell gets Bruce Grobbelaar off the mark.

RAYNAUD'S A Better Understanding

In 1984, the first book in layman's language entitled Raynaud's - A Better Understanding was written by Mr Kevin Lafferty for Raynaud's patients and also those involved with the care and welfare of sufferers of this painful and often misunderstood condition.

Poetry from members

These poems were sent in by members who wished to express their feelings on having Raynaud's:

Raynaud's

Don't like to be morbid
Hate to be sad,
But sometimes this Raynaud's
Really is bad.

But then just knowing
That you are out there,
Suffering likewise,
Knowing you care.

Boy what a lift
Does that give to me
'Cause I really believed
There only was ME!

E Hodges

Comfort

Getting your newsletters
Knowing you care
A great sense of humour
Then I'm halfway there.

Fellow sufferers
Nationwide
A smile on your face
What pain do you hide?

What funny stories
Do you have to tell?
I'm sure that you have some
That you can foretell.

It's not always easy
If we can just grin
With help well at hand
Us Raynaud's will win!

Thanks to the people
For forming this group
We owe them a lot
A wonderful troup!

E Hodges

A Christmas Wish

I sometimes wonder how great Christmas would be,
If my wife for a while of that disease she was free;
To see her for once not crying with pain,
For a very short time to live normal again,
And maybe for once walk alone in the snow,
Not worried to death of letting my arm go.
So with Christmas coming and time of good cheer,
Let's hope there's good news coming,
Not more months of fear.
So let's not wish for a New Year
Full of money and greed,
But for somebody, somewhere
To cure this disease.

You're not alone

It's not much fun when the weather is cold
Trying to keep warm if you're young or old
In layers of clothes we venture out
Full of hope and full of doubt.

Reality strikes, this weather's not kind
But we plod on relentless in body in mind
Our feet are numb our hands are blue
We wear thick socks and mittens too.

When other folk come up and say
Don't you think it's much milder today?
We have to nod and say 'Oh yes'
To explain what it feels like they could never guess.

To hang out the washing is really a chore
Fingers go numb and pegs fall to the floor
Peeling potatoes is a difficult task
And how does one manage to make pastry I ask?

When shopping for food at the 'Cash out' you stand
You can't hold the goods and you can't feel your hand
On opening your purse you fumble inside
Your fingers are clumsy and the coins start to slide.

But don't be downhearted and try not to moan
The main thing to know is that you're not alone
A sense of humour we must try to keep
And a tot of whisky to help us to sleep!

AHM

A touch of humour

Bridget Ferguson from Wilmslow wrote to tell us how for some years her two young children were under the illusion that their mother's condition was some dire disease contracted by driving her 'Renault' car. Renault's Disease - drivers beware!

Local meeting

On 29th June 1984, Carol Black gave a talk at North Staffs Medical Institute. This was a most enjoyable and informative meeting attended by 95 members. At the meeting Carol Black was presented with a cheque for £7,000 for a thermographic camera.

Dr. Carol Black receives a cheque for £7,000 from Anne Mawdsley

First Branch

The first branch, pictured above presenting a cheque to the Association, was formed in Stockport by Ann Barber, Janice Coborn, Joyce Harrison and Lindsey Bloor, followed later by a Scottish Branch run by Maureen Dorman.

Glasgow venue for Conference

The Annual Conference in 1984 was held at Glasgow Royal Infirmary, the registration fee was £5 with bed & breakfast just £10!

One letter we received following the conference and which we thought would interest our readers was from a London member, Connie Radway, who had a good sense of humour despite the problems she experienced.

Very many thanks for all the hard work you put in to make the Glasgow Conference such a success. I personally enjoyed it immensely. It was wonderful to meet Raynaud's friends, doctors, lecturers and everyone concerned - people who genuinely understood. It was sad saying goodbye to you all on Sunday morning, but as I had annual leave from work until Tuesday I thought it might be more interesting to learn a little about Glasgow than speeding back to my bedsitter flat in a noisy tower block in London. After you'd gone, I walked into town to meet a lady I had made friends with at the conference. Together we found a restaurant for lunch then caught a bus to the Burrell Collection. We spent a happy time together, kept warm as and when we could and both saw the funny side of part of the stained glass within the museum showing a 15th Century man warming his bare hands and feet over a wood fire and cooking pot. I wonder if he had Raynaud's?

On Monday after breakfast I left the warmth of my cosy room at Murray Hall and wended my way round Glasgow. Unfortunately, it was a local public holiday and all shops were closed. There weren't many people about and the weather was decidedly chilly. Just where, I wondered (as always) could I go to find warmth enough to de-pain my hands and feet? I turned into Central Station hoping to get a hot cup of tea to curl my fingers round. Even this failed because in the first place the buffet was cold and draughty, plus my hands by then were too 'dead' to hold a cup. I turned away and slowly walked down Union Street and noticed several people entering a building. Something was open! Whatever it was I was going in. It turned out to be a darkened fruit machine/bingo arcade. That didn't interest me in the slightest, but the warmth floating within did. What was more, at the back of the shadowy hall were clean looking toilets. Imagine my delight when I found not only hot water but also an Automatic Hand and Face Drier!! Revelling in the hot water, followed by the warm air hand drier, I found I could also shoot hot air into my face by moving the nozzle. Oh, it was sheer bliss - and I know only another true Raynaud's sufferer could understand what I mean. As usual, bliss was fleeting. Stepping back into Union Street and a few minutes walk to the station to catch the 1.10 pm train to London, which was crowded with passengers, was enough to enable the 'deadness', to take over again.

I arrived home at 7.30pm. and immediately lit the oven part of my cooker, soon to sit with my feet in the oven. At the same time I took my postcard of the 15th Century man from my handbag and couldn't resist a good laugh - so little has changed - that 15th century man warming his bare hands and feet over a wood fire and cooking pot, while 20th century Raynaud's sufferers do likewise in modern gas oven!!!

Back to work on Tuesday, I didn't look forward to it one bit. We moved offices to a new building last February. Many of my colleagues love the modernity but I dislike the open plan, fluctuating air-conditioned atmosphere. I find the stress factor predominates and I don't feel the same person any more. Most of my colleagues cannot understand my problem. Despite despondency within one's own environment, it's comforting to know there is an enthusiastic band of Raynaud's friends through the country.

Again I send my grateful thanks for giving so much of your valuable time to further our cause. It was a lovely meeting.

Connie Radway

Below is another amusing letter which we received from Connie.

Dear Anne

After showing one of my office colleagues some of our newsletters, I thought the following conversation might raise a smile.

HER: "I find your magazines very interesting, but I can't understand how you caught such an odd disease".

ME: "Oh, one doesn't catch it".

HER: (quizzically) "Well, how do the animals pass it on to humans?".

ME: (astounded) "Animals?".

HER: "Yes, 'cos it's not as if you live in the country and meet any foxes to pick up the virus they carry".

ME: "Foxes! Virus!".

HER: (in all seriousness) "Isn't that what foxes are called - Reynard's?"

Raynaud's Research Team - take heart - just catch that wily old Reynard the Fox!

International Contacts

In the summer of 1984, Anne and her family were on holiday, staying with friends in America, and took the opportunity to make contact with several groups such as ours. There were many scleroderma organisations but none at that time specifically for Raynaud's, even though it was becoming evident that over 90% of people with scleroderma also had Raynaud's. Their Branches were called Chapters and the first one which Anne contacted was in Phoenix, Arizona where the temperature was around 100 degrees. Not surprisingly, their activities were quiet between May and September but they still have problems with Raynaud's, especially with air conditioning. While there Anne also met a lady who had erythromelalgia, whose feet and lower legs were bright red and burning with pain.

Anne made contact with Diane Williams who in 1975 was responsible for setting up The United Scleroderma Foundation which has chapters throughout the USA. In New York she met with officials of the Scleroderma Research Foundation, a group primarily concerned with raising money for research and patient treatment and diagnosis. She also met with the President of the International Scleroderma Federation of which The Raynaud's Association had recently become a Charter Member. We discussed many aspects of the work being carried out by our respective groups and it was most encouraging and exciting to exchange ideas and keep in touch with news of research abroad. They were most interested in knowing who was interested in these conditions in the U.K. and Anne was delighted to put them in touch with experts, such as Dr. Carol Black, who later became one of their medical advisers. During 1984 we also began to have regular correspondence with Irene Case at The Australian Scleroderma Association of New South Wales.

Sponsored Bath Pull

£400 was raised by a sponsored bath pull. The bath on wheels, was loaned to us by Twyford's Bathrooms Ltd. and visited four South Cheshire towns commencing at Twyfords in Alsager. It was pulled by eight Twyford's employees and two workers from a local pottery.

Holiday Park Donation

In the photograph, comedian Don Maclean is seen handing over a cheque for £1,764.48 to Anne Mawdsley, which he accepted on behalf of the Association at Highfield Holiday Park in Clacton-on-Sea. On the left is member Pauline Harrick and in the centre, Shirley Burchfield who approached the holiday park at the start of the season.

Fund Raising in the Village of Bildeston

"Bildeston may only be a small village in Suffolk with a small population but when we organise a Raynaud's market the whole village turns out and it is well supported. The first morning market we arranged was in July, 1984. We thought if we held it outside we would attract more people, so I wrote to the Parish Council and we were given permission to hold it on the market square. We were hoping for a find day and it was hot and sunny. My husband printed some cards and we pushed them through every letter box in the village. The people were marvellous in giving and buying. People came from near and far and we were able to raise £307 for the Raynaud's Association. The same day the Bildeston Horticultural Show presented me with £24 from the sale of their produce. We had Webb Ivory catalogues and sold Christmas cards and gifts, the profit from the sale for Raynaud's. Then a friend said she would like to help, so she opened her home and we sold all sorts of things to raise money.

In June we organised another morning market. We had permission once again to have the market square but our summer being as it was, it decided to rain, so we had to change our plans and hire the village hall. We thought we would never raise as much money but we did. I wrote around to several Raynaud's sufferers in the nearby towns and villages and was delighted to meet some of these people at the Morning Market. It's good to keep in touch. We were able to send £368 to the Raynaud's Association. You really get a lot of fun out of organising such functions. Two friends had a car boot sale for us and raised over £50. Our next sale will be in November in a friend's home and we will sell anything we can get our hands on but mostly Christmas cards and paper, etc.

The most wonderful thing about all this is three years ago I could not sew or do anything like this to raise money. My arms and hands were so painful, my husband even had to dress and undress me, then my specialist at the hospital suggested that I went on to steroids and I became mobile once again. I still have off days, days when I can't do anything which increases when the weather is cold, but I am so grateful for the better days. It's good to be able to raise money for such a worthwhile cause".

Chris Buckledee

A Raynaud's Poem

If you suffer from Raynaud's it's not very nice
'Cos it makes your hands as cold as ice.
Your fingers go dark purple and blue
That's Raynaud's - have you got it too?

I wash my Mum's hair with the greatest of ease
She can't do it she's got Raynaud's disease.
Raynaud's can be bad and sometimes very sad
But when you've got electric gloves you'll be very glad.

In the spring when you read your Newsletter
This will occupy your mind and help you feel much better.
When you get desperate get yourself a whisky
But don't drink too much that might be risky!

Andrew Mawdsley
(Anne's 9 year old son)

Coffee time at Freda's

Mrs Freda Todd's home at Crifel Road, Parton was crowded to the door for a coffee evening she held in aid of Raynaud's Research. Proceeds topped £100 for Mrs Todd's contribution to the Raynaud's Association. Mrs Todd, second from left in the front, has had the phenomenon for six years.

My year for Raynaud's

Fund raising for Raynaud's can be very good fun,
I'll give an account of the things I have done
Last Christmas I raffled a cake and some sherry,
I thought to myself, "that will make someone merry".

I then did a talk to the Young Wives in town,
All about Raynaud's, and watched them all frown,
They didn't know much about this disease,
So I explained all in detail, and felt quite at ease.

Then came the marathon - Oh, what fun
To see all the runners start after the gun,
Looking for Bill who so kindly said
He'd not run for nothing, but for Raynaud's instead.

Then hubby and me went asking around,
If any kind person would give us a pound.
We walked and we walked and covered some miles
And got a nice cheque from the Whitehaven Lions.

Then came a surprise from grandchildren, all six,
They had up their sleeves a box full of tricks,
A garden sale was what they did plan
To help out our charity and please their dear gran.

A splendid effort it was indeed,
After rain and storm the sun took the lead.
Its Christmas again, my hubby did cry,
We've got to do something, we really must try.

There's going to be a mass charities fair,
It's down in the town, so we'll take our stall there.
We're knitting and sewing and baking as well.
We are working so hard to have plenty to sell.

And after it's over we'll sit down with pride
And count all the money, with delight we can't hide.
And when the year's over, just one thing you hear,
Best wishes to all and a Happy New Year!

Freda Todd

New Handbooks

During 1985 two handbooks were written by Anne Mawdsley, one on Raynaud's and the other on scleroderma. These proved to be very popular as very little patient literature was available at this time.

Sponsored Swim 1985

During the week of 18th-22nd February 1985 a mammoth Sponsored Swim involving 450 children and adults, took place at Alsager Leisure Centre in aid of Raynaud's Research. Over 280 swam a mile or more and were presented with medals by comedian Don Maclean at a medal ceremony on 2nd March, at which over 600 people attended. Sporting personalities who took part in the swim included Stoke City footballers, Mark Chamberlain, Peter Fox and Chris Hemmings.

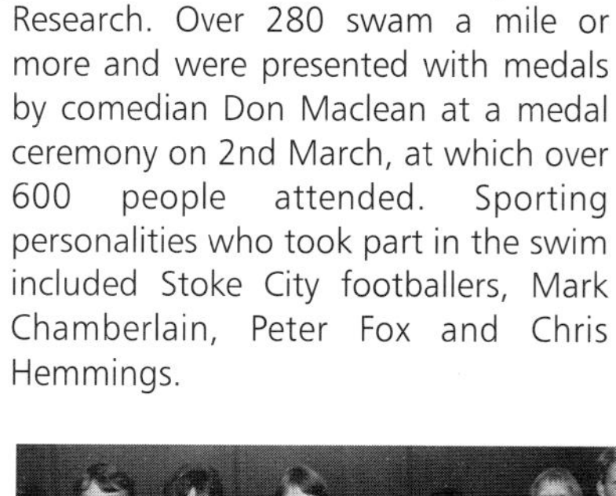

Stoke City Footballers Mark Chamberlain, Peter Fox and Chris Hemmings are seen here before taking to the water for Raynaud's Research.

Don Maclean with youngsters who received medals for swimming a mile or more during the sponsored swim.

Annual Conference 1985

The 3rd Annual Conference was held in Bristol at which experts in the field of Raynaud's presented up to date accounts of research in their specialist area. The conference was attended by 150 members, doctors, nurses and social workers. It was a most successful day and probably the most informative and interesting meeting we have held. Each speaker answered many questions put to them by the audience and this was one of the most important aspects of the conference.

British Telecom Supports Raynaud's

Fiona is 11 years old and until 15 months ago was a healthy, lively youngster. Tragically, Fiona became a victim not only of Raynaud's but also suffered from all three of the conditions which are associated with Raynaud's - rheumatoid arthritis, scleroderma and systemic lupus erythematosus. She wears electrically heated gloves to maintain warmth and try to arrest the ravages of arthritis on her tiny, bent fingers. At night she sleeps with her legs clamped in plastic splints and her hands bound to a plastic moulded hand to halt the twisting of her joints. The skin on her thin fingers where scleroderma has taken hold, is tight, tough and frequently becomes ulcerated. Fiona is a brave little girl and her parents have a sensible attitude towards their daughter's condition, encouraging Fiona to lead as normal a life as possible under the very difficult circumstances they face daily" (see update on page 83).

In the photograph, Fiona Sable, one of our younger members is seen with the High Wycombe half marathon runners from the British Telecom teams. When British Telecom staff heard about Fiona they decided to run in the High Wycombe half marathon to raise funds for Raynaud's research.

Woe is me

My name is Fiona
I'm so full of woe
For I get cold
Wherever I go

The summer's not bad
For which I am glad
Now winter is coming
I'm sure I'll be sad

Out come the heated gloves
Woolly scarf and hat
It's times like this I wish
I was a big furry cat!

Fiona Sable age 11

A sign of the times

Many, many years ago, in times beyond recall
My hands were delicately pink and never cold at all,
Knitting, sewing, crochet, were all tackled at a pace
And some of it when finished was as whispery as lace.

Then gradually the years rolled by, and now it must be said,
My hands are seldom warm but cold, and white and blue and red.
To darn or sew a button on, is just a dreaded task,
And I'm wired to the finger tips - "What for?', you may well ask.

"I'm a sufferer of Raynaud's', I explain in accents clear,
And with a look of puzzlement they say, "What is that, me dear?'
"The make up of my blood" I say, "is not the same as most
It doesn't go round fast enough to keep me warm as toast".

And when my time on earth is o'er I'll see the pearly gates
Where gentle friend St. Peter stands and patiently awaits.
I will explain how difficult t'would be to play the lyre
And know that he will understand and lead me to the fire!

Beryl Bradley

Vibration White Finger

Vibration White Finger was added to the schedule of prescribed Industrial Diseases on 1st April 1985 which meant that benefit would be payable to those in certain specified occupations who suffer from the severe form of Vibration White Finger. The earliest known case of a man being awarded compensation for VWF occurred in 1946. In cases settled in 1984 average sums in excess of £14,000 were awarded in the High Court.

Research Donations

Funds were distributed to Dr. Jill Belch at the Glasgow Royal, for a laser Doppler flowmeter, Dr. John Tooke from the Charing Cross Hospital and Westminster Medical School and Dr. Mike Martin from the St. James's Hospital, Leeds for support in setting up a television microscopy system to measure finger blood flow within the nutritive skin capillaries. A thermographic camera was donated to Dr. Carol Black and she was also awarded funding for a technical assistant for a year.

What's in a name?

We thought you may be interested in a few of the spellings of our condition which were on envelopes addressed to the Association. Why couldn't an Englishman have named the condition?!

Reynard's
Renauds
Rheynoes
Rayners
Rainoids
Raynolds
Rayndes
Raynons
Ranaurds
Renaults
Rhinos
Ranar's
Rainaults

Raenards
Rayno's
Raynews
Rainos
Renod
Reyno
Reynauds
Renous
Rhaines
Reynolds
Reynoulds
Reynauds
Reanauds

Rends
Raynors
Rainauds
Ranose
Rainors
Ramos
Renoes
Rainows
Raynoz
Ragnos
Raynards
Ranaults
Rynauds

Raynose
Rheynose
Reynose
Ranards
Rainards
Raynau
Renoides
Raymouldphen
Raynords
Raylaud's
Raynaruds
Raynauld's
Rhanoilds

Biography of Maurice Raynaud 1834-1881

MAURICE RAYNAUD, the son of a distinguished university professor and a nephew of the well-known surgeon Vernois, was born in 1834. He studied medicine in Paris and received his doctor's degree in 1862. He later became professor agrege, was made officer of the Legion of Honour in 1871 and was elected to the Academy of Medicine in 1879. His inaugural thesis 'Sur l'asphyxie locale et la gangrène symétrique des extrémités', which was published in 1862 described the striking local asphyxia and symmetrical gangrene since known as Raynaud's disease. Raynaud was greatly interested in the history of medicine and his work, 'Les Médicins au temps de Molière', is an interesting and charming account of the practices and customs of the profession that was the target of so many bitter shafts from the great French dramatist, Moliere. Raynaud's great ambition was to obtain the chair of medical history at Paris, but this was denied him because, as his friends maintained, of his devotion to the Catholic Church. He suffered for several years from organic heart disease and in 1881, after dining in apparently good health and playing with his children was suddenly seized with a heart attack and died three hours later. He was forty-seven years of age at the time of his death. Raynaud was a man of great integrity, of spotless character, and recognised for unusual intellectual attainments. He was at the same time a physician, a savant, a philosopher and a man of letters.

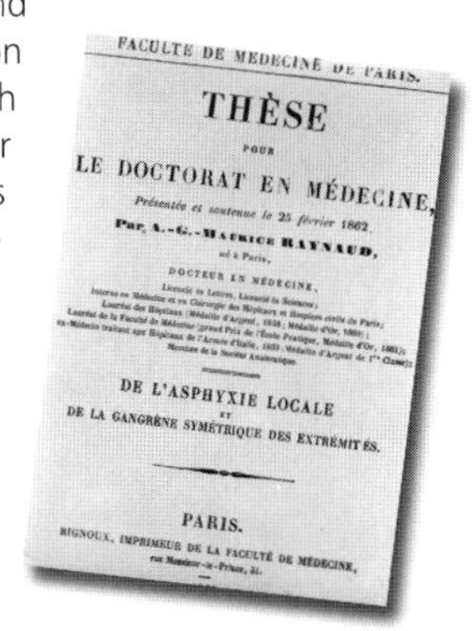

FACULTE DE MEDECINE DE PARIS.

THÈSE

POUR

LE DOCTORAT EN MÉDECINE,

Présentée et soutenue le 25 février 1862,

Par, A.-G.-MAURICE RAYNAUD,

né à Paris,

DOCTEUR EN MÉDECINE,

[illegible]

DE L'ASPHYXIE LOCALE

ET

DE LA GANGRÈNE SYMÉTRIQUE DES EXTRÉMITÉS.

PARIS.

RIGNOUX, IMPRIMEUR DE LA FACULTÉ DE MÉDECINE,

rue Monsieur-le-Prince, 31.

Awareness Week

During Raynaud's Awareness Week, there was a tremendous interest from the media. The BBC filmed for Northwest Tonight, at the home of member Janice Coborn, in Stockport, showing the difficulties of coping on a day to day basis with household tasks and Anne was invited to appear on the BBC Breakfast Time programme where she was interviewed by Selina Scott. She was joined on the programme by younger member Fiona Sable and as a result of this publicity, the Association received over 1,000 requests for information.

Questionnaire

Dulwich Hospital involved the Association in the first Raynaud's questionnaire. A total of 571 completed the questionnaires, 531 by women and 40 by men. The main benefit of this survey was to be able to give more positive answers to some of the questions concerning migraine, angina or the various related diseases. Sadly no definite pattern appeared to exist to explain why certain treatments benefit some people but not others.

Raynaud's Song

Member Mally Melia from Liverpool wrote and recorded a Raynaud's song which has over the years proved to be very popular and a source of amusement at meetings.

New Technology

Anne learns new technology from Howard Lawton from ICL who helped to set up our computer system.

A Day in Life of ......

7.15 am. and a familiar sound - something is being forced through the letter box - it bangs shut before being opened again and again. I lie there semi conscious until the 7.30 am news comes on the radio and I know I must get up and start another busy day. Craig, my 13 year old son, goes downstairs and calls up that there are hundreds of letters. This is followed a few minutes later by Andrew, my 12 year old, who has gathered up the brown and white mass which had carpeted the hall floor, calling "It's alright, Mum, there's only 95 today". I can feel the adrenaline rush through my body when I realise what is in store for me during the next hour.

"Mum, where are my socks? Is my football kit washed?" I throw on my tracksuit and head for the kitchen, prepare the necessary packed lunches, load the washing machine, feed the cat and make sure the family have all they need for the day. The mail by now has been placed in a precarious pile on the table and I have a very quick glance through. Today there are three from America, two from Australia and one from Spain. There are also six typed envelopes which have been franked rather than stamped, which may or may not contain good news of donations from companies. 8.35 am and my sons leave for school and my husband for work. I put on the kettle to heat up the tea which I didn't have time to pour and look sadly at the empty bread bin. Was that really the last piece of bread that went into the toaster only five minutes ago? I make a mental note to call into the village for a loaf on my way home at lunch time.

Breakfast things washed up, I get a letter opener and prepare to attack the mound of mail. As it is opened each letter is put into a pile. All enquiries with an s.a.e. are put together for an early reply; those without are put into a separate pile as these take much longer; letters containing cheques and membership forms are put aside for Anna to deal with before they come back to me; enquiries from hospitals, doctors and letters from companies are sorted and finally letters from existing members giving tips or accounts of fund-raising activities, or just general interesting letters, are put in another pile. This morning most are enquiries from Woman's Weekly, Breakfast Time and local newspapers from all over the country. Three toy companies and one health food company have offered to donate goods for our Christmas Fayre and one letter is from a company prepared to donate by way of advertising in our Christmas Newsletter.

9.15 am the door bell rings - a photographer has arrived from a local magazine to take a 'mug shot' as he called it, to accompany an article which a reporter had interviewed me for the previous evening. Click, click and it was done. Back to the letters for a final attempt to open the last couple of dozen. 9.30 am and running out of time. Dash upstairs to make the beds and get ready for work. Phone goes and a dear lady from Cornwall rings with a problem. Front door and Anna has arrived to help me with the mail. She stays to sort out and prepare cheques and monies for the bank and also tries to decipher my scrawled letters which require typing. She then makes a start on my filing system and opens any letters which I haven't had time to open. Ten minutes to get to work - I quickly put on my battery, plug in my wires, put on my electrically heated gloves (which I've had warming up for five minutes), throw on my anorak, jump in the car and off to work. From 10 am to 12 noon I teach four half-hour classes of children to swim. There are approximately 35 pupils in each class and today the teacher tells me to work them hard as they are very lively. For two hours my energies are directed into the satisfying and rewarding task of improving strokes and giving confidence to those who need it. Any pupils not taking part, have been given the job of taking stamps off envelopes for our collection!

12 noon - Dash to the shops for bread and a quick snack for Craig's lunch. We arrive home at the same time. There is a black bin liner under the carport. A quick glance tells me it is jumble for our sale. I take it indoors and see the cat sitting patiently waiting to be let out of the back door. On opening the door into the porch I see that the second post has been delivered through the cat flap. Poor postman must have

decided he couldn't face the letter box. As I bring it in, I notice the washing is still in the machine waiting to be emptied. A flick of the switch and the emptying process begins. While this is happening I go upstairs to check for messages on the answering machine. There are three calls - one is an enquiry leaving an address, one from Bristol CVS and one from a local lady asking me to collect jumble. Dash downstairs to put the washing out in the hope that it may dry. The wind is cold so only manage to get half of it on the line dropping at least 6 pegs in my attempt before coming in for a warm. The phone starts ringing - an enquiry from London. Craig has the local Radio station blaring out pop music, he finishes his lunch, hurriedly puts the finishing touches to some homework and shouts 'goodbye". Is it really 12.45 pm? The rest of the washing is put on the line and I realise I haven't had any lunch. Thank heaven for instant soup and sliced bread. Switch the answering machine on and off to work. From 1 pm until 3.45 pm I have another five classes. I have to remember to ask each group for second-hand toys for our Toy Fayre. All the schools are very supportive and I would imagine almost every child in Alsager knows something about Raynaud's, even if it's only that their swimming teacher has blue hands every morning and she's always asking for something!

Lessons over - I need some articles photocopied so a quick dash over to reprographics in school and the copies are done. Collect jumble from a house on the way home. Why is it that there are always road works when you want to get somewhere in a hurry? Arrive home and the phone is ringing. By the time I have managed to get the key in the door the answering machine has swung into action - I'm too late but no doubt if it's important the caller will ring back later. Into the kitchen and put the kettle on to make a cup of tea ready for Craig who is due any minute. The phone goes again - a lady asks if I am anything to do with Raynaud's Disease! She sounds most relieved when I say I am, as she has had difficulty in finding the number. I decide to ring Telecom straight away and ask for Raynaud's to be entered into the next telephone directory in addition to my own name. This sounds a simple procedure but when I spell it out I am told it is a business and can't be entered. I protest and explain that we are a charity. The lady will ring back when she has sorted it out. Take off my gloves and coat and make a pot of tea. Craig has arrived home and I ask how his day was. I Pour the tea and take mine upstairs to my office (a curtained off section at the end of the landing). The red button is flashing three times on the answer phone, indicating three messages. The first caller has decided not to speak to the machine; the second one is a lady calling from Bucks. and she leaves a number to call; the third is another enquiry leaving an address for information to be sent. I deal with this straight away and make a note to ring the number in Bucks after 6 pm.

Second post is still sitting on my desk - 38 unopened letters. This is my next task and I start the opening process. If letters are not dealt with and replied to within a couple of days, I get a feeling of panic that I am behind. Manage to do about 25 'standard' replies and then start on the ones requiring a personal reply. So many of these are from people who feel lonely, afraid or have a problem and require some help or information to put their mind at rest. The phone goes - would I like a three piece suite for the jumble auction? I thank the caller but decline her offer owing to the fact that she needed it transporting. She says she will ring the council to collect it. I suddenly realise that I have some important phone calls to make - three to our local free papers requesting publicity for our Christmas Fayre and asking for contributions of cakes, bring and buy items, etc. The first number is engaged so I try the other two and then get back to the first one. This done, I need to place advert in the evening paper for Friday night's jumble auction - then a call to Radio Stoke who are always most helpful in advertising events. They promise to broadcast both the events at the appropriate times.

5.15 pm and our evening meal is not yet prepared - or even thought of! I fly down to the kitchen and put some potatoes on to cook and then think what we can eat with them. Stick some frozen peas into a pan and look in the food cupboard. The phone rings - Janice, a friend and member from Stockport is calling to check on one or two things for the sponsored pub crawl she has organised for the following weekend. We get chatting and I become aware of a burning smell from the kitchen. I explain in a couple of words that I have a problem and charge downstairs, only to find that I hadn't put enough water in the peas - the third burnt pan in a month! Potatoes are cooking well and I reach for a tin of M & S Chunky Chicken from the cupboard, open it and put the contents in a saucepan. I rescue the peas which were not touching the bottom of the pan and sling the rest in the bin.

5.35 pm and time to go and collect Andrew from table tennis club at school. Craig is instructed to keep an eye on the potatoes and lay the table. Drop a carrier bag full of letters into the mail box, collect Andrew and home again within five minutes. Craig has dealt with two phone calls, one from either a Scottish or Irish lady who will ring back and the other from Father Christmas checking on which day he is due to be at the Christmas Fayre. Into the kitchen to sort out the meal - close the curtains only to see shapes against the sky. The washing is still out: Andrew is called and instructed on how to make an Angel Delight while I dash out and collect the cold, damp washing from the line. 5.50 pm my husband comes home and we're ready to sit down and eat our meal. You really couldn't tell about the peas - the only clue being the odd brown coloured one and the smell of the air freshener! I make a mental promise to prepare a proper meal the next night. As we start to eat the phone rings - a lady requesting some sponsored slim forms. As I put the receiver down it rings again, this time it is a gentleman from West Sussex wanting some information on Vibration White Finger. I help with the washing up and then go back up to the landing to continue with the mail and sign some letters which Anna has left for me. She has also left some membership forms from new members which need feeding into the computer. The computer system is on the landing - it's a good job that the family are fairly slim as they have to squeeze past it to get to their bedrooms! I remember to return the call to the lady from Bucks. 6.30 pm and my treat of the day - a nice, hot bath, after which I can put on my old jogging suit for the evening. I half fill the bath with tepid water and then get in, always amazed by how my fingers and toes turn white on entering the water. As soon as they become a normal colour (what's normal?), I add more hot water until my whole body is glowing. A beautiful feeling to be warm all over. The phone rings and I can hear my husband coming up the stairs with my portable handset (donated of course!). It's my dear Mum ringing to check on the price of some items she has made for the Christmas Fayre. I'm relieved that it's not a call requiring pen and paper as it's difficult, though not impossible, in the bath. She enquired about the distant sound of lapping water.

I decide to leave the phone off the hook for a precious few minutes and enjoy the warmth and peace of the bathroom.

7 pm and Lynda arrives. She drives over from Wistaston at least twice a week to help with various things. She collects stock for sending out to members and tonight has brought posters for the Christmas Fayre, together with some cartoons which she has done for the Christmas Newsletter. We laugh and joke about some of the possibilities and she threatens to write an article accompanied by a cartoon of me, which she says she will get to the printers one day without my knowing. She thinks you should all know what it's really like working with me! We look at the new banner which she and her mother have just finished making. It looks good in a very rich red with white lettering. Time to go into the loft where we keep all the stock. I get the ladder down and Lynda disappears into the darkness to put on the light. The phone rings - another person wants information. Everyone has a tale to tell and I find it is good to relate to people who are so delighted to know that someone understands and believes them. While Lynda is sorting out pens, pencils, etc. in the loft, I make a start on the computer. My aim tonight is to try and enter all new members and print out some area lists for existing members. Unfortunately, the programme takes so long on the BBC computer, that much time is wasted in waiting for each county to load before I can type in the names and addresses. Lynda finishes sorting the stock and comes down frozen! She then starts on the Father Christmas gifts and we decide we need another 90. Her next task is putting together some packs of information ready for the next batch of mail. After two hours my fingers are sore and my eyes aching from working on the computer. We decide to have a drink. I say goodnight to the boys who by now have disappeared into their rooms. Lynda and I then draw a plan of the hall at the Civic Centre, deciding on which stalls will go where. We then have a discussion on the Christmas Newsletter which is filling me with horror at the very thought of it. Why did I ever think we could do a special edition? It's now 11 pm and Lynda leaves for home laden with all the things she has to do before her next visit. I turn on my electric blanket and return to my desk determined to get all the letters up to date. By 11.45 pm I can do no more and retire to bed. I take with me two papers which I want to read, one is a newsletter from the Australian Scleroderma Society and the other an article on 'Calcium Channel Blockers and Raynaud's Phenomenon'.

My bed is beautifully warm with my blanket and hot water bottle. It's now midnight and I slide under the covers. Why are the days so short when there is so much to be done? My husband has forbidden the use of my hand-held dictaphone in bed, so I let my mind and body give way to a deep sleep, aroused only by the subconscious thoughts which keep passing through my head - thoughts like, "Have I done this?" "Have I remembered that?" and then the dreaded, "I've just had an idea", which always frightens my friends.

7.15 am - it's that letter box again...

The above article written by Anne appeared in Issue No.14 Christmas 1985.

Anne Mawdsley

Members of the Association, their friends and relatives were invited to a meeting at Crewe Hall where Dr. Jill Belch from Glasgow Royal Infirmary, gave a most interesting talk on current treatments and research. Following the meeting, members were given a tour of the building which is the property of the Duchy of Lancaster and as such belongs to the Crown. Since 1399 the title of Duke of Lancaster has been held by the Sovereign.

Members and guests have a guided tour of Crewe Hall.

Research Donations

Recipients included Dr. Jill Belch, Dr. Alan Silman, Dr. Peter Maddison, Dr. Kathryn Darton, Dr. Carol Black, Dr. John Tooke, Mr. Peter Vowden and Dr. David Wilkinson.

Barbara Fletcher with her stall.

Support from the Dalstonians

Barbara Fletcher wrote to tell us about the support which she received locally:

My village of Dalston is situated 5 miles from the centre of Carlisle in Cumbria on the fringe of the Lake District and 15 miles from the Scottish border. By now all the inhabitants must know that I am a Raynaud's sufferer and fund raiser for our research, from the various newspaper articles and Radio Chat Show to advertise our need to support a research programme; also from my stall which appears annually at the Dalston Agricultural Show which attracts over 10,000 people.

After the rush of the Christmas Charity Card and Gift Fairs, for which I make my own cards, I wrote to Anne to say, "thank goodness the pressure is off, I can now relax" and hardly had the words been written when a chance remark I made at a small local Whist Drive prompted one of the ladies to say, "Why don't you have a Coffee Morning in the Village Hall?". Not having a committee to discuss the proposition with, the ladies said, "We'll help, we'll bake, you fix the date, advertise in the Parish Magazine, put up some notices in the village shops, ring up Radio Carlisle, write to the Cumberland

Newspaper, write out some cards and pop them through the letter boxes, get some prizes for a raffle, and we'll do the rest!". I took a deep breath and started to prepare. Most of this was achieved in a day, apart from the raffle prizes and notes for the local letter boxes. Two weeks to go and by the time the day arrived, we had loads of donations for the raffle and in addition, the milk, tea, coffee, biscuits and sugar had all been donated. I was completely overwhelmed.

The morning arrived and when I looked out of the window to see our first snow of the winter, my heart sank into my furry slippers. I thought nobody would turn out on a day like this but then it was Pension Day at the Post Office, so maybe they would. "Pull up your socks, put on your boots', I said to myself, "and pull your woolly hat over your ears, plug in your gloves, put on a smiling face and get out in the snow". How broad was my smile when my helpers were already there to help unload my car and set up. The cake stall was bending in the middle with the weight of all the goodies being placed upon it. The gift stall was only half large enough to hold all the gifts and we had to rescue another table. The ladies had taken over the kitchen and were well organised by the time the first customers arrived. In no time at all, the hall became a hive of activity and alive with the buzz of conversation. What a happy morning it turned out to be. One quickly forgot the cold and the snow outside with the warmth and generosity from inside. One couple had ventured from a village 12 miles away to hand me a cheque for £20 and Ruth, a fellow sufferer telephoned to apologise because she could not get through the snow. "There is a cheque in the post for you', she said.

We raised £260, it had been a very successful social occasion and a few more folk knew something about Raynaud's. However, it didn't end there, the next post brought a cheque for £10 from Ruth, a few old stamps were exchanged for £5, so now I had £275 for our fund. Imagine my surprise and delight when the following post brought a letter from a Carlisle fabric printing firm, informing me they had decided to send a cheque for £50 direct to Anne Mawdsley. It is all so easy - one thing leads to another and I had a good start in 1986. Perhaps I can have my rest now!

The next date is a Flea Market on Easter Saturday and I shall be there with my stall. Easter Saturday blew in with rain yet again. The Flea Market as originally organised was cancelled due to lack of support from local charities, but it was decided to hold a smaller version in the Old Town Hall which had limited accommodation. I trundled off to town with my wares but there was not a single soul about in the town or the Town Hall. I must have the wrong day, the shops were all shut. I waited an hour and someone came. "Is it today?". "Yes, 11 o'clock". I'm sure I was told to be here for 9 o'clock. I could have had another hour in bed and it didn't look like being a busy day. A helper was writing a large notice advertising our stalls - coffee, tempting sandwiches and hot soup. Just the menu for this Easter Monday but where was she going to put it? The Railway Station, because three special trains were arriving in Carlisle at mid-day. Where could they all go to when all the shops and cafes were locked up for the day? To the Town Hall, of course, where they had a warm welcome and a profitable day was had by all.

On 26th April,it was the turn of my Charity to have a spot in the covered market especially to sell my raffle tickets. The wind howled around my fur-lined boots and did nothing to ward off my Raynaud's spasms. My helper came along for the morning session and all went well until 2 pm and by this time my parking clock was overdue, my circulation only working at half-cock and the loo was too far away to leave my stand unattended. I packed up and went home, having beaten the traffic warden! May 5th "Would you like a stand at our Car Boot Sale?" said the notice from the Boy Scouts. "Come at 10 o'clock" the invitation read, so I went at 10 o'clock and there was hardly any room left for me. "They were here at 8 o'clock this morning" said the Scout man. It was a cold, grey and very wet day but business was fairly good, so my hot soup stayed in its flask. At 1.30 pm the heavens opened. Have you noticed Bank Holidays are never favourable towards people pursuing outdoor activities? This fund-raising business has its ups and downs - the 'downs' are when I am outside and its cold, wet and windy. The 'ups' come when I am warm and cosy at home counting up the takings and writing cheques for Anne. At one of the early meetings I remember Anne saying, "Contact your local businesses and factories. You will be surprised how generous they are', so I wrote to Nestlés whose factory is on the outskirts of my village, to ask if they would consider donating coffee or a raffle prize for my forthcoming coffee morning on 7th June. Two or three days later a 500g tin of coffee was personally delivered to my door with Nestlés compliments. The coffee morning was a great success and I had £172 to send to Anne plus £121 for raffle tickets.

The next event was the 4 Peaks Race over 46 miles, including Lakeland's 4 highest mountains, on 21st June. Graham Bell offered to run for Raynaud's if I arranged the sponsor forms, so after having a chat with Anne at the Glasgow Conference, she said she would send some official sponsor forms. He completed the run in 19 hours and now I had to gather in the 25 forms, hopefully with plenty of donations. News of a Car Boot Sale on the village green came to my ears whilst my sister was visiting me from New Zealand. "What on earth is a Car Boot Sale?" she said, so I thought I would introduce her to one and take her along with my stall. It was a fairly quiet Boot Sale but a pleasant afternoon and we had £40 in the kitty. It is nearing the Dalston Agricultural Show Day which I am looking forward to, especially as I have got a super shelter on permanent loan from a factory in Carlisle to protect me from the wind and rain.

The phone goes at 7 am on the Friday before Show Day. It's George, my stall helper to say he has "flu and cannot collect my stall from the factory nor erect it on the Show Field for me. I shall need to telephone 'Odd Job' in the village later on to see if he can take a trailer to Carlisle, pick up my stall and put it up on the Show Field today. We arrive at the factory with the car and trailer half an hour before they shut down for the weekend, only to find it requires a lorry not a trailer to transport it. Oh dear - what a headache! No time to rearrange transport now, so 'Odd Job' plans to hire a lorry in the morning to get my stall to the Show. The stand must be ready for judging by 9 o'clock and he is only collecting it at 8.30 am. We missed the judging and I didn't need the stall after all. It was the brightest, warmest day of the year - the first day this year without any wind. The Street Market at Carlisle Great Fair is quite an occasion for one week each year and I have an opportunity to take the Charity Stall for one day. It was a pleasant and warm day and I almost sold out of stock. What a contrast to last year when the stand blew away in the gale. I wonder what will happen next year?

Barbara Fletcher

Seasons

Springtime I come alive again,
In summer I really bloom,
Autumn I begin to fade away
And I wilt in the winter's gloom.

Edith Williams

Robin Redbreast

I looked out the window and what did I see,
A little robin sat on my tree.
He has no boots to keep out the cold,
Yet he sits there so comfy and very bold.

I throw out some scraps as a special treat,
But then I come in with cold hands and feet?
His breast is red like a glowing fire,
You can't help but look or even admire.

How does he survive the snow and the sleet
When I'm in the warm with blue hands and feet.
Mother nature is strange and God made all creatures,
Then between them both gave different features.

Some cope with heat and some cope with the cold,
But for me it's the same, I must be old!
Fifty-one is not old - on that you agree,
But I can't survive sat under a tree!

I know there's no cure for our complaint
But if we could find what they have and we aint,
And why they survive without extra clothes,
Then perhaps we could find a cure - who knows?

Pearl Waterhouse

Anyone for Whist?

Anne said "Get with it and raise us some lolly
For Raynaud's funds'. I thought, "That's jolly,'
What could I do in the winter-time
When the wind blows cold with the frost and grime

And I feel so chilled right to the core
When it's too bad to venture outside the door.
A whist drive perhaps, well it's worth a try,
I'd search for all the players nearby.

(I'd send for some leaflets from our Lynda's store
She keeps a good stock of posters, and more).
I found Bessie and Bertha and Sidney and Dee,
Who apart from the whist, come for chatting and tea,

And oft during play should a person revoke
They'd get off quite lightly with these friendly folk.
Mrs 'B' comes, she's a sweet little soul,
Who knows all the rules so can keep tabs on all.

We get into muddles with only three tables
And ladies play 'Gent' and forget to wear labels.
It has really caught on and it really is fun
Though no-one knew Raynaud's until we'd begun.

Pat Trott

New office

Official opening of the new office in Crewe Road, Alsager in October 1987. The red ribbon was cut by Kerry Wilson, a local television personality, impersonating Margaret Thatcher. Also present, the Mayor & Mayoress of Congleton Borough Council, Anne Mawdsley, staff and volunteers.

Moving On

Research Grants totalling £108,500

Totalling £77,000 to Mr. Bruce Pardy is to investigate whether local surgery, apart from conventional finger amputation, is of value in severe Raynaud's phenomenon; Mr. Richard Morgan of the University of Wales College of Medicine requested financial assistance for the purchase of a thermographic system; Professor Morris Brown, Addenbrookes Hospital, Cambridge requested a Periflux Laser Doppler Flowmeter; Mr. Leonard Cotton, King's College School of Medicine funding to continue their programme of research into the diagnosis and treatment of Raynaud's phenomenon; Dr. Stuart Roath's department at Southampton requested money for equipment and a research assistant and Dr. Carol Black and Dr. Darton to continue working with the thermographic equipment. Dr. G. Laurent from the cardio thoracic Institute at the Brompton Hospital in London; Professor Malcolm Jayson, Hope Hospital and Professor Morris Brown at Addenbrookes Hospital, Cambridge.

Raynaud's Questionnaire

We received an excellent response to the questionnaire distributed to members of the Raynaud's Association. Of approximately 2,600 sent out more than 1,420 responded, a response rate of 54 per cent. Very few of these were unsuitable for analysis so that it has been possible to obtain a good overall picture of Raynaud's in 1986/87 as it relates to members of the Association. Here is a summary of the results. These relate to the mean figures though there is in many cases a wide range. As expected, most of those who have Raynaud's are female (85.6 per cent) and most are middle-aged (however one lady aged 92 years completed the questionnaire) and in most (74 per cent) the disability had been present for less than 20 years, 50 per cent less than ten years. About two-thirds have primary Raynaud's and one quarter (360) had scleroderma or other associated diseases. However, almost one patient in ten was uncertain regarding their diagnosis and we are uncertain what this means. Only one-quarter of the responders had mild disease measured as either short lived attacks (less than 15 minutes), infrequently and with only slight pain. The fingers are, of course, most commonly affected. Our interest is in the other extremities involved and if there is a difference between primary and secondary Raynaud's. The statistician is still working on these but the preliminary figures suggest little difference does exist.

With regard to therapy, half the responders use some form of hand warmer, usually heated gloves. Also some form of oral therapy (tablets) taken to produce or attempt to produce an increase in blood flow to the extremities has or is being used. Fourteen drugs in this category were named. By far the most frequently used drug was, or is nifedipine but even this is used by just less than a quarter of the responders. It was pleasing to note that very few individuals with Raynaud's have had tranquilisers or are using them at present.

Finally, we wish to thank all those members of the Raynaud's Association who gave their time and interest to answer the questionnaire.

E D Cooke MD

Open Day at Eaton Hall Gardens

Our afternoon at the Duke of Westminster's Estate on 29th May 1988, was a most successful occasion. Members came from all over the country and it was wonderful to see so many friends. Our sincere thanks to everyone who donated the food, cakes, drinks, cups, plates, etc. for the refreshments and to everyone who made handicraft items, potted plants or helped in any way. We even managed to have a self drive van, free of charge, to transport everything! Over 70 people helped on the day to organise the car parking, gate money, refreshments and stalls. It would be impossible to name everyone who helped but we would just like to say a special "thank you" to Alsager Lions Club and their wives for playing a major role in the organisation. The weather was reasonably kind and a couple of heavy showers turned to our advantage as the stalls and refreshment area was the only covered place for people to shelter.

The wonderful news is that we raised a total of £2,000!

In the photograph taken at Eaton Hall, from left to right - Jane, Joan, Anne, Anne, Barbara and Tricia.

It's all Buloni!

"Think about it and let me know and I'll do you a nice Buloni amputation on Friday." Well, I'd heard of tibias and fibias but bulonias or bulomias? The penny soon dropped and now I talk glibly of below knee, through knee and above knee as if they were a part of everyone's everyday conversation. Unfortunately, "below knee" is now a part of my everyday conversation - and I mean every day. I find myself telling complete strangers on the telephone, "I shan't be at the office on Monday, I'm being measured for a new leg". One of the side effects of such a serious operation and, in consequence, of being the centre of so much attention, is that one's conversation is decidedly self-centred. Friends would visit, followed by other friends who would ask questions about the first friends which I couldn't answer because the total topic of conversation had been me and Moomin. Moomin is the name I give to my stump because, when the knee is bent, the bit of calf which I can still call my own looks just like Moomin who, for those who don't know is a cartoon hippopotamus.

As I am still nervous about shaving the leg too close to the scar, it is a hippopotamus with moustache. Actually Moomin is losing weight, which means I hope soon to be measured for my final leg. I was disappointed with the first one. It didn't look too bad, but they called it a pylon and try as I might I have never been able to tune in to Radio 3, and we have had so much rain lately, I worry about rust; at least we don't now have to worry about woodworm! I am told that the final version will be more glamorous and one kind cousin suggested I should request a mould to cover the other leg so that I should have a matching pair! "Look at that lovely curve" the doctor said, but she wasn't talking about my legs, she was admiring the graph on the computer which showed such improvement to my blood after a month's daily dose of Iloprost jungle juice. Such beautiful graphs but my toes still hurt! Any fellow Raynaud's sufferer who has had ulcerations or gangrenous digits will know what I mean when I say it was such a relief to be free from the pain once I had had the Buloni amputation.

Many say they cannot understand how I can be so cheerful, but I had cried so much before that Friday, that it is easy to be cheerful. I enjoy learning new skills and try to treat it all as a game. Of course, occasionally I wake up to the fact that the 'fun' is here to stay and I can't say, "I'm tired of that game, let's play another', and I'm paranoiac about the colour of my other foot and watch it like a hawk. The people I admire are those who remain cheerful through their pain and I love being the centre of attention. So many cards, so many flowers, so many visitors (on average about 6 a day), so many friends and relatives who care; such kind and attentive doctors and nurses, who forgave me fighting and swearing at them before and after the operation, who forgave me for always being in the way doing wheelies in my wheelchair or for always being missing while I visited other wards, or the shop, or the library, who always came running to cuddle me (the nurses not the doctors), every time I said "ouch" or burst into tears at the sound of a Norwegian waltz, international folk dancing being my hobby.

Last Saturday I went to my first dance workshop - mainly to watch and show-off to my friends. I did manage one dance, a Norwegian song dance, quite easy, arm-in-arm in a circle, just step, close, step, close, step on your partner's foot and both nearly collapse, step, close. I still move a bit like Frankenstein's monster, but I'm working on it.

(See update on page 51)

Kelsey Blundell

Fighting a mystery disease

Six years ago Chris Buckledee found that she was having difficulty in performing everyday household tasks because her hands seemed to be increasingly immobile. As the weeks passed, her condition got so bad that she couldn't even dress herself. In 1982 Chris of Brooksfield, Bildeston, underwent a series of exhaustive tests at a local hospital before specialists finally diagnosed Raynaud's Disease. Now, thanks to the medicine she takes, she can undertake tricky tasks like making soft toys to raise funds for research. Her condition started over a period of about four weeks when she noticed her fingers were becoming colder and she was fumbling when trying to pick things up. Eventually her fingers turned blue and she was afraid she had a heart problem but was reluctant to go to the doctor. Chris says, "One day when I was peeling potatoes, I had a severe attack of cramp. I could not hold the knife which fell to the floor with a crash and I could not pick it up again - I decided it was time to see a doctor." Chris has enjoyed helping The Raynaud's Association as she feels her fund raising activities give her an interest in life. Over the past few years Chris' efforts have raised thousands of pounds and in 1988 alone she raised £525.

Chris with some of her handmade toys.

Joyce Simpson from the West Midlands receives her mile medal and a big hug from Matthew Kelly.

1989 - Sponsored Swim Raises £8,500

A sponsored swim organised by Anne Mawdsley raised £8,500 for Raynaud's Research. Approximately 400 adults and children took part in the event at Alsager Leisure Centre, swimming distances ranging from 1 length (25 metres) to 18 miles. The youngest swimmer was 3 years old and several were senior citizens. The effort made by the swimmers and their sponsors was tremendous and Anne would like to thank everyone for their support. All who took part were presented with a certificate and those who completed distances of a mile or more received a medal. The medals were donated by Alsager Lions and Alsager Rotary Club and presented by TV personality Matthew Kelly. We were most grateful to Matthew for attending a special presentation ceremony on 31st March which proved to be a most entertaining event in itself, with over 1,000 people being present. Alsager Comprehensive Sixth Form Band and Uncle Phil, our friendly magician, giving their services to make it a memorable occasion. In addition to local people who participated, several members who read about the event in the newsletter, organised their own sponsors and swam at their local baths. Mr. Barber from Corwen, Clwyd made a superb effort by contacting many local companies and traders who supported his swim, resulting in a total of £908 and Meda Grant of Rowington, Warwickshire surprised herself by raising £500. Thanks also to Dorothy Young who raised £160, Louise Green £80, Pat Ridyard £76,. D. Angell £71 and Joyce Simpson £50. All told us that they enjoyed their swim and were surprised how much support they had been given. We would like to thank members who sponsored 8 year old Stephanie Burwitz who achieved a personal best of 12 lengths.

Matthew with some of the youngsters who took part.

New Publications

Raynaud's - A Guide for Health Professionals

This new book has been edited by Dr. Stuart Roath, consultant haematologist and senior lecturer at Southampton General Hospital and the University of Southampton, for the Raynaud's Association. It provides a full introduction to the phenomenon and its treatment, clinical and epidemiological aspects of Raynaud's, differential diagnosis and overview of the latest investigations into it is discussed. Finally, the book details the current methods of minimising symptoms, approaches to the prevention of problems by medication and a guide to treatment of the more extreme forms of the disease. The book will be of interest to sufferers as well as health professionals.

There Are More Questions Than Answers

A new booklet entitled 'There Are More Questions Than Answers' has just been published by the Association. Written by Anne Mawdsley and illustrated by Lynda Palin, the booklet contains over 100 questions and answers on Raynaud's and other related conditions such as scleroderma. It is intended as a clear and straight forward guide to a condition which affects thousands of people but for which there are still many unanswered questions. The Raynaud's Association would like to thank Dr. Jill Belch and Dr. Carol Black for their advice and Dr. Mike Smith, a patron of the Association, broadcaster, writer and specialist in community medicine, for writing the Foreword.

Diseases don't respect borders

I had the fantastic experience of attending your Annual Conference at Alsager on 23rd September. It was an overwhelming experience. All the lectures were very instructive and the doctors present were willing to answer questions, sometimes with a lot of humour. It was wonderful to see the interest of the participants and experience their strong support of your Association. Most wonderful of all was the warmth and interest with which I was received by Anne and other participants at the conference. Our Danish Scleroderma Society has existed since 1985 and we have only around 100 members, so our Society is much smaller than your organisation. Your Association has members from many different countries and I have myself just become a member. International co-operation is important now and in the future. Diseases do not respect national borders so co-operation is necessary to support research and distribute information to patients and the public. We face different problems in different countries. In Denmark we are facing a cut down in health budgets, which makes it very difficult to be treated at our National Centre of Scleroderma. Patients can often only be treated at local or county hospitals where they usually have none or very little experience in treating scleroderma. As another consequence of the situation it is very difficult to be diagnosed in the right way, so patients have no diagnosis or are diagnosed wrongly with other diseases. The problems described, have made the Danish Broadcasting Corporation interested in making a TV programme about our situation, as an example of the problems of small patient groups. In future we have to focus more on patients with Primary Raynaud's phenomenon, and perhaps we at the same time should change our Scleroderma Society to a Raynaud's Association.

Niels Bo Sorensen
Chairman of the Danish Scleroderma Society

Office Extension

In the photo from left to right, Ian Foden (architect), Anna Burwitz, Raynor Lancaster, Lynda Palin, Anne Mawdsley & Mayor of Congleton Borough Council, Trevor King, who cut the ribbon.

The need for an extension to our existing premises was becoming apparent and so in March this year we decided to launch an appeal both locally and nationally, to fund the building project. By June we had raised sufficient funding and the work began in July. Foolishly I thought there would be little or no disruption to the running of the office and presumed everything would go to plan. Completion by our conference at Alsager in September seemed a possibility and we had hoped to show off the new premises, complete with toilet facilities for people with disabilities. September came and went as did our only toilet and water supply. To add to this problem the heating system packed up and was irreparable. I approached British Gas and after some gentle persuasion, they very kindly agreed to put in central heating to the extension and the existing building, free of charge. Glow-worm donated the boiler, a Combie Express, an essential part of the system which will mean that we will have hot running water for the first time. We are most fortunate in having a good friend and helper, Joan, who lives across the road from the office, without whom we would not have been able to go to the toilet or have a drink all day. The last drink I had out of the old system was the last straw. Raynor made me a cup of coffee which at first seemed fine but as I got to the bottom of the mug, it tasted gritty - it contained half an inch of builder's plaster!! October came and went, every day bringing more mess, dust, dirt and noise. The end did not seem to be in sight and the builder was reluctant to give a completion date. It was all very frustrating, particularly as it was probably one of our busiest times both with mail and phone calls following Raynaud's Awareness Week in October.

November arrived and a message from British Gas to say they were coming to install the central heating. Good news indeed but first the old pipes and radiators had to be stripped out. Again I thought we would cope. Then reality hit, as every inch of the building had to be turned upside down. Raynor sensibly took a weeks holiday, Anna said she would work from home if necessary and I settled in the corner of a room with a telephone, notepad and fan heater to keep the communication system alive! A day was enough so I put the answerphone on and set up a temporary office across the road on Joan's dining room table, where we opened the mail together. I kept popping across the road to check the answerphone. Inevitably the phone rang when I was there and I'm sure the person at the other end of the phone must have thought we were in a building which was being demolished, with all the knocking, banging and drilling going on! The gas men did a superb job and after a week, Lynda and I began redecorating the office, one room at a time.

My room was a priority as Raynor and I both work in there and also the other two front rooms still needed new windows fitting, the old sash windows having given up the ghost! We cleaned and scrubbed and hoovered and dusted until finally we were able to paint the walls a lovely, clean rose white. Lynda did the ceiling, I did the walls and we both glossed. The curtains were washed, ironed and put into place - it looked wonderful. It had taken us all weekend but was worth it. Monday morning and business as usual. Feeling positive that the end was in sight I was feeling much brighter than I had the week before. Just then a face appeared around the door. It was the electrician "Sorry luv, there's a problem with the electrics in the extension below, I'm afraid we'll have to take up the floor boards in here!" So Raynor and I moved our desks and continued to open the mail and answer the telephone with wires suspended across the room and the floor boards leaning against our newly painted walls. The other two rooms were still under dirt and dust sheets, so on Monday night we worked for hours to get Anna's room cleaned and painted - almond white this time. On Tuesday morning Anna arrived complete with typewriter which she had taken home during the turmoil and started work. About 11 am she came upstairs and said there was a glazing company van outside and was it anything to do with us. You've guessed - it was! Out came the dust sheets over everything except Anna, who continued to type while the window came out and cold air came in. Raynor and I still had our floor boards up but we answered the telephone as Anna couldn't have heard for the traffic.

A local Building Society had donated the money for the windows but when they were put in there was a slight problem - they were three inches too short! Still they did their best to rectify the situation and I managed to get them to knock enough off the original quote to pay for the fencing at the rear of the office, which a timber company were erecting free of charge. They even threw in a roll of lead stripping and a template for Lynda and I to put on the windows when we find time and can borrow a long ladder! I guess this compensated for the putty which was trodden into the newly cleaned carpet tiles. Fortunately we all have a sense of humour or I think Anna, Lynda, Raynor and I would have gone mad with frustration at the problems which have arisen during the building of this extension - raising the money was the easy part! We are not out of the woods yet. The plumber arrived to do his work, which he is doing at no cost, only to find the toilet donated by Twyfords had been concreted into the wrong place by the builders. This still had to be moved before the water supply could be turned on. The heating was on for a day - what bliss amongst the mess - surely nothing else can go wrong? Sadly there was a fault on the new boiler which although not a big job still had to wait to be done. This meant that every ten minutes or so the electricity cut off and Anna couldn't type a letter without disruption.

The completion date is now 25th November. I am not sure which will be ready first, the newsletter or the extension. I only know that next time I have an idea, I must make sure it doesn't lead to four and a half months of chaos. The good thing is that we raised every penny by donations and gifts from companies. Electrolux donated a small fridge, a luxury we haven't had before, so none of the money raised for research has been used for this project. Various pieces of furniture including several chairs, have been donated by local people. On November 27th we are opening a Charity shop three doors away from the office, thanks to a generous local business man. I am not sure how we will be organised by then. We haven't really got very much to sell but somehow once it starts items come from everywhere. The people of Alsager are very supportive, so we hope to raise a few hundred pounds in the three weeks up to Christmas. We look forward to welcoming you to the office, where we hope there will be a warm welcome! It really will be so much better when it is all finished as there will be a new room downstairs, toilet facilities for people with disabilities and a car park with wheelchair access into the premises. The official opening by the Mayor of Congleton Borough Council is planned for the week before Christmas.

Anne Mawdsley

Charity Shop

Having previously borrowed premises for a temporary shop with good results we now had more space so in order to raise some funds we opened the downstairs of our office as a Charity Shop on two occasions. The result being £1,000 for sale of Bric-à-Brac. This was only made possible by recruiting local volunteers and we would like to thank in particular the ladies from Alsager Widows Club who manned the shop on the first occasion and Joan Farrall who helped every day during the second opening.

Volunteers Joan Farrall and Dorothy Dudley displaying goods on sale.

10 year old Andrew Robinson, played the violin outside the office on Saturday mornings when the shop was open. He collected over £30 in coins from passers by.

You don't have to be mad to work here ....

I've never worked anywhere quite like this office before! First there is the office itself, it's like Dr. Who's Tardis, that is, it seems to be about twice the size inside than it looks from outside. You're thinking that I mean it is spacious, aren't you? No such luck, every accessible and some inaccessible places are filled with leaflets, posters, books, used stamps, bric-à-brac etc. I'm not physically able to climb the ladder to the loft but from the amount of things that do ascend that ladder, the roof space must pass the length of the road. We have self-filling filing trays and a letter box that must be permanently open. There is one telephone line but at least three phones in use at any one time which explains why when you ring, either two of us answer or we all look at the phone expecting someone else to answer it. We never throw anything away, which is a good plan in theory but in practice does mean that things become progressively harder to find. Then there's the staff. First there's Anna, who always manages to do two or three jobs simultaneously without a permanently worried expression. I'm jealous of her because she doesn't have my fear of the computer and types at such a speed that even the typewriter can't match (it squeaks in protest until she slows down). Lynda does the artwork, 'they' tell you. What 'they' don't say is that artwork means posters, Christmas cards, office walls and ceilings. She's also our furniture mover, stamp warehouse, stock controller, collecting box organiser and Director handler. I did mention that she also has a full time job and unlike the rest of us lives five miles from the office.

The dreaded phrase in the office is "I've had an idea!" which emanates at regular intervals from 'The Boss'. This invariably means pain for one of us and trouble for all. There doesn't seem to be anything she can't do, she somehow manages to acquire anything and everything and has the cheek of the devil. She occasionally takes a holiday when we think we'll just calm down and takes things slowly but then she telephones or if she's abroad, she writes with the familiar phrase "I've seen something that would be perfect for the office and I've had an idea". It's true I haven't ever worked anywhere like this before but I've never enjoyed myself so much either. It's probably the thrill of the unexpected!

Raynor Lancaster, Welfare Officer

Calm Chaos

"Recently I had to go to the Raynaud's office to collect some Christmas cards and stock to sell at a Charity Fair I had been invited to attend on the Association's behalf. It had started out as a beautiful morning and Harry and I looked forward to a pleasant drive through the Cheshire countryside. Typically, halfway there, the heavens opened and we slogged through unfamiliar lanes in pouring rain - so I was looking forward to a cosy office and a good gossip with Anne over a warming coffee. I knew there were some alterations being made whilst a disabled toilet was installed and the old kitchen was moved and altered to make way for a small consulting room. How quickly our dreams are shattered, gone was the usual neat front office, instead there was one small space where Anna was trying to type - never mind I thought, the back will be alright. Oh no - no access, the newly laid floor was not dry and no one was allowed through until the following day, so even if the toilet had been working, no chance of using it. No tap water either, and that had been the case for over two and a half months! Next upstairs to Anne's office where we did get a very welcome coffee - undisturbed chat we did not. The telephone never stopped ringing - a sister from Guy's Hospital in London; Lynda to check that the reprint of this years Christmas cards were ready for collection; a member with a query regarding a forthcoming event; someone from the local paper to check copy about the recent Halloween party and finally Raynor had to walk all the way around the block to give a message to the builders (you haven't forgotten it was pouring down, have you?). I thought we had been in a mess when we moved into our bungalow last year and had a loft conversion and new fitted kitchen, but how they have coped since the beginning of July I don't know. All I can say is that I now understand how the Association has grown and prospered in the short time it has been in existence, with such a willing group of helpers and with Anne at their head. I wish them well when everything is again ship-shape and back to normality, but I doubt if that telephone will stop ringing for very long"!

Anne Main

Mum's terror as child suffers sudden attack

Emma Vaughan with her mother, Jane

The following article appeared in the Evening Sentinel on 17th October 1989.

Perhaps the most terrifying experience for a mother is to see her child turn blue in a sudden, mystery attack. Jane Vaughan's immediate thought when it happened to her youngest daughter was that the toddler had developed heart problems. In fact, it wasn't until several months after the first incident that Emma, now two, was diagnosed by a hospital consultant as a victim of Raynaud's Disease. By then, the lively little girl had suffered numerous distressing attacks during which her lips and cheeks turned blue and her hands and feet went icy cold. Doctors had carried out tests on her, but could find nothing wrong. So, by the time the correct diagnosis was made, Jane felt only relief to know exactly what was wrong with her daughter, who is now under the care of a consultant at Hope Hospital, Salford. "Emma had the first attack last year', recalls 30-year old Jane at her Werrington home. "I was taking my eldest daughter, Sarah, six, to school one day. Emma was in her pushchair. Suddenly, her face turned blue. I rushed her to the doctor and he told me to take her straight to hospital. The doctors there couldn't find anything wrong. They thought it was an isolated occurrence which can happen with children. I was told that if it happened again, I should get in touch with the family doctor". Another attack followed a week later. Emma was sent to hospital for tests but again nothing was found. "The attacks continued, Emma was having them three or four times a day in winter. She looks really poorly when they happen. She gets very upset and cries if she has a bad attack. The doctors said it was not her heart and all the tests were negative. When she turned blue, I panicked and immediately thought it was her heart. Then in January this year, she was discharged by the hospital. The doctors still didn't know what was wrong, but one said he thought it could be Raynaud's. I had never heard of it.'

Jane's health visitor knew of the condition and contacted Anne Mawdsley at the Raynaud's Association office in Alsager. Within two days, Anne and the charity's welfare officer, Raynor Lancaster, visited the family and advised Jane to ask her G.P. to refer Emma to a consultant at the Salford Hospital. "When we saw the consultant for the first time in March, he confirmed that Emma had Raynaud's Disease', Jane recalls. "I was relieved really because I could put a name to what was wrong with her. I can cope now that I know what it is". Emma has now started going to a playgroup twice a week where helpers are aware of her condition. She needs to be kept warm, even during the summer. The heating is kept on at home. Now, when the toddler feels an attack coming on, she puts on her own coat, hat and gloves. "She is brilliant, considering that she is only two', says Jane, who has joined the Association. "She is so lively and mischievous. If she was a docile child, having Raynaud's would probably be worse for her. If by publicising Emma's condition, it helps other mothers and sufferers, then it will have done some good".

Jane Vaughan

Top cricketers hit by Raynaud's

Several articles in national newspapers have featured cricketers who have developed Raynaud's. Paul Jarvis, Yorkshire's England bowler, and Glamorgan bowler Simon Dennis were given infusions of the drug Iloprost, over several days, in order to alleviate their condition. Dennis found his career with Yorkshire threatened when gangrene set in so badly that amputation of his left index finger was considered. However, the treatment he and the other cricketers received enabled them to continue with their sport. Chris Lewis who is at present bowling for England in the West Indies suffered so badly with his hands last season that it kept him out of the county championship side for almost two months. He found that delivering a cricket ball caused numbness, blisters and persistent ulceration of the fingertips and he was required to rest during July and August. He said that he found it hard to grip the ball and didn't know where it was going when he bowled it. The longer he bowled the worse the condition got.

Research grants awarded

Professor Colin Roberts and Mr Paul Baskerville of Kings College School of Medicine & Dentistry requested a salary for a clinical research fellow; Dr. Alan Silman of The University of Manchester - junior programmer/analyst salary and Dr. Carol Black of The Royal Free Hospital - Salary for post-doctoral research fellow.

These grants total £51,400 for one year.

Trickery!

Recent research by the USA Army indicates that the body may be tricked into circulating blood to the hands even in cold weather. Three to six times each day Raynaud's patients sat indoors with their hands submerged in warm water. Then they were put into a cold environment where their body was exposed to cold temperatures except their hands, which were submerged in an ice chest filled with warm water. After 50 rounds of this treatment, 150 test subjects were able to go out in cold weather without losing circulation in their hands. More research is needed to determine if this treatment will work for many people over an extended period of time.

Raynaud's and Sticky Blood

One question which is often asked at meetings relates to whether blood in a Raynaud's patient is thicker than normal. The following article explains about the properties of blood:

One of the first problems that a Raynaud's sufferer notices is an alteration in hand and finger colour in the colder weather. The fingers may initially go white reflecting spasm in the arteries and therefore decreased blood flow. They may then go blue as the blood trapped by the spasm in the finger vessels loses its oxygen and finally they may become red as the spasm relaxes and blood rushes back into the fingers. This is the classical Raynaud's attack. Pain can be a feature of all these three phases of colour change as can numbness and tingling, making even the smallest job difficult to carry out. However, although these Raynaud's attacks are very distressing and often interfere with the sufferer's lifestyle, the blood does return to the fingers and all is well until the next attack. In a few patients, however, with the more severe form of Raynaud's, the tissues can become damaged and small cracks and ulcers appear over the tips of the fingers. The reason for this is that not only is the vessel spasm stronger, but these people may have blood that is slightly stickier than normal. Of course, blood is meant to be sticky - when one cuts oneself it is the sticky properties of the blood that stops the bleeding. However, some Raynaud's sufferers have blood that clots in an intact blood vessel, this blocks the vessel, blood cannot flow and the small piece of tissue at the end of the blocked vessel dies and so an ulcer or cracks begins.

Blood consists of three main cell types suspended in fluid (plasma). The red cell carries oxygen, the white cell fights infection and the third cell, the platelet, is supposed to be sticky and stops bleeding. The plasma which carries these three cells in the circulation is also rich in nutrients such as sugars, proteins and hormones. Changes in all of these four blood constituents can lead to an increase in blood stickiness. Let us look at each in turn. The red cell measures about 7 microns. The small blood vessels in the fingers measure only 5 microns. To enable passage through these small vessels the red cell must bend or deform. Nice healthy floppy red cells have no problem passing, but in Raynaud's the red cell may be stiff and hard and may get stuck in the small vessels. The white cells, although much fewer in number, are almost 2,000 times as hard as the red cell and in the same way these cells can be harder than normal in Raynaud's and block the vessel. The white cell is also sticky and it uses this property to stick onto viruses and germs before destroying them. In Raynaud's, however, they can sometimes stick to the blood vessel wall, silting it up much like soot in a chimney. The third cell type, the platelet, is supposed to be sticky. When it comes in contact with a broken vessel this cell, which is initially round, puts out sticky little feet just like a starfish. These intertwine first with each other and then with red cells so that a blood clot is formed. In Raynaud's, platelets start to make these little feet even in the absence of a broken vessel and a clump of platelets can form, obstructing the flow of blood. The plasma can also contribute to blood stickiness. Plasma contains fibrin though only in small quantities. It is formed when required to stop bleeding. Fibrin is like a spider's web which is spun over the area of a breached vessel. Normally fibrin is kept at the right level by enzymes which digest the strands. However, in Raynaud's, there may be too little of this fibrin digesting enzyme and so the vessel silts up. In addition to spasm of the vessel, therefore the sufferer may have hard red cells, sticky white cells and platelets and too many fibrin strands. These findings have been very helpful to the medical profession in trying to find treatments that are useful for Raynaud's. Of course the main treatment aim is to stop spasm but the ones that seem to be most successful are those which also decrease blood stickiness.

Dr. Jill J. F. Belch

Gastrointestinal Problems

Many patients with scleroderma have problems with the intestinal tract but may not be fully aware of what is happening. The skin and joints can be seen but once food enters the mouth it is not obvious what happens next.

Once food enters the mouth cavity the function of the mouth area is to chew it up and make it easily transportable into the stomach. One of the problems in scleroderma is that the size of the opening of the mouth may be reduced by the scarring that occurs in the tissues, making the mouth less mobile and less able to be opened wide. This makes it difficult for some patients to eat large pieces of food. Another problem may be due to a related condition, Sjogren's Syndrome, in which there is reduced production of saliva from the salivary glands. Saliva is necessary to lubricate the food so that when it is chewed, it is softened and then becomes more readily swallowed. In addition to Sjögren's Syndrome, some drugs can also cause a reduction in the production of saliva. The most important area where problems can occur is the oesophagus. This is responsible for passing food down from the mouth to the stomach. In doing so, it passes through the diaphragm, passively at first because the majority of people eat upright so that there is a gravity effect. More important is the fact that the passage of food is assisted by muscle contraction which is completely involuntary. However, for this contraction to work the muscle has to be able to contract, the nervous control has to be intact and a valve has to function at the lower end of the oesophagus to prevent food coming back up.

Approximately 50% of all patients with scleroderma have problems with this area. So why does this happen? There are several reasons. The first and most important is that in the lower end of the oesophagus, there is a lack in the ability of the muscle to contract although very often the upper portion works quite well and food is moved down but gets to the point of the junction between the oesophagus and the stomach and the muscle contractions become inco-ordinate, causing very weak contractions which are not propulsive and therefore create no forward movement, so that food just sticks there. Another problem is with the valve at the junction between the oesophagus and the stomach which can be faulty in one of two ways. Firstly, it can be faulty in the sense that it doesn't relax and just stays closed in a tight spasm so the food comes down and is blocked from passing into the stomach, or it may be unable to work and remains open. The food then comes back up instead of staying in the stomach. The movement of food from the stomach up into the oesophagus is called reflux and the opening in that region is called a hiatus hernia. A hernia means that there is a wide opening and this creates a further problem. The food in the stomach refluxes into the oesophagus and causes irritation and inflammation because the stomach contents contain hydrochloric acid. Continual inflammation can cause excessive scarring in the oesophagus, producing a stricture which is a tight band or narrowing, usually due to reflux. So what will a doctor do when presented with a patient who describes these swallowing problems? Usually a barium swallow will be taken during which X-rays are taken of the oesophagus. Having made the diagnosis of the particular problem, there are several treatments which are available. If the patient has a stricture this can often be helped by having a tube passed down which dilates the oesophagus. The majority of patients, however, can be treated very effectively by regular medication to reduce the production of acid by the stomach. Surgery is rarely required. If problems are recognised and treated early they can usually be controlled.

Another significant area in the gastrointestinal tract is in the small intestine. The small intestine starts after the stomach and ends up in the large intestine. The function of the small intestine is to absorb nourishment. The food, after it has been chewed, swallowed and partially processed in the stomach, goes into the intestine where a large number of enzymes break it down into simple products, which are then absorbed and used by the body. The intestinal tract has to move the food along because it can't stay fixed in one area, it therefore has contraction waves (peristalsis) the same as in the oesophagus. In a minority of scleroderma patients, the food in the intestine cannot pass on correctly. The small intestine is normally sterile, i.e. containing no germs, but when there is an abnormality and the contraction and food doesn't move along freely, then there is a risk of overgrowth of bacteria. There is a breakdown of food products by bacteria which are irritating and paradoxically produce diarrhoea. This diarrhoea has a major side effect, which is the problem of absorbing food and therefore the possibility of losing weight and not having adequate nutritional ability. People who have this problem can easily be tested by a variety of tests which include X-rays. Treatment with long term antibiotics can be sampled for bacteria. Certain long term antibiotics can be used to control bacteria growth in the bowel and help relieve that particular problem. The last part of the bowel can also be affected. Probably the worst problem for patients when this occurs is difficulty in controlling the bowel function. This is very difficult to treat but fortunately rare.

Vibration White Finger

The fight for compensation for workers claiming compensation for Vibration White Finger (VWF) continues. In October 1987 during Raynaud's Awareness Week, Thames TV's helpline programme featured a short discussion with a London Branch member and referred to a number of claims being made for compensation by workers employed by British Gas, who had developed Vibration White Finger over the course of many years of their employment. It is estimated that many thousands of workers employed by British Gas and other utility companies suffer from VWF. So far hundreds of workers have put forward claims which are being processed. It is therefore pleasing to report that there have been a number of settlements recently, and in particular two former workers who suffered significant symptoms and were laid off have succeeded in obtaining out of court settlements in excess of £50,000.

VWF has been a prescribed industrial disease since 1985. The more recent changes have meant that only a small proportion of VWF sufferers can expect to receive benefits from the State, because of the method of assessment. Civil compensation claims against employers therefore represents the only practical way of obtaining some level of security for those workers who cannot, because of their condition, continue to be employed in their pre-conditioned employment. Many of these workers are now severely restricted in what they can do, because of the general problems which affect them, which are particularly prevalent in winter. Despite the growing awareness of the dangers of exposure to excessive vibration, workers continue to suffer from VWF and still stand the risk of losing their jobs. The fight for compensation for those workers continues and in the examples referred to above, it should perhaps be noted that the claimants in question would not have been able to have financed their claims without the support of their union, the GMB. In 1989 the Health and Safety Executive published the report concluding that as many as 150,000 workers could be regularly exposed to vibration from tools which may expose a risk of Vibration Induced White Finger. The HSE have committed themselves to preparing guidance on VWF and its prevention.

David Pipkin, Rowley Ashworth Solicitors

Raynaud's Phenomenon in Young Children

Professor Malcolm Jayson

Circulatory problems, and in particular Raynaud's Phenomenon, are extremely common. We see large numbers of young adults who develop Raynaud's Phenomenon and in the majority of these no underlying disorder is found. It is then known as Primary Raynaud's Phenomenon. Recently we have seen several young children with precisely the same problem. This was a great surprise as we had not appreciated that small children can suffer from this disorder and may be severely distressed because of the symptoms they suffer whenever they become cold. We saw one youngster at the age of 17 months who had suffered from cold hands and feet since birth. When she became cold her hands became blue or purple and then red on rewarming and she would cry because of the pain. Another female child first developed problems at the age of 6 months and we saw her when she was two and a half. When she became cold her fingers, hands, toes and feet became red and then purple and she became very upset. The third girl was first seen at the age of 2 years and 2 months and had a history of being very sensitive to cold since the age of 16 months. Changes in temperature made the hands, feet, lips and cheeks turn blue and then bright red on rewarming. She would become extremely distressed and cry with these episodes which could last anything from a few minutes to several hours.

We investigated these children in detail and could not find any evidence of any underlying disorder. We even managed to do capillary microscopy in one young lady. This was a considerable achievement in such a young patient but I am pleased to say that it did not upset her and we found her capillaries to be normal. They therefore fall into the class of Primary Raynaud's Phenomenon, very similar to the problem which we find in many adults.

This is not the first description of Raynaud's problems in children but previous reports generally refer to older children and many of these had connective tissue problems such as scleroderma or lupus. Since we first presented our report it has become apparent that Primary Raynaud's Phenomenon is not rare in children and a number of further cases are now being sent to us. From the point of view of treatment the most obvious priority is to keep warm and avoid exposure to cold. The children should avoid going out when it is extremely cold and if they are outside then they must be adequately dressed. Not only does this mean warm clothes but also mittens and socks are important. A warm hat is very helpful as a lot of heat is lost through the scalp. One of our children was so badly affected that the Raynaud's Association arranged for electric gloves. We were worried about how she would manage at this young age but we were delighted to learn that she could use them and indeed was happy with them and did not experience any problems.

The question arises whether we should use the medicines which improve the circulation in adults in children. Clearly we want to avoid the use of all drugs in children if at all possible but if the symptoms are very severe there may be little alternative. We have had some experience of the use of vasodilator medicines. They have to be given in liquid form and in very small dosage. In our very limited experience it has been helpful with no real problems. It is clear that Raynaud's Phenomenon does occur in children and may not be as rare as previously thought. Very careful assessment is needed to make sure that there is no underlying problem and to plan the treatment programme.

Malcolm I. V. Jayson,
Rheumatic Diseases Centre University of Manchester

The effect of female sex hormones in Raynaud's Phenomenon

Raynaud's phenomenon is a condition that is predominantly seen in women of child bearing age. On average about nine women have the disorder to every one man. The reason for this sex difference is unknown but one possible explanation may be to do with the female sex hormones. These sex hormones, of which there are several types, change throughout a woman's life. In childhood these hormones circulate in the blood in low levels. With the onset of puberty these hormones increase in concentration and adopt a cyclical pattern which changes during the menstrual cycle. Pregnancy increases considerably these hormone levels. After the menopause these hormones are no longer required for reproduction and so are no longer produced. These four periods of the female life are associated with marked changes in the number of Raynaud's attacks each sufferer may have. In general Raynaud's phenomenon is rare in young children but common in teenagers who usually grow out of the symptoms by their 20's. The majority of women start exhibiting symptoms in their 20's and 30's. The condition may improve during pregnancy and also after the menopause. Moreover, women on the oral contraceptive pill may find their Raynaud's phenomenon becoming worse. Occasionally some women are advised against taking the pill but this should only be done after consultation with a doctor. Whether the female sex hormones are responsible for these findings is unknown. Certainly the studies performed on how the role of the menstrual cycle affects Raynaud's phenomenon is conflicting. These studies have demonstrated that women without Raynaud's phenomenon react to cold in a similar fashion to women with Raynaud's phenomenon during menstruation, around mid-cycle when the ovum is released, and one week before the onset of menstruation. Whether the attacks are associated with pre-menstrual syndrome again is unclear. Although female sex hormones may influence the severity of Raynaud's phenomenon in some individuals it cannot explain why men suffer from the condition or why some women have the first Raynaud's attack in their 50's or 60's. It is probable that there are several factors which alone are unable to cause a white finger attack but when combined with other factors, may do so. In one individual one factor may dominate and in another person, another factor may dominate. This would explain individual variation. More research is needed to define the exact role of female sex hormones in Raynaud's phenomenon.

Dr. David Greenstein,
St. James's Hospital, Leeds.

We've changed our name

In 1990 we changed the name of our Association to The Raynaud's & Scleroderma Association Trust. At the Trustees meeting in July, Mr. Alan Golding proposed the change and this was unanimously agreed by the other two Trustees, Mr. Robert Holmes and Dr. Carol Black. It has taken three months for this to be made official due to all the forms which have to be filled in and approval given by the Charity Commission following our announcement in a national daily newspaper.

The reason for the change came about as a result of requests from members for more awareness to be given to scleroderma. Over a third of our members have scleroderma in addition to Raynaud's and we are supporting research into both Raynaud's and scleroderma. The majority of members who are most severely affected and who need support from the Association are those who have been diagnosed as having scleroderma. Many have only skin involvement but others also have internal problems. We have concentrated during the past eight years on bringing about an awareness of Raynaud's and still have a long way to go. In the coming year we intend to highlight scleroderma equally. Scleroderma is one of the more severe underlying conditions. Dr. Carol Black describes it as follows:

"Scleroderma is one of the most uncommon, extraordinary and fascinating of the connective tissue diseases. These types of disease affect the joints, muscles, tendons, bones, skin and the connective tissue which supports and surrounds the blood vessels and internal organs. The fact that scleroderma can affect so many different parts of the body probably explains why patients are referred to so many different kinds of doctor e.g. rheumatologists, dermatologists, lung, heart and gut doctors, vascular surgeons and even specialists in the kidney. The word 'scleroderma' comes from two Greek words 'sclero' meaning hard and 'derma' meaning skin. However, many patients with scleroderma not only have problems with their skin but also with their circulation and other parts of their bodies. This is the reason why the disease has a secondary explanatory name, systemic sclerosis".

A Scleroderma Family!

You will have heard that it is very rare for scleroderma to run in families but there is a scleroderma family of mushrooms!

Terrestrial species. Fruitbodies subglose to somewhat flattened, or pear-shaped with a stalk-like base of varying prominence and a firm leathery to thick rind.

Scleroderma citrinium has a thick,leathery, coarsely scaly wall.

Scleroderma areolatum has a thinner wall and is more finely scaly.

Scleroderma verrucosum. In section this species is seen to have a thin flexible tough rind and brownish-black spore mass.

Common Scleroderma Scleroderma aurantium, is a 'Poisonous' mushroom, which can be recognised by its almost kidney like shape and yellow-brown colour. The conelike warts upon the surface also help you to recognise this as a potato type mushroom. The inside is a dull white with a purple black centre. As soon as you split this one open, you can see the centre already starting to change to a purple black, so beware of this mushroom. This one grows around old stumps and rotten logs in the woodlands. It fruits in late summer and fall.

New Medical Adviser

Dr. John Bewley

Dr. John Bewley, General Practitioner in Alsager, has recently joined our medical panel. Dr. Bewley has followed the progress of the Association since it was founded in 1982. He was Anne's G.P. when she was first diagnosed in 1975.

Aren't I the lucky one?

Below is an excerpt from the talk which Kelsey gave at the Conference in 1990 having had her second leg amputated.

A minicab driver said to me one day "You're one of those lucky people who can park anywhere they like". Well, up to a point he was right. I am and I can. The first time I took advantage of my orange badge, it took me so long to get out of the car into the stream of traffic that I ended up climbing over the gear stick and getting out on the passenger side, which wasn't easy and I still had one leg then!

I'm getting to know many of my neighbours for the first time. There's one little girl (she's 5) who hasn't quite grasped the situation and keeps asking to see my bandaged toes. Her mother told her she was always to ask me if I needed any help. "You can walk a little bit, can't you?". "Oh, yes, I can walk a little bit." "It's just that you're very slow." "That's right, I'm very slow." "That's 'cause you're old." .... It's the everyday things that are difficult, like getting dressed without falling over, pulling the dining room chair up to the table when you can't put weight on a bended knee, straightening your skirt when you sit down, especially when getting into the car (I've given up hope of ever wearing an uncreased skirt), putting the rubbish out, carrying a plate or a cup of tea, carrying anything. Like packing up your house in order to move out to let the builders in. I'd worked out that it was no good packing the books near the bookshelves, because I wouldn't be able to move the box afterwards. The box had to be placed where it was going to stay and the books brought to it, but it was a slow process because the furniture kept getting in the way. The cardboard boxes were flat so first I had to put sticky tape round them before packing. Normally, I would get down on my hands and knees, but it's impossible to get on your hands and knees, when you can't flatten your toes or turn them sideways. (I tried it once and fell flat on my nose.) So you sit on the wheelchair and bend forward to reach across the box and that's when you drop the scissors beyond the box! In order to bend forward you must have the brakes on, but then you need to move the chair to pick up those scissors, so you have to let go of the sticky tape to take the brakes off and move the chair, then you drop the sticky tape and the box, which in any case is in the way of the wheels. Eventually I'd have a box the right way up and I would proceed to put the books into plastic bags before packing them in the box. Invariably I'd find that the plastic bag that I was using would be trapped under the wheels of the chair! I have one of those 'helping hands' picker uppers. But what do you use to pick up the picker upper when it's the picker upper that you've managed to drop on the floor?

Another way in which I'm lucky is that I don't mind. What I mean is, I'm not embarrassed to be seen in a wheelchair or to be seen legless. It's frustrating not being able to do the things you used to be able to do, like Flamenco and Greek dancing but I don't care about other people noticing. When I visit friends, if my legs are tired, I usually ask permission before removing them, but at work, if necessary, I just take them off and put them under the desk. I'm aware that sometimes other people are a bit disconcerted, but as one friend said to me that's our problem and we have to deal with it, not you. And if people get used to seeing me legless, then they might not stare so much when they see others with perhaps a greater disability or, more to the point, a greater sensibility to their condition. So I feel I'm doing my little bit to break down the barriers. More than one person has felt it necessary to say to me "think how lucky you are" and it is something that I'm very much aware of. I do have a lot to be thankful for, and I have a lot of people to be thankful to. I have Anne and everyone in the Raynaud's Association to thank for a great deal. The hand controls and power steering on my car, the donation from Casio of a small television while I was in hospital, the many cards and little presents like the foot, the finger, the abacus. The letters I received from so many members, many of whom I had not even met and many I'm sorry to say, I didn't even get around to replying to.....

After having the traumatic experience of a second leg amputation, Kelsey is now back at work. The good news is that the Association was able to finance the conversion of her car which included power steering, so that Kelsey could drive again. In her letter Kelsey said a big "thank you" and sent us this photograph of herself with her newly converted car.

"You're one of those lucky people", the taxi driver said. Well, he's right. Not everyone is able to drive a car, or can afford to run a car or belong to an organisation like this one, who gives so much moral and practical help.

Kelsey Blundell

My first efforts for the Association

Being a new member of the Association I decided to attend the AGM at Alsager College on September 22nd, 1990 to obtain some information about aims, objectives and developments in research. Little did I think I would return home realising the urgent need to promote funding for the Association and also endeavour to motivate the general public to support what was now the Raynaud's & Scleroderma Association. Awareness Week. was obviously not an opportunity to be missed but shortage of time was a major problem. First of all, armed with literature, I approached the Manager of the local Cornbow Shopping Centre in Halesowen to ask if he would permit a display stand for the whole of the week. The answer was YES! Success! Then the real work started, borrowing stands, displaying posters, visiting firms, seeing newspaper reporters, cajoling a printer friend to make cards, the right size to head the display stands. So many things to do and not enough hours in the day. Was I being too ambitious? On Thursday, 18th October I thought I would have to forget the whole idea - my printer friend had gone into hospital the day before - and not even a title for the stand! BUT THEN A MARVELLOUS SURPRISE, my very first donation, incredibly from the manager and tenants of the Shopping Centre. An enormous teddy bear, donated by the manager had been raffled, (a member of the security staff sold the tickets) and raised the sum of £141.00, so without doubt I had to continue.

On Friday and Saturday I was still in the process of borrowing and collecting items I would need to set up the stand on Sunday, and I also had to persuade volunteers to assist me during the week by manning the stand. (Can you imagine morning, noon and evenings without visiting the smallest room or having a coffee!). I forgot to mention, I have not long moved to Hunnington and consequently the number of people I knew in the area was limited, let alone persuading the ones I did know to help with something they knew nothing about. Nevertheless, seven volunteers rallied round offering three or four hours during the week, only one of whom knew anything about Raynaud's and this because she herself was a sufferer and a member of the Association. To sum up, I was exhausted and Awareness Week was very tiring but overall the result was worthwhile. Not only were members of the general public now more aware of problems in their own community, but in addition offers of support have been forthcoming in small ways to raise funds. One or two visitors to the stand said they may hold coffee mornings or evenings with my support, or hold raffles amongst their friends and colleagues. The reward was knowing a lot of people suffering from Raynaud's and scleroderma, and members of their families knew that every effort was being made by the Association to continue funding research until a cure could be found. One must stay optimistic! Two collecting boxes on the stand resulted in donations totalling the sum of £94.30 and a further sum of £35.20 was achieved by the sale of small items. A total of £270.50, and with any luck more donations may be received. Hopefully I shall be able to continue to promote the aims of the Association in any way feasible, time and stamina permitting.

Alicia Shirley

Sell-a-pen Appeal

Sell-a-pen Appeal raised £2000 which enabled us to provide a wheelchair, three bedrests, two sets of electrically-heated gloves, two Careline telephones, a nebuliser and an electric heating pad - also transport costs to and from hospital for several members.

Take-a-Break!

Member Mary Munns from Kings Langley won a three minute Supermarket 'grab' in a popular big-prize family weekly magazine. Rather than keep the prize she very kindly donated it to our Association. It was quite a surprise when we received a phone call from the Head Office of Take a Break telling us that we had been donated a three minute trolley dash at our local Safeway Supermarket in Nantwich. Although the prize was donated in Anne's name she decided that Lynda's hands were in a better condition for grabbing items from the shelves and the organisers agreed to Anne pushing the trolleys while Lynda filled them. We went for several practice 'runs', only to find the night before that all the shelves had been moved around for Christmas!! It was quite a nerve wracking experience at 8 o'clock in the morning to dash around a Supermarket while being timed by a stop watch. I think the store was quite glad to see us go as Lynda managed to demolish several of their Christmas displays! Anyway we did very well, clocking up £527.80 worth of goods which we sold from the office to raise funds for research.

In the photograph with the trolley goods, from left to right: Lynda Palin, Anna Burwitz, Olwyn Lancaster, Anne Mawdsley, Raynor Lancaster and Muriel Rigby (complete with stop watch!.)

The Magic Million
One million pounds raised!!

In less than 10 years since the Association was founded in 1982, the money raised has enabled numerous research projects to be funded at hospitals throughout the country where funding had not previously been available for research into Raynaud's and scleroderma. The Association's welfare fund has also been very active, helping members where and when necessary. We are appreciative of all donations received towards both research and welfare. There is still a long way to go and it is vitally important that research is continued. The next few years could prove to be most exciting, leading to improved treatments for both Raynaud's and scleroderma patients. Our present commitment exceeds £200,000 a year, all of which comes from donations and fund-raising activities. We are hoping to maximise our efforts during our 10th Anniversary year.

Back in Circulation

Our new video, Back in Circulation, was launched at Crewe Hall, the U.K. Headquarters of the Wellcome Foundation which was a beautiful setting for the occasion. After seeing the video, members, friends and local supporters were given a tour of the Hall by Marketing Manager, Mr. Tom Protheroe. Dr. John Bewley, General Practitioner, was most impressed by the quality of the production and felt that it was particularly easy for the lay person to understand. He emphasised the importance of research and increasing awareness of the conditions as well as the excellent facilities offered by the Association for the welfare and counselling of sufferers. During the evening, Joan Adamson, Manageress of the Crewe Branch of Marks & Spencer, presented Anne Mawdsley with a cheque for £2,000. This was a donation from Marks & Spencer Head Office towards the welfare side of our work and is part of their continuing support. We are most grateful for this donation. The video explains how the Association works, relates sufferers' experiences and demonstrates how they have coped with their physical problems. Doctors outline some of the treatments and tests which are available to patients and the need for ongoing research.

The following members of the Association took part in the video:

Caroline Turner aged 22. Her Raynaud's came on suddenly a year ago. She was waking up in the night with really bad pins and needles in one finger. She had very bad finger ulceration, her fingers were constantly purple and she was told that at least one finger would have to be amputated. Caroline read about the Association in a local newspaper and came for advice. After being referred to a specialist centre in London, Caroline had local surgery called a digital sympathectomy, which has made a great improvement to her circulation. No amputation was necessary and she was able to return to work. The youngest member to take part was 3 year old Rhianne Meakin. On the video her mother Joan talks about how Rhianne's hands and feet used to turn blue even though she was a summer baby. At about 15 months she was quite poorly and went into hospital - even in the hospital ward her hands turned blue after a bath. She explains how it is the change in temperature which causes the biggest problem - not easy to avoid in such a young child.

Eileen Henry, age 55, had problems for many years before Raynaud's was diagnosed. Her condition worsened and her weight dropped from nine to five stone. She was vomiting and generally feeling ill. Then she happened to visit an event organised by the Raynaud's Association. She called into the office for advice and it was arranged for her to attend a specialist centre for tests. She had many tests, ECG, lung function, lung tissue etc., but they couldn't find out what was wrong. Then a lung biopsy was performed and scleroderma was diagnosed. It had affected her heart, lungs and stomach. She had oesophageal reflux, felt very bloated and her fingers were also ulcerated. Eileen was devastated when she had to give up teaching but has acquired new values in life. She is very much better healthwise and is most grateful to the doctors who have done so much to help her.

Helen Kelsall is 17 years old and attends the local comprehensive school. Raynaud's was diagnosed two years ago during a very cold winter. She describes how she would be fine in the house but as soon as she went outside she suddenly wouldn't be able to feel her hands - she couldn't bend them because when she did they were very painful. Helen tells how her feet used to go blue at night but it was the pain which affected her more than anything. She went to night school to do pottery but had to stop because the clay was so cold. Suddenly her symptoms disappeared, as often happens in teenagers, and although she is still very careful in cold weather Helen now manages to live a normal life. Another teenager, 14 year old Angela Billings, is seen attending a local G.P.s surgery, presenting with typical Raynaud's symptoms which occur mainly when she goes from one temperature to another. Pat Trott participates in lung function and thermographic tests, while Dorothy Parker is seen being assessed by a physiotherapist and an occupational therapist for gadgets in order to help her daily living. 82 year old Vera Warburton is seen coping with household chores such as peeling potatoes and taking off jam jar lids, also wrapping up warmly when going out and Alan Golding describes how scleroderma has affected his swallowing and also the facial changes which have taken place. Anne Mawdsley describes the work of the Association and how support and advice are available for sufferers. She stresses the importance of sharing problems as so many people feel that nobody understands their condition and consequently, many become depressed and feel alone.

Dr. John Bewley emphasises the importance of early diagnosis and urges patients to go to their G.P.s. Often there are no visible signs at the time of their appointment but this should not embarrass the patient. Mr. Nick Goddard discusses surgical removal of calcium deposits and the operation called digital sympathectomy. Dr. Carol Black goes through the screening tests which she would carry out on a new patient, in addition to taking a careful history and examination, in order to try and detect features of underlying disease. Dr. Black has helped with all the medical input and we are most appreciative of her support. The Association is grateful to His Grace the Duke of Westminster for his introduction of the video. "We have come a long way since 1982 and drug treatments are now available to alleviate both conditions - but progress is still needed to improve our understanding, develop better remedies and raise general awareness". Our thanks to British Gas for sponsoring the production of this video.

Coping with Raynaud's

You just have to laugh about it. Here I am sitting in the living room with woolly mittens on my poor cold hands, big, thick socks on my feet, the central heating on full - and it's the middle of summer! Having Raynaud's Disease means I have to do some rather odd things, but the pain is so excruciating when I have an attack that I really don't mind my family having a laugh at my expense, just so long as I can keep myself warm and prevent that dreadful pain. Having cold and painful feet seems quite a normal thing to me. My mum always complained about her cold feet, and I always used to wear socks in bed because of mine. Lots of people complain of cold hands and feet during the winter, but with Raynaud's Disease it's not quite that simple. When I have an attack, my fingers suddenly turn white and go numb, then

Sue Jackson

they turn blue and I just can't do anything with them. Once they start to get warm again, they turn bright red and then my fingers or feet go from feeling heavy and dead to a dreadful burning, tingling pain, just as though they are in a fire. Life gets more difficult in winter, but attacks can happen at any time of the year. For the half an hour that the attack usually lasts I just have to stop whatever I'm doing - and concentrate on warming up. I usually have about two attacks a day. I've got three children and once they were all at school I went back to work. That's when I realised how bad the pain had become and how much more often I seemed to be getting attacks. I was working as a school dinner lady, where I would walk around the school playground whatever the weather and the children would hold on to my fingers, making it impossible to wear gloves and my hands often went dead.

That was seven years ago, and my husband said he couldn't stand seeing me in so much pain any longer, so I went to see my G.P. He told me that I had Raynaud's Disease and told me to wear woolly mittens to prevent attacks. It was the middle of summer and I didn't want to have to wear gloves. I felt cross that I had to learn to live with the pain, but relieved that at last I understood what was causing my symptoms. I knew I had bad circulation because I've got varicose veins. It just seemed another ailment to add to the list so I accepted it and tried to cope as best as I could. When I realised I had keep warm, I decided to change my job and went to work in a shop but it was a cold shop so it didn't help. I next went to work in a bakerery shop but I had problems there too as sometimes my fingers would go into spasm. Three of them would be dead and sticking out at an odd angle and I'd be stuck trying to put buns into a bag using only the other two fingers. I then tried working from home. I love handicrafts, so I set up my own knitting business, but sitting at a knitting machine all day meant that I wasn't moving and I would still get very cold. I felt as if I just couldn't win. I made sure that I was always well wrapped up. I soon worked out that a warm bath before I go to bed helps to keep me warm right through the night. Being a mum with Raynaud's isn't always easy. Holding heavy shopping bags quickly brings on an attack. If I'm ironing, I just have to stop when my fingers go cold because I can't grip anything.

An attack prevents you using your hands, and as for getting anything from the fridge or freezer - that's just wicked. If I put my hands in either, I have an instantaneous attack. I have to wear my oven gloves - it's not easy, but you've no choice. Cold water is also a problem. When I'm peeling potatoes or doing the veg, I do it under a warm stream of water, not cold and if I'm doing hand washing, which often brings on an attack, I wear rubber gloves for extra insulation. I still get dead fingers when I'm doing these things and suddenly I'll drop whatever I'm holding but every precaution is worth it as it helps to prevent you being in pain so often. When you get dead fingers you can't tell if you've cut yourself peeling the spuds because you can't feel the knife. I used to be involved with the Girls' Brigade but I've stopped that now, mainly because coming home on cold nights causes such agony for me and I'm sad to say that Raynaud's does affect other things I enjoy doing such as sewing, knitting and walking. A walk in the cold, or even just a sudden cold wind on a hot day, turns my nose blue and dead, my ears go numb on the outside and inside my ears and head I get a numb, heavy aching. When they warm up again, the pain and stinging are dreadful, so I wrap up in a snood to keep my head warm.

The best thing that happened to me was when I discovered the Raynaud's Association. It was wonderful to discover that I wasn't the only one with the disease and to be able to share experiences and tips with other sufferers. I was so relieved. In all the years I'd had it, I'd never met another sufferer. Just after that I gave up my knitting business and went to work in a store's fabric department. It's been tremendous because the shop is so warm that I rarely have an attack, and if I do have one and can't cut the fabric, everyone is really understanding. My teenage daughter, Michelle, seems to have it too. I'm sad that she is suffering as I've done but I'm grateful that neither of us seems to be affected as badly as in some rare cases. I'm an expert on keeping warm now but if it gets worse, I'll go back to the doctor. My hands mean so much to me - life would be unbearable without them. It's bad enough having to put my sewing and knitting down when I get an attack - and I intend to keep on knitting into my nineties".

Sue Jackson

Chrissie sews for others

Member Chris Buckledee from Bildeston has been busy raising funds for the past eight years, which has resulted in £6,000 for research.

Chris tells us how she dreads the icy mornings, as the cold causes excruciating pain in her fingers, particularly when she has to hang out the washing. She wears gloves most of the time and her heating bills have doubled since she developed Raynaud's in the cold winter of 1982. We asked Chris to write a short piece for our newsletter, so that members would know how she has raised this money, in spite of her painful fingertips:

"I start sewing in January and sew all the year round. People see what I make, they buy and then their friends buy. At the moment I have a run on clowns made with Suffolk puffs (these are small pieces of material pulled together into a puff). People seem to like anything made with pretty materials. I have lots of orders for Christmas so I have to start now or I would not get finished in time. The Morning Market in Bildeston involves more people and so we are able to raise even more money. I was very encouraged to meet Mrs Backhouse, a member from Sutton, and her lovely family. Mrs Backhouse has had both her legs amputated and is confined to a wheelchair but her bright cheerfulness amazed us all. We have a Christmas sale in a friend's home in November where we sell Christmas cards, paper etc. I also have Webb Ivory catalogues circulating around at the moment.

That's how I have raised £6,000 for research since I started. May I say thank you to all who have helped in any way to make fundraising successful. It has helped me and also created a lot of community spirit.'

Chris Buckledee

HTV

In June,1991 Anne Mawdsley was approached by HTV West for the Association to take part in an item on the Good Neighbours Show. This was filmed in Bath, at the home of Jean Howie, a member who has a severe form of scleroderma. Both Anne and Jean were interviewed by the programme's presenter Sherrie Eugene. Jean was filmed in her kitchen, showing how she copes with various gadgets and also demonstrated her expertise in tapestry. Her fingers are permanently bent and damaged making any task difficult but in spite of having many problems which involve her spending several weeks in hospital every year, Jean manages to stay bright and cheerful. She has a very positive attitude to her condition, telling viewers that there is no point worrying about what you can't do but to concentrate on what you can.

Shirley's Sale

Shirley Roe who has been selling her own design notelets, sent a cheque for £100. She then became more ambitious when a friend suggested that she should hold a nearly new sale in her home. Together with some supportive friends they planned the day - coffee, tea and homemade cakes all day. She charged an entry fee and ran a raffle. Her dining room was converted into a sale room of two rails of clothes and a bric-a-brac stall and a little side room was the changing room. Shirley said that the shrieks of laughter, the fun and success of the day was indescribable and they took over £1,000!! The sorting and pricing was very important in order to hit the right price and get a fast turnover. Well done Shirley and friends!

My Coral Castle

Julie McMahon

I was diagnosed ten years ago with scleroderma, the most rapid and severe case they'd seen. It took nine months before I finally knew what was happening to me. Early in the year my hands and feet were puffy and tender and I was experiencing great fatigue. Even after a good night's sleep I seemed to be exhausted. Eventually I went to the doctor in May. He took blood tests but couldn't find anything wrong. He gave me fluid tablets which didn't help. He metaphorically patted me on the head and said there was nothing wrong. In July, I went to another doctor as by this time things were worse. I had pain in my arms and legs but not in the joints. She thought there was definitely something wrong yet she didn't know what it was. She couldn't get me into the rheumatologist that she wanted so she sent me to a physician. He was not sure what it was. He ruled out Lupus and sent me home for twelve weeks to do nothing while I waited to see the rheumatologist. Aged 28, full time in school and involved in everything that was going, I nearly went round the bend. I loved sport and had coached our boys in Australian rules football. Now I sat all day doing nothing. The big event of the day was to walk to the letter box at the front fence to see if there was any mail. I knew how many steps it took to go from my room to the bathroom, kitchen etc. By the time I eventually saw Steve Millazzo the rheumatologist, I could hardly walk. My fingers were banana shaped and yet Raynaud's was not something that I had noticed although the beginnings of it were there. The skin over all my body had tightened, my lungs, oesophagus, kidneys and bowel were all affected, but it was externally that the disease was rampant. The O.T's made full leg and hand splints in the hope that it would help, but it didn't. The D-Pencillamine seemed to make it worse. I appreciated the doctors' honesty in saying it was out of control and they didn't know what to do. They thought I would end up like a block of wood unable to move. At 28, this was very frightening. They assured me I could get a bed at the 'Home for Incurables". What was happening to me?

I felt, as I'm sure many of you do, that we have been invaded. This disease was not welcome but it came just the same and while we thought of fight and flight, it kept insidiously encroaching on us until we had to learn to breathe underwater. If we are to live in this coral castle, we must adapt. This may mean changing our way of living and thinking. We need to pace ourselves as we experience loss of job, hobbies, abilities to do household and personal things. We have to settle for being able to achieve a tenth of what we used to do and yet I can say ten years on that this unwelcome invader has been a gift; not one I wanted or would have chosen, but nevertheless a gift. Our society tells us that pleasure is good and suffering is evil. I think they are neither good nor evil; they are opportunities for growth. However, my glasses are not that rose coloured. I realised it is usually only in hindsight that we see things as opportunities. In the middle of it, it is sheer hell, blinding pain, frustration, depression, confusion and fear. Yet for those of you at this stage, there is hope - hold on! There is a fine line that people with chronic illnesses have to tread. On the one hand you need to be a fighter and not give in and on the other hand you have to make your home a coral castle and breathe underwater. You have to accept there is something that will not go away and learn to live respectfully with it.

This grief process takes time before you learn to walk the tight rope and then, like all people, it is natural for you to stray to either side at times. The people you live with have to grow to know a new person. Someone who looks different, who has different abilities and needs and yet someone who is the same but is trapped in a dysfunctional body. This can cause pain, misunderstanding and resentment. I have been fortunate to live with people who have been supportive and patient. My daily life is often enriched, because I appreciate little things as gifts, like the ability to walk and talk at the same time. I used to concentrate so hard on walking that I couldn't talk. To be able to get on a bus is another achievement. Who in their right mind would think that catching a bus was a gift? Only someone who couldn't do it for years! To see the veins in your arms reappear and be able to pinch the skin on your neck and arms after years of tough, hard, shiny tissue is wonderful. I feel that support groups like yours and ours are invaluable. Not only do they give emotional and practical support and information, but they give opportunities to become involved and to contribute. The groups also foster friendships with people who really do understand your situation.

Australia is a vast country with only 17 million people. We have 6 groups in Australia with the Scleroderma Association of New South Wales as the main group. We are not connected into a federation but we do have close contact and get together whenever possible. The largest groups are New South Wales, Victoria and the Hunter Region which are autonomous. The smaller groups such as our own, the Queensland and Tasmanian ones are connected to the Arthritis Foundation. We are lucky to have their support as we couldn't exist without them.

The above article was taken from a talk given by Julie McMahon who was a guest speaker at our Annual Conference in 1991. Members were very impressed by Julie's positive attitude to her condition and it was a pleasure to spend the weekend in Julie's company.

Why tat? Why knotterie?

We started trying to raise money in the mid 80's but as beginners we had a number of disappointing if not disastrous events. However, we think we learnt a little from our failures e.g. which venues to avoid and certainly no jumble sales for us (no storage space available!). We then started running a tombola at boot sales, and this we have developed so that we give a prize for every ticket. How we manage this is too long a story for now! However, the main hazard with boot sales is the weather, too windy and the prizes blow away, too wet and they spoil, too hot and we sizzle! An additional idea was needed to work in parallel with tombolas. I had learned to tat in the early 50's but owing to pressure of work had a 30 year gap of non-tatting. Perhaps if I started again we could sell the items at Craft Fairs (under cover!) I began tatting motifs which Irene mounted in frames or paperweights. Slowly we began to sell them and gradually built up a stock. In November '89 we had a stall at a Soroptimist Craft Fair and sold over £100 worth with many follow up orders. We felt we had at last taken off. To have a more colourful display meant buying more balls of cotton. Prices ranged from £1 to nearly £2 for the smallest balls. It was then we decided to make a request in the Newsletter. The parcels started arriving from all parts of the country - a wonderful selection of colours and thicknesses, even shuttles. Friends also have provided us with card - we are now able to make gift tags. Our next hope is to find a firm or shop which will supply us with small pieces of velvet. The obsolete pattern books would be perfect. All this has changed our way of life considerably. I now tat 'daisies' whenever possible - in the car (I don't drive), on coach tours, in hospital waiting rooms etc. Complicated patterns are worked at home. Irene, however, can only do her part of the work at home, so has many housebound evenings. We have found that people watching me tat find it hard not to talk to us so, as an added bonus, we feel the exercise is also a publicity stunt for Raynaud's. Why Knotterie? The answer is simple. When applying for stands at Craft Fairs we found we needed a 'Trade Name'. We're not terribly inventive and as tatting is a series of knots we decided on Knotterie.

Joyce Bailey & Irene Cammegh

If only you knew!

The following article from Marion Robinson doesn't even begin to describe how hard she and her husband Mike have worked during the past four years to raise funds for research. They have raised a staggering £15,000 in spite of Marion having Raynaud's, scleroderma and rheumatoid arthritis. She is always cheerful, willing to help all she can (ours isn't the only charity she helps), yet she is constantly in pain. Mike is a tower of strength, helping with her market stalls - she could not do all the lifting and carrying without him.We would like to say a very big thank you to these two very special people - whose efforts are very much appreciated.

Raising Money Can Be Fun!

Here we go again to Wendover or Tring Market. It's 7 am or thereabouts and the car is packed with about 10 apple boxes full of garments and bric-a-brac, with the clothes and rail piled on top. So many people have deposited bags on our doorstep and occasionally Lynx carrier delivers 10-12 very large boxes of goodies from Head Office. I have a wonderful time sorting them all ready for sale. Some need repairing, ironing or general sprucing up as my clothes rails always hold good, clean items and people are getting to know that they can get a bargain from my stall. Once the stall is set up (outside) and it's not raining (don't go if it is), we meet some lovely people who are most sympathetic when they see my hands. Some know of a friend or relation with similar problems and leaflets get passed around. We can also have a listening ear for those in distress.

At the Antiques Fair (not very antique) in Wendover Village Hall, the organiser very kindly offered me the Charity Stall at no charge. This is monthly but it doesn't bring in as much money as an open market. I have to be more selective and no clothes rail. If I have anything valuable, i.e. vases, china, silver, gold, linen, etc. I can sell to other stall holders and they give me a fair price. This has led me to dealers in books, records and coins, so in fact we are doing each other a good turn. Mike goes weekly to RAF Halton Thrift Shop with two bags full containing around 20 garments. The friendly ladies have named our charity for a donation of £200. I cannot drive or carry heavy items at the moment, that's why my lovely Mike goes. He's getting quite good at selling and comes with me to markets as he carries the boxes, etc. while I lay the tables. The rag man collects about 10 bags from us every 8-10 weeks and gives us £3 to £4. It all mounts up.

Marion Robinson

Collecting Box Champion

Jack Miles who holds the record for the greatest amount in a collecting box which he raised by doing odd jobs.

Hands

Anna & Raynor seen with some of the hands which have been donated during the past few years and which are displayed at Head Office.

Our collection of hands continues to grow thanks to companies who are invited to donate and members who send hands which they have spotted on holiday or at car boot sales. For new members who don't know what we are talking about, a couple of years ago we began to collect hands (the hand being our symbol). The collection now numbers well over 100 and includes hands made of pottery, china, porcelain, glass, wood, plastic, brass, stone, terracotta in fact almost everything and anything!! Our latest donations include a pottery hand from Malta given to us by Kathleen Belfield and a small decorative china hand from Chris Buckledee. 87 year old Mr. Gove from London has made us a very special hand in marquetry which is of the original logo of the Association. Portmeirion Pottery made a donation from their British Heritage Collection - 'Hand with Flambeau' and 'Hand with Tulip'. These really are very beautiful.

An Irish welcome

Our video 'Back in Circulation' has been in great demand and was requested for a meeting to be held in Dublin on Sunday 26th April 1992. On April 1st a copy was sent but by 22nd April it had not arrived. Another copy was sent by Datapost to be delivered on Saturday morning, the day before the meeting. I received a phone call at 7 pm on the Saturday to say it still hadn't arrived and not wanting to let the group down, said I would personally take a copy over. First thing on the Sunday morning, I found myself driving to Manchester Airport, boarding a plane and heading for Dublin. I had no idea what to expect but having said I would go, I was asked if I would speak at the meeting. On the plane journey (which went far too quickly!) I sorted out my talk and overheads. At the airport I was met by Phyl Keaveny and Nicky O'Reilly who seemed very relieved that I had arrived safely, complete with video. We went straight to the hotel and on the way I learned what was happening with the Irish Raynaud's Society which is affiliated to our Association. They had been working hard to get their Society off the ground and had just published their first newsletter. When a member joins the Irish Society they also become a member of our Association and receive a copy of our newsletter. We send the required number of copies to Dublin and they are then distributed to the members from the Irish group, together with their own newsletter.

The meeting had been advertised in newspapers but no one knew how many people would turn up. Mr. Vincent Keaveny and Dr. Barry Bresnihan were due to speak on Raynaud's and scleroderma and then our video was to be shown. I was very honoured to meet such lovely people and to have the opportunity to meet with members who had joined our Association several years ago, along with new members who had recently joined both groups. 175 people attended and it took me back to our first beginnings in 1982 and our first newsletter. Everyone was so delighted to be able to talk to others who shared their problems and to be able to ask questions of the doctors present. It really was a wonderful experience, to be part of this group. Vincent and Phyl Keaveny invited me to stay for the night and the next morning at breakfast there was a phone call asking me to do an interview on the Pat Kenny Radio Show in an hour's time! This gave me the opportunity to thank everyone for their hospitality and to spread the word about Raynaud's and scleroderma and the existence of the Irish Raynaud's Society. As the show was live and not to miss an opportunity, I asked for donations, help with fund raising and for sufferers to contact the group. An hour later I was on the plane back to Manchester and heading back to the office. A phone call from Dublin followed to say that they had received a tremendous response from the radio appeal. I eventually received reimbursement of my air fare from Datapost!

Anne Mawdsley

When Cold Hands Simply Mean 'Cold Hands'

Icy fingers may not necessarily mean Raynaud's syndrome. Women tend to feel cold more intensely than men do.

This could be because:

- **In general, women are smaller, which means that their blood vessels are smaller, too. Smaller blood vessels carry less blood.**
- **In women, blood vessels in the extremities constrict more quickly, sending blood back to the internal organs.**
- **Fat distribution in women is uneven. While breasts and buttocks tend to be well-insulated, other areas are not.**
- **Women have less muscle tissue (which burns calories and generates heat, even at rest), so less heat is generated.**

Surgery in Raynaud's and Scleroderma

There are essentially two aspects to surgery for the affected hand with scleroderma. One is confined to surgery for calcinotic nodules. Surgery in this case is largely reserved for those fingers where there is infection in association with the calcific deposit. It is important that when removing infected calcific deposits as much skin as possible is preserved and where possible, for the larger lesions, the defect covered by a split skin graft. The second aspect of surgery in Raynaud's and scleroderma concerns the augmentation of blood flow to the affected digits. It is now widely recognised that cervical sympathectomy has only a transient benefit and has been widely discontinued in the light of the discouraging results. Many patients of course, can be helped using traditional conservative methods such as drugs which dilate the blood vessels e.g. Nifedipine, Ketanserin, Diltiazem and, more recently, Iloprost. There are still however, a significant group of patients whose symptoms persist despite conservative treatment and it is this group that may benefit from digital sympathectomy.

Digital Sympathectomy

The operation itself requires the isolation of the terminal branches of the sympathetic nerves, the division of these nerves and then finally stripping adventitia (the outermost layer) from the digital arteries. This is done under general anaesthetic under tourniquet control exposing the individual digital nerves and arteries from the distal palm of the hand to the middle of the fingers. It is then usually possible to identify two or three communications between the digital artery and the digital nerve which can then be divided. Then using standard micro surgical techniques the adventitia around the digital artery is removed circumferentially for a length of approximately two centimetres, so effectively removing any remaining connections of the sympathetic nerves. It is important that the remainder of the artery (the media and intima) is not damaged lest this result in thrombosis and subsequent occlusion of the vital blood flow. Brisk return of circulation is confirmed following release of the tourniquet. Theoretically one should expect an immediate response but this may occasionally be delayed due to relatively high level of circulating adrenalin. Generally the response is observable several hours following the operation and by the following morning the finger is usually warmer and the temperature difference between the adjacent digits apparent.

We now have a series of thirteen patients with twenty one fingers and one toe having been operated on. To date we have had no complications and our early results are encouraging. In particular, any ulcers have healed rapidly and generally within two weeks of surgery. Also the distal pain has largely been alleviated. There has only been one patient in the series in whom wound healing proved to be a problem and this patient had extensive scleroderma. Importantly and significantly we have lost no fingers as a result of surgery. All of our patients have been thoroughly assessed pre and post operatively with thermograms and it appears that the results in our series are long lasting. This bears out other worker's experience which suggests that digital sympathectomy is a relatively uncomplicated procedure. It is effective in the majority of patients and there is no recurrence of symptoms following treatment. We will continue to further evaluate our patients and hope to present our long term results in due course.

Mr. Nick Goddard,
Orthopaedic Surgeon, Royal Free Hospital.

Cervical Sympathectomy

The Association is continually being asked questions about the operation called 'cervical sympathectomy' as a treatment for Raynaud's. We have included several articles on this subject in our newsletters in the past but felt that it would be appropriate to discuss this further. Maurice Raynaud's theory in 1862, was that the cause of the condition lay in the sympathetic nervous system. He thought that it must be overactive, making the arteries so narrow that not enough blood could get through to the extremities to keep them alive. In 1901 an English doctor called Hutchinson supported this theory. By the turn of the century surgery had advanced to a degree where the sympathectomy was performed regularly and safely for various conditions including Raynaud's phenomenon. Initial reports suggested that sympathectomy produced great benefit in vasospastic disease but as time went on it became clear that any benefit from the operation in the upper limb soon wore off or did not help at all. Surgeons initially blamed these failures on inadequacy of sympathectomy due to poor surgical technique and more extensive operations were devised but produced the same poor results.

Mr. Kevin Lafferty, M.S., F.R.C.S., author of the book 'Raynaud's - A Better Understanding', concludes that "cervical sympathectomy for Raynaud's phenomenon" (i.e. bilateral symmetrical episodic digital vasospasm) has been shown time and time again to be of little or no benefit." A point of interest on this operation, which was previously done through an incision in the neck, is that it can now be performed via a telescope inserted in the armpit. It is used for a condition called 'hyperhidrosis' (excessive perspiration).

Results of a questionnaire which was completed by 571 members of our Association, and analysed by researchers at Dulwich Hospital, showed that 81.4% of sympathectomies had failed, the majority within a year. In Dr. Stuart Roath's book 'Raynaud's - A Guide for Health Professionals', Dr. Derek Waller states that "there is probably no place for cervical sympathectomy in patients with resistant Raynaud's phenomenon". In the BMJ dated 12th October, an article entitled 'Raynaud's Syndrome and Similar Conditions', stated that "The indications for cervicothoracic sympathectomy are few". Beneficial effects, especially in patients with connective tissue disorders are difficult to achieve and are shortlived". Mr. Bruce Pardy, Consultant Surgeon at Newham Hospital, says "I believe that today there is almost no place for upper limb sympathectomy in the management of patients with Raynaud's phenomenon".

Treatment for Calcinosis

The Association recently funded a video entitled 'Drilling for Calcinosis' made by Mr. J. H. Webster, Consultant Surgeon to the Southampton University Hospitals.

Mr Webster wrote "I am most grateful to the Association for their generous support in helping me to make a short teaching video. The subject of this video is the management of one of the unpleasant complications of the CREST syndrome, (calcium deposits in the fingers). The technique shown in this video is to drill out the calcium with a dental drill. This procedure is long established but hardly anybody seems to know about it. It is well shown in the video which seems to have caused quite a lot of interest. The video was shown at a recent meeting of the Association of Surgeons. The great advantage so far as I can see over other methods of treating this condition is the remarkable lack of post-operative pain, and patients having it done go home the next day".

Mr. Nick Goddard who has been performing digital sympathectomies at the Royal Free Hospital was most interested in this video and has in fact used this technique recently with very good results.

Review of dietary therapy for Rheumatoid Arthritis

This article has been based on the talk given by Dr. Gail Darlington at our Annual Conference in 1991.

Introduction

The idea that dietary manipulation may alter symptoms of rheumatoid arthritis (RA) is part of the folklore of the disease. For decades patients have adjusted their diets to try to reduce symptoms, until recently with little scientific support for their actions. Many conclusions from early studies of diet for arthritis are based on inadequate uncontrolled data and poor study design, and the possibility that food and rheumatoid diseases may be interrelated has not been studied scientifically until fairly recently.

Definitions

Dietary therapy for RA may be divided into two types: supplementation therapy, in which foods are added to the diet, and elimination therapy, in which foods are removed from the diet.

Dietary Supplementation Therapy

Among dietary supplements, the best studied are fish oil, evening primrose oil (EPO), New Zealand green lipped mussel and selenium, but vitamins, herbs, kelp, royal jelly, ginseng, cider vinegar, garlic and honey are also popular among patients.

Fish oils

Enthusiasm for fish oils is widespread among rheumatoid patients but doctors have been cautious. Eskimos on their traditional diet rich in marine oils, have a low incidence of inflammatory disorders. Fish oils are used in the production of chemicals in the body which are less inflammatory than those derived from saturated fats, and work to date on the use of fish oils for rheumatoid patients is interesting and promising and the treatment appears to be safe. Long-term toxicity studies are needed however, and also studies to determine whether low-dose fish oil (as taken by patients without prescription), is effective, since many of the good results so far reported have been in studies using only high-dose fish oil concentrates not available without prescription and fairly expensive to prescribe.

Evening Primrose Oil

Evening primrose oil can be used as a building block for the production of chemicals which are less inflammatory in the body than those produced from saturated fat. The data so far reported from using evening primrose oil for rheumatoid patients appear promising but need to be confirmed by further work with long-term toxicity studies. One multicentre study incorporating 300 - 400 RA patients treated with EPO has already been planned in the U.K. but others are needed. As yet, EPO cannot routinely be prescribed for rheumatoid arthritis and patients have the considerable expense of this long-term treatment, so further studies are therefore needed to clarify its therapeutic role.

New Zealand green lipped mussel (Seatone)

Seatone is an extract of the New Zealand green lipped mussel, Perna canaliculus. It was found to have some anti-inflammatory activity in rats and was reported enthusiastically in the press. On the other hand, the evidence to date that Seatone has significant value in rheumatoid arthritis is slight, although it has an undoubtedly powerful placebo effect and may have mild anti-inflammatory activity. There is no definite evidence that the product is effective orally and it is expensive for patients to buy.

Selenium

Abnormalities in the metabolism of the essential trace element Selenium (Se) have been implicated in rheumatoid patients. Selenium concentrations were found to be relatively low in the serum of rheumatoid patients when compared with healthy controls. Review of studies, however, shows that oral Selenium therapy appears to have a limited value in the management of rheumatoid arthritis.

Dietary Elimination Therapy

This therapy involves removal from the diet of those foods which cause symptoms, preferably after the latter have been determined specifically, rather than by the exclusion of large groups of foods which may or may not be culpable. The dietary programme falls into three main parts: Firstly, the removal from the diet of any foods which might be causing symptoms, to determine whether symptoms improve on their removal i.e. the exclusion phase. Secondly, if symptoms do disappear, foods are then re-introduced, one at a time, to discover which ones produce symptoms i.e. the re-introduction phase. Thirdly, for credibility in a research context, the results of such diets need to be confirmed by double-blind challenge, now recognised as essential to confirm subjective results from the first two dietary phases. Although all elimination diets work on the same principle, there are several possible variations in method, ranging from a total fast for one week, with the exception of bottled spring water, to a diet of fish, pears, carrots and water, the latter being nourishing, acceptable and not too demanding. Such dietary manipulation takes approximately 6 weeks to perform and is at present the only accurate and reliable way to confirm reactions to foods. It should be remembered, however, that this approach may lead to nutritional difficulties and social disruption, and there are dangers in the unsupervised use of diets, especially for infants and young children who may become seriously malnourished if the diet is taken to extremes. Elimination diets, therefore, should only be undertaken under medical supervision. Careful studies to assess dietary manipulation are important because RA relapses and remits spontaneously and because rheumatoid patients have a high placebo response rate. Many studies now suggest that dietary elimination therapy is of benefit to at least some patients with rheumatoid arthritis although the exact mechanism is as yet unknown. Weight loss and allergy do not seem to be relevant to the success of treatment but there is some evidence that particular foods are more troublesome than others and that cereals are high on the list of culprits.

On a practical note, patients should be discouraged from reading books on dietary treatment of RA available to the public, since a review we undertook of 21 such books in 1990 showed that advice on diets was conflicting and varied from book to book and various books were mutually contradictory.

Possible reasons for improvement on diets

Improvement of patients on dietary therapy may be the result of a number of different mechanisms, acting singly or in combination. Possible reasons for improvement include a placebo-response which certainly occurs in rheumatoid patients but which would not be expected to persist for more than a few months, and in fact, in at least two studies, much longer improvement has been reported. There could be an acute allergic reaction but no evidence of this has been found in studies so far performed. It is possible that the ability of the gastrointestinal tract to absorb may vary i.e. it may be increased in some rheumatoid patients, particularly those taking anti-inflammatory drugs and this may increase any tendency to absorb food antigens and/or bacteria. A reduction in permeability on dietary treatment may be beneficial. It has been suggested that the bacteria present in the gut may be affected by dietary manipulation in some way which is beneficial and which suppresses the inflammatory process in which such bacteria may play a part. This is still controversial but very interesting work and various different bacteria have been suggested as having a part to play. There are now sufficient good scientific studies, from the United Kingdom and abroad, to suggest that, at least in some patients with rheumatoid arthritis, dietary therapy may influence at least the symptoms and possibly the progression of the disease. Since dietary treatment is safe and may reduce or avoid the need for drugs, it is appealing to patients, who are increasingly anxious about potential drug toxicity. It must, however, be medically supervised to avoid misinterpretation of results, to protect patients from taking diets to extremes, with resultant malnutrition, particularly in children, and to prevent patients from persisting with ineffective diets when they should be receiving drug treatment. Medical interest in dietary treatment also ensures that patients discuss their diets with orthodox practitioners rather than being driven by our scepticism into the hands of unqualified people who may exploit patients' interest in the subject.

Summary

More research is needed: dietary supplements not yet assessed scientifically need assessment, fish oils need further investigation e.g. to determine whether low dose fish oil has any value or whether it is only useful in the concentrated form so far used in controlled studies. Evening primrose oil needs to have its therapeutic value confirmed and its safety determined. Dietary elimination therapy needs investigation with double-blind challenge, its long-term efficacy needs further documentation and individual dietary components need to be considered in detail for effects on arthritic activity rather than empirical exclusion of whole ranges of foods. More work is required to determine the possible role of gut flora in RA, with investigations of any link between dietary manipulation and gut flora and clinical remission. Finally, the whole field of possible antibiotic therapy to alter gut flora and possibly, thereby to affect clinical activity in RA needs to be explored. Much remains to be done but the potential for benefit is great.

Dr. Gail Darlington

Sjögren's Syndrome - Do we know the cause?

We do know that auto immunity is involved in Sjögren's Syndrome. The immune system appears to be overactive and attacks its own organs, such as the salivary and lacrima glands. Abnormal proteins or antibodies are produced and these proteins circulate in the blood. Over the past ten years, there has been evidence that viruses are probably involved. These may be specific viruses or several different viruses. There is some evidence that the virus which causes mononucleosis (Epstein Barr Virus) may trigger Sjögren's Syndrome. Certain genetic factors are involved as are hormones, and this condition primarily affects women.

Diagnosis

How does one diagnose Sjögren's Syndrome when it varies from person to person? Clinical suspicion is the major ingredient of diagnosis. If you don't know what a disease is you can't make a diagnosis. Once that suspicion is there, depending upon symptoms, the diagnosis may become apparent through an eye examination by an ophthalmologist. He or she may use a Schirmer test to measure the flow of tears, or staining of the eye to see if there are areas of dryness in the cornea. In some individuals who do not have dry eyes, a dry mouth is the main complaint. Here the salivary biopsy usually of the lower lip is more often used. Testing the blood for anti-Ro and La is also useful. The eyes should always be examined because people may have asymptomatic dry eyes and be unknowingly developing damage to their corneas.

The above has been extracted from an article based on a presentation by Dr. Arnett, Professor of Internal Medicine, in the Division of Rheumatology at the University of Texas Medical School at Houston. It appeared in the Moisture Seekers Newsletter from New York.

Rose promoting the Association at a Car Boot Sale.

TV star in the making!

When Granada Television approached the Association to take part in an appeal film for the Telethon in July 1992 we had no idea what they had in mind or who would take part. Still, it was a challenge and one which we felt would help to promote the work of the Association. A few local members were invited to the office where they met a researcher for the programme and spent several hours, before deciding the best way to present the appeal. We wanted the film to feature a positive theme yet at the same time show the problems experienced by sufferers. Rose Woodward from Congleton had all the qualities we were looking for and was chosen to represent the Association. Rose is 56 years old, her hands are very badly disfigured from scleroderma but she has a staggering determination.

The following is Rose's story, taken from the script before it was edited:-

"I've had scleroderma for 15 years and it has been very gradual - going through different stages of joint discomfort and muscle discomfort. You're never really free from some part that aches, you feel tired, very lethargic and the next day you feel as if you're going to move mountains - you don't, but it gives you that little bit of a boost because you do feel that perhaps the next day you can do this. At first physically you feel very slow, you will feel sorry for yourself but you've got to be strong, tell yourself that you're not going to give in and just keep on pushing yourself. Not to the extreme that hurts but don't just sit and do nothing about it - keep going, think what you did weeks ago, try to tell yourself you're going to do that again tomorrow as best you can. Keep your clothes and your hair nice and really help yourself a little bit. It's a very depressing illness because people will say you look so well - well just tell yourself that you do feel well. It's very difficult if you feel like a little cry - go into your bedroom, tell your best friend, tell your husband but try to keep a good face for outside and you will find you get a lot more help if you help yourself. In the beginning the skin is quite supple and then gradually you feel you'll reach out one day and the skin feels so tight that you think it is going to split - it's a very tight, pulling feeling all the time. When the face is affected you feel that you really want to stretch your face, like a snake wants to shed its skin, you feel as if you could just take that skin off and then your face would be able to move how you feel you want it to move. For some reason mine has softened a little. Whether it's the help of medication, I don't know, maybe it's my own feeling of relaxing into the condition. The more tense you are, the more stressed you are, the worse the condition feels and also I've found that with the Raynaud's, if you get stressed, you have an attack. Apart from the temperature dropping, I think being stressed sets off an attack of Raynaud's, so if you can relax through some tension, I think you'll find the attack will gradually go away on its own.

I think a lot of us will find the relationship with our loved ones will alter, as with any long term illness. They gradually stop being your lover and stop being your husband and they tend to feel this too because they're no longer this part of your life. They are more a helper and nurse, sometimes you get very cross with each other. It's got to happen because this isn't the role you married your partner for. You vow for better or worse but sometimes I'm afraid a little bit of the worse comes out when things are not being done as you like to do them and he thinks he's doing it the correct way. But you have to be very patient with each other, very tolerant. I think my husband over the years has been both patient and tolerant. Don't get me wrong, we still argue when he is trying to dress me but we really do try to pull together. We've lasted 15 years with this condition and 38 years of marriage, so I think we can continue a little bit longer! I think this is where the funds for welfare would help enormously. If you could have someone perhaps a couple of hours a day 2 or 3 times a week even, just to relieve your husband from the pressures. Help is available on the NHS but it is so few and far between. If you could get help on your own to relieve the tension between you, it would help enormously. You have to be positive and help each other. You only get out of this world what you put into it, and the stress and strain is going to tell on everyone because it is a very, very long, tiring illness.

Fortunately, I've always been a strong character. I think maybe I've found great difficulty in accepting people's help. I've always been so independent and probably a bit too strong a character. I think people hesitate to help. My tongue is still a little bit sharp perhaps with some people but I think at this stage, I really do appreciate help.

There comes a time when you know you've got to accept it, but do not give in. To cheer myself up, I usually borrow my husband's wallet and do like all normal women and skip off to town, find someone to come along with me and help me choose a pretty blouse or take myself away for a weekend - to break the monotony for both of us. If you're down then your partner is going to be down and then it is only you that can help by setting out and achieving something to cheer you up. If you come back smiling as usual, then it will cheer up all the family, helping them to carry on and help you through a little bit more. I think the Association is a wonderful thing. I didn't discover it until quite recently. I live on the doorstep but just in the short time I've found it so beneficial to ring up the Association for any help. If you're feeling down, speak to Anne or someone at the Association and you will feel so much better - they do such tremendous work for Raynaud's and scleroderma patients".

Following the Appeal which went out not only in the Granada area but also on National network, the Association received many calls from sufferers who had not heard of us previously. Rose wanted very much to help our Welfare Fund, so she organised a stall at a Car Boot Sale and then went around the field in her wheelchair selling our raffle tickets.

Floral Tribute

This floral display was created by Congleton Borough Council Park's Department to commemorate our 10th Anniversary. Members from all over the country have been to see this beautiful tribute to our charity. We would like to thank the Council most sincerely for all the work which they have put into the design and creation of this flower bed.

Welfare Donation

The Association has received generous funding from Marks & Spencer Plc over the past three years, towards our welfare funding. Pictured here handing over the last £2,000 installment on behalf of the company is the Crewe store department administration manager Dorothy Bratherton (right) with Anne Mawdsley (centre) and Welfare Officer Raynor Lancaster (left). The group are shown in front of the Association's floral carpet, which is situated opposite St. Mary's Church in Alsager.

Anniversary Conference 1992

This year's conference was very special being our 10th Anniversary. More people attended than at any other meeting since the Inaugural Conference in 1983, and there was a tremendous atmosphere with many new friendships being made, particularly amongst those who stayed over the weekend. We were most grateful to our speakers who gave up their valuable time to join us. A good mixture of humour and up to date information was the order of the day and all who attended felt that not only had they learned more about their condition but had enjoyed themselves as well.

After the dinner on Friday evening Dr. Black gave a talk about scleroderma overseas and she read out several messages which had been sent to congratulate the Association on our 10th Anniversary.

The following quotes are taken from these letters:

"Congratulations and best wishes to the Raynaud's & Scleroderma Association of Great Britain on your 10 year celebration. You have come a long way in these 10 years with lots of dedication, enthusiasm and hard work. Congratulations and I look forward to many more years of association and friendship".

Barbara Roberts, Scleroderma Society of New Zealand.

"On behalf of the members of the Scleroderma Association of New South Wales, Australia, I would like to extend to you and your members our sincere congratulations and very best wishes for your 10 year celebration. Your dedication in making life a little easier for people with Raynaud's and scleroderma has been an inspiration to all of us. We hope that it will not be too long before your hard work is rewarded with the realisation of our common dream for the future.

With kind regards to all of you from your brothers and sisters 'down under'".

Irene Case, Scleroderma Association of NSW, Australia.

"The members of the Lupus Scleroderma Group of the Arthritis Foundation of Australia - South Australian Branch - send greetings and best wishes for a successful 10th Birthday celebration and conference to the Raynaud's & Scleroderma Association of Great Britain. We are most appreciative of the contact we have had with you and access to information we have obtained from your publications and the 'Hot News' Newsletter.'

Sr. Julie McMahon, Arthritis Foundation of South Australia, Ashford.

"Our best congratulations to your 10th Anniversary of the foundation of the Raynaud's & Scleroderma Association and also our best wishes for the future for your organisation. We assume it was a long and hard way up to that Anniversary but in any case a successful one. Because of the fact that the origin of this disease is still unknown, the self-aid organisations do a lot of work in helping each other in initiation and mobilising a new vital energy to their members, so that life becomes a little bit more worthwhile.

We wish you to go ahead in this way and to have further success with your work, and we remain with our best regards.'

Antje Heinrich, Selbsthilffegruppe
Sklerodermie in Deutschland E.V.

"To the assembly of the Raynaud's & Scleroderma Association of Great Britain we like to congratulate you with your first decade of good work. May many decades follow!'

Enjoy the memorable day of 12th September 1992.

Peter Bakker, Nat. Vereniging
L. E. Patienten in The Netherlands.

"We wish you and your Association a successful celebration of your 10th Anniversary. We are with you in spirit. To express our thanks for your co-operation we are sending a small donation of £76.

With kind regards from the Raynaud's sufferers in Holland.'

Bart van Zenderen, Vereniging van Vaatpatienten,
Bunnik, Holland.

"Happy Anniversary! The 12th September is indeed a benchmark for patients suffering from scleroderma or Raynaud's syndrome, not only in Great Britain but also in other countries. What you and your colleagues during the past ten years have achieved is remarkable and wonderful. You have made the diseases known in the general public, you have co-operated with doctors across many specialisations and supported research and you have made it possible for all of us to know more about our diseases.

Unfortunately we are not able to join you at your annual seminar this year, because we on the very same day have arranged our own seminar for the second time. It will take place in Odense, the town of the fairytale writer, Hans Christian Andersen. The idea of having Summer seminars we have got from you. This year we will have nearly 80 persons attending the seminar. We are happy to be part of your international network and look forward to co-operate with you in the future.

As a token of our appreciation and support of your work we enclose a cheque for £200 as our birthday present to you.

From all of us to all of you - Happy Birthday and all the best in the future.

Niels Bo Sorensen, Danish Scleroderma Society.

"On behalf of the Executive Body and Membership of SRF, we send Best Wishes to the Raynaud's & Scleroderma Association of Great Britain on its 10 Year Celebration.

Working together to help find a cure!'

Emanuel A. Coronis, Jr., Scleroderma Research Foundation,
Columbus, New Jersey, USA.

"Congratulations and good wishes to the Raynaud's & Scleroderma Association of Great Britain on your 10 Year Celebration.

Keep up the good work - you have done a great job!'

Arkie Barlet, Scleroderma International Foundation, Pennsylvania, USA.

"Congratulations and best wishes to our good friends of the Raynaud's & Scleroderma Association of Great Britain as they celebrate their 10th year of fine work.

All of us at the Scleroderma Federation wish you many more years of success. Let us hope that one day soon our efforts will be rewarded with a cure!'

Marie A. Coyle, Scleroderma Federation, Massachusetts, USA.

A view from Holland

Tired but very happy, that is how I felt after the 10th Anniversary Conference in September. I remember feeling really at home in the office the day after (Sunday) and saying to Anne "if there is anything I can do". She looked at me and said: "Yes as a matter of fact there is. Could you write a report on the conference for our Christmas Newsletter?" To be able to write about the conference I have to go back to the very beginning and start with how I prepared myself to go - mentally I mean. Once upon a time a Dutch doctor went to England to a conference about Raynaud's and met Anne. He came home and told me about the Association, I became a member and for years I read the leaflets and Newsletters. They diagnosed me with very severe Raynaud's. I went from one university centre to another ending up hating doctors and with a fear of investigations. I was so fed up with being a patient that I decided I only wanted the drips that made my life easier and, encouraged by other doctors, I refused any investigation until now. Meanwhile I didn't renew my membership but let it slip away. I thought if I didn't pay any attention and kept on seeing only the bright side then this is just a nightmare and it will go away. But it didn't. I changed doctors and came back to the one that made me a member in the first place. He thought I should contact England as soon as possible. I did and found myself talking on the phone to Anne who never made any reproach - she just was there and listened to me. I was really panicking because I just found out that acting as an ostrich wasn't too smart. Anne invited me to come over to the conference and Annie, a friend, said she would travel with me.

Marjolein (right) with her friend Annie.

We took the aircraft on Friday afternoon 11th September

- our journey had begun. We were met at the Airport by Raynor's Mum and Anne's Mum was driving. She doesn't live in the area so she didn't know the way but we enjoyed a ride through the countryside and had time to adjust ourselves to England! When we finally found Alsager we went past the lovely flower display and thought about what laid ahead. I was really very tired, tensed and worried but I needn't have been. People were so nice and friendly! We were received with a 'cuppa' and sandwiches at the office, we really felt in England among friends. Anne had put me on the ground floor with Annie in a room next to me and I began to relax, sure that it would be a nice weekend! Friday evening it all began with a welcome dinner. Anne opened the Conference with a word of welcome to us from Holland. We enjoyed dinner with nice people. Dr. Black talked about research around the world and she read out congratulations from other associations abroad. After dinner we were invited to a room where the Anniversary Draw would take place. We had to wait several minutes before the doors opened and I was so cold, I started shivering and clacking my teeth. Suddenly somebody came next to me and started to warm me up. I was so surprised, people without me asking, helped! Thank you Kathy. After the Draw, which had raised a lot of money, we did some Christmas shopping. I bought a little bear and a snuggler, a modern version of the good old hot water bottle which can be put into the microwave, very handy and much safer for me than coping with hot water and a bottle.

Later that evening and the following day people asked me how I felt and if I was warm enough. I was really moved about everybody's concern. I never experienced anything like this before, complete strangers who turned out to be friends. Somebody said to me later on we're all in the same boat, we know how it feels. After a short night, a big breakfast and registration we received a conference bag and notebook. We were fully prepared for whatever the conference might bring. Beforehand I had a little chat with Dr. Black who gave me a glimmer of hope for the future, things were not as bad as they had told me in Holland! The conference itself was really interesting. I learned a lot and we enjoyed ourselves. British humour is admirable! The atmosphere was very good, serious matters combined with a big birthday party. Afterwards with tea and biscuits there was plenty of time to talk to people. I met a lot of new friends. Then there was dinner again for those who stayed overnight. It felt as if we were at a family reunion. We watched the video about Raynaud's and scleroderma and Annie had the splendid idea to take the video home so people could see where we had been and what an excellent job is being done in England. I took it to the hospital where I get my drips. Most nurses are fully ignorant about the condition and don't have the faintest idea what scleroderma is. Now they will know! We watched the Last Night of the Proms, and according to those present, we saw the British at their most eccentric! On Sunday we had time to be in the office together before the aircraft took us back to Holland. In a few days, after what had begun as a somewhat scary adventure not knowing what to expect, we felt at home! Raynor and Betty took us to Manchester Airport and it was difficult to say Goodbye. I felt as if we had left good friends behind and I miss you all!

Thank you all very much for being there.

Marjolein Taanman

Further extension to the office

Members who have called at the office will be aware of the need for more space and those who have called recently will know what a mess we are in now that the builders are in action! However, it will be worth it when it is all finished. Our thanks to BT who are sponsoring the project and British Gas who are putting in the radiators and extra heating free of charge. Local firms have been more than generous by giving discounts on materials and we are most grateful to Redland Bricks for donating the bricks, Ensors for the breeze blocks, Audley Builders Merchants and Jewsons for the sand, cement and Maldon Timber Ltd. for the double glazed window. and Scanlans who donated a skip to remove the rubble.

We are not finished yet so there is more begging to be done!!

The new extension to the office was opened by the Mayor of Congleton, Mrs Shirley Jones on 23rd February 1993. In the photograph from left to right, Anne Mawdsley, Rose Woodward, Sheila Clothier (BT) and Shirley Jones.

Welfare support

Welfare help has been given to several members. These include donations towards a holiday, a specially-adapted car and a battery operated wheelchair for Jean Howie in Bath.

Jean writes:

"I just had my 70th birthday the day before, so full of surprises I thought I would never be surprised again, when I had a visit from Anne and her mother, Muriel. They had both been to see me on previous occasions but that particular visit left me speechless. Anne knew that I had borrowed a lightweight wheelchair as I can no longer walk around my flat and she had called to tell me that the Association would like to buy me my very own chair.

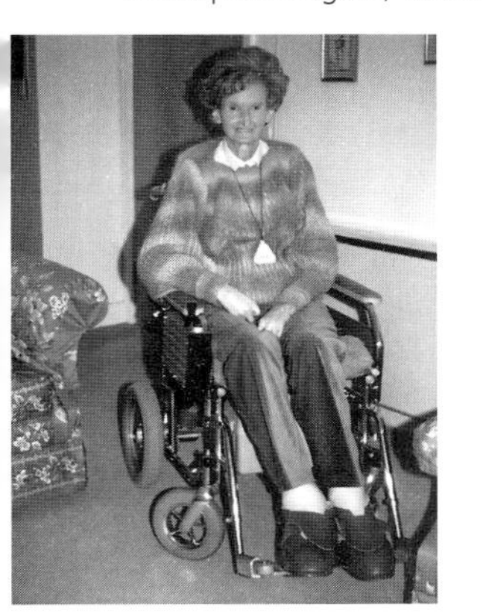

Jean in her new wheelchair which helped to give her independence.

Two weeks later it arrived and what bliss! The doors, walls and furniture have taken a few knocks but I'm getting better now. Up until June I was able to get around my flat with the aid of a 'walker' but after being in hospital for two months, I simply could not walk anymore.

Without this wheelchair I would be completely housebound, dependent on friends to do my shopping but now I can get to Waitrose in Bath each week, visit friends and I really move quite fast!

I cannot ever thank the Association enough for a simply wonderful gift which has made my life so much easier and more independent".

New Publication

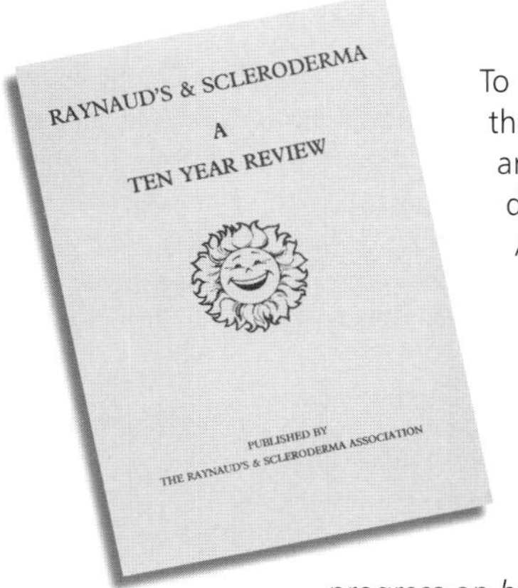

To celebrate our 10th Anniversary a book was launched at the 1992 Annual Conference on 12th September at Crewe and Alsager College. The Anniversary publication contains details of research which have been funded by the Association during the first 10 years. It is unique in that it is the only book containing research developments nationwide. All doctors who have received grants from the Association have contributed, Dr. Carol Black edited the material and The Duke of Westminster wrote the Foreword.

"...this book is a good straightforward read. It couldn't be a better symbol or guide to the work in progress on behalf of present day sufferers".

Dr. Mike Smith

"...we are working together to make the future brighter for those who suffer from Raynaud's, whether primary or secondary, and we must continue to do this with enthusiasm, hard work and belief in a better future".

Dr. Carol Black

Artists at risk?

Spotted by member Mrs Gilham in The Independent Magazine - In the 'Lancet' in early 1988, a report by a research team in Copenhagen indicated that artists using bright colours are at risk. It concluded that Rubens, Renoir and Dufy who tended to use brighter colours than their contemporaries, all suffered from rheumatic disease while Klee suffered from scleroderma. All seem to have been victims of slow poisoning with heavy metals from their paints. Lead is not the only culprit, of course. Bright yellow paint contains lead, arsenic and cadmium. Bright red contains cadmium and mercury. The dangers are increased if you fail to wash your hands before eating.

Paul Klee

(See article on Paul Klee on page 189).

Still going strong

Research Update

Projects currently being supported by the Association, costing a total of £342,896.80 of which we still have an outstanding commitment of £196,169.96, are as follows:

Royal United Hospital for Rheumatic Diseases in Bath - Professor Peter Maddison. Project title 'Antinuclear Antibodies in Systemic Sclerosis Patients and their Relatives".

Royal Brompton Heart and Lung Hospital - Dr. Ron du Bois. Project title 'Lung Disease in Systemic Sclerosis - A Study of Highly Sensitive Indices of Inflammation in Detection and Monitoring Disease Activity'. This work continues the research previously funded by the Association and is to run for two years.

Hope Hospital - Professor Malcolm Jayson. Project title 'The Study of the Role of Hypoxic Reperfusion Injury in the Pathogenesis of Raynaud's and Systemic Sclerosis'.

King's College Hospital - Mr. Paul Baskerville. Project title 'The Endothelial Cell in Raynaud's Phenomenon and its Relationship to Oestrogen/Progesterone'.

Southampton General Hospital - Dr. Don Marcer. Project title 'Psychosocial and Behavioural Factors in the Causation and Treatment of Raynaud's Disease'.

Royal Free Hospital - Dr. Carol Black. Project title 'Molecular Pathology of Lymphocyte Adhesion and Phenotypic Surface Antigens in Dermal and Lung Fibroblasts in Scleroderma'. In addition to funding Rama Vancheeswaren, on this project, the Association also provides funding for Dr. Black's department to help with her clinical research work. Our contribution in this area totals £110,000 to support the salaries of Kevin Howell, Dr. Geraldine Brough and Dr. Xu Shiwen.

Nucleolar antibodies in Scleroderma

During a hospital visit, most patients with Raynaud's or scleroderma will have had a blood sample taken in order to identify any auto antibodies which may be present. Antibodies are part of the body's natural immune response against infections. For reasons which are not yet known, most sufferers from connective tissue diseases make antibodies against components of their own cells. These so-called auto antibodies are produced in a highly specific manner. Only a limited number of types have been discovered, and a single patient only rarely presents with more than one or two of these. Furthermore, the particular auto antibody found in a given patient, and its quantity in the bloodstream, is a good indicator of the exact form of their disease, and can be an important diagnostic aid. This information can also help the physician to choose the most suitable treatment for the patient concerned, and can indicate which systems of the body require special attention or investigation.

The association of particular auto antibodies with disease subtypes has been much studied in related diseases such as systemic lupus erythematosis. Much work has also been done on the two most common scleroderma auto antibodies, anti-Scl-70 and anticentromere. However, several more types are also found in this patient population, known as anti-nucleolar antibodies, they are much more difficult to detect, requiring a special technique known as immuno precipitation. Once identified, however, they are equally good indicators of the clinical picture, assisting in specific diagnosis of disease subtype, and aiding prognosis. These more unusual antibodies are being studied at Bath Institute for Rheumatic Diseases. The large number of patients with connective tissue disease passing through the hospital allows the perfect opportunity for studying the distribution of the antibodies in the different forms of the disease. Genetic factors are also being looked into, in order to help establish the risk-factors and causes of the disease, which may be genetic or environmental. Since the start of this work six months ago, good progress has already been made in optimising the technique of immuno precipitation. Hundreds of samples of DNA and blood have been obtained from our patients, and most of these have had a preliminary auto antibody screening using a technique known as immuno diffusion. Another screening test, particularly good for anti-nucleolar antibodies, called fluorescent immuno localisation, is also underway. Following the completion of screening, immuno precipitation will be carried out on all samples. Together with the results from concurrent DNA-finger printing and immuno blotting studies, we will be in a good position to gain a more detailed picture of the relationship between disease expression, genetic profile and anti-nucleolar antibody specifities, giving doctors additional information, helpful in the diagnosis and prognosis of their patients. The study will also provide further information about genetic and environmental factors operating in the expression of disease-specific auto antibodies, which may contribute to an understanding of the causes and development of the disease.

The generous support of the Raynaud's & Scleroderma Association in funding this project is greatly appreciated.

G R Harvey, Bath Institute for Rheumatic Diseases

Family study in Raynaud's

The following is an interim report on a study of families suffering from Raynaud's in order to determine the natural history of the condition.

Originally this study set out to look at 50 families with three or more members suffering from primary Raynaud's Phenomenon. Raynaud's is a common usually benign phenomenon, present in families. Using information from previous studies it was expected that this would give us more than 150 existing cases of Raynaud's Phenomenon and sufficient healthy young adults such that around 50 of these would develop Raynaud's within 10 years. At the same time, material was to be gathered for the study of the genetics of Raynaud's Phenomenon. Each family was to be visited once at the beginning of the study and again after two years. The visits were to consist of a clinical assessment - involving the filling in of a detailed questionnaire, taking blood samples and using a high powered magnifying glass looking at the blood vessels around the base of the nail. It was also important to educate the family to report any changes in their disease or any new members developing Raynaud's. On my appointment to the unit in January 1992 I was given a list of 35 initial contacts who had responded to articles in the Raynaud's & Scleroderma Association newsletter, Saga magazine, or were patients of Dr. Black. After a period of training I contacted those families and found that only 15 of them fitted the inclusion criteria i.e. at least three members of the family had primary Raynaud's Phenomenon, sufficient members of three generations were willing to take part in the study and there was no known family history of any connective tissue disease (with the exception of rheumatoid arthritis).

In order to recruit more families, I contacted the Raynaud's & Scleroderma Association again and also the ARC who organised press releases in several womens' magazines, local and national newspapers. I designed a poster for display in rheumatology and vascular units across the country and wrote to as many consultant rheumatologists as possible. From over 300 replies from potential volunteers I found another 25 families who fit all of the criteria giving a total of about 40 multi-case primary Raynaud's families and at least 150 Raynaud's sufferers. Most of these families have between 10 and 30 members willing to take part in the study. I expect the numbers to increase as it is only when I start to visit families that I am able to persuade more members to take part. I have on file a second group of families with multi-case Raynaud's Phenomenon, but only two surviving generations. These could be included at a later date if more families are needed. To date I have bled at least part of the majority of the families. Most families are very co-operative and will get together for visits, but others need almost one visit per person. Due to work commitments, many people require evening and weekend visits. After each visit the bloods are spun, separated and stored in a minus 70°C freezer, the family tree is entered on a computer programme and a copy of the consent form is sent to the G.P. A second follow-up questionnaire has been devised to be sent out to all participants at six monthly intervals. So far, no investigations have been carried out on the blood samples collected, so it is not yet possible to attempt any correlations using the data provided by the questionnaires. However, as soon as some results are available we will inform the Raynaud's & Scleroderma Association to whom we are very grateful for their continuing help with our research. We would also particularly like to thank those members who volunteered to give up their time and their blood for this study! Without these volunteers our research would be impossible.

Helen Wilson, Royal Free Hospital

Chilblain Research

Magpie Research carried out a survey on behalf of Pharmax Healthcare to determine the incidence of chilblains in the U.K. The survey was carried out during October 1992 and involved 772 housewives across 4 regions (Tyneside, West Midlands, Greater London and South West).

The results of the survey are detailed below:

a) Approximately 1 in 12 (8%) of the survey reported that they, or someone in their household, had suffered with chilblains in the last 2 years.

b) Sufferers were spread across all ages (including children), but incidence of chilblains was slightly higher in 35-49 years age group.

c) The incidence of chilblains was higher in the North/Midlands than in the London/South. 1 in 9 suffer in the North/Midlands compared to 1 in 20 in the South.

d) Females are the main sufferers of chilblains.

e) 70% of the survey who suffered from chilblains had done something to treat the condition. Of these, 45% had obtained medication from the chemist, 25% have visited their G.P. and 11% had used a homemade remedy.

From analysing this research, we estimate that there are 4.58 million people in the U.K. who suffer from chilblains.

Chilblains and Raynaud's

Many Raynaud's sufferers are prone to chilblains. They are caused by extremes of temperature - if in winter you are sitting close to the fire to get your feet warm, the blood will rush to the end of the toe. Then you walk away and your feet get cold again, and the blood supply gets cut very suddenly. This causes what look like bruises on the end of your toe when they first start, and that is a chilblain. Because of the poor blood supply, these bruises don't heal readily and often become infected. If your chilblains aren't broken you can use an ointment which will increase the blood supply to the area. You just rub a small amount into the top of your toe and that will increase the blood supply. (Balmosa is a product which can be bought inexpensively in a pharmacy). If they break, you have to be careful that you are not going to get them infected, so they have to be dressed regularly and you should see your G.P. or chiropodist to see what can be done specifically for your chilblains. Most chiropodists will look at a chilblain and know what it is. When you see a chilblain on your foot it gets quite a hard skin over it. The corns that you sometimes get in those areas can be either the result of the chilblain or they can cause the chilblain because it is a pressure area. You treat the chilblain by keeping socks on and keeping your feet at an even temperature. No hot water bottles in bed, and when you put your slippers on, try to warm them so that they are a nice even temperature. If you walk from a carpeted area onto tiles, for example in a bathroom, you are getting the feet cold, then if you take a shower the change in temperature again causes the blood to come rushing in because it is warm, then gets cut off on a cold floor.

In Memoriam

We were very sorry to hear that Mr Leonard Cotton had passed away in November 1993 after a short illness. Mr Cotton, Dean of Kings College Hospital, was one of the first doctors to become involved with the Raynaud's Association.

Mr Leonard Cotton

A success story

In 1985 we ran a story about an eleven year old girl called Fiona Sable (see page 27). Fiona suffered from Raynaud's, rheumatoid arthritis, scleroderma and lupus. She tried to live as normal a life as possible in spite of the problems she had to cope with.

"Fiona wears electrically heated gloves to maintain warmth and to try to arrest the ravages of arthritis on her tiny, bent fingers. At night she sleeps with her legs clamped in plastic splints and her hands bound to a plastic moulded hand to halt the twisting of her joints. The skin on her thin fingers where scleroderma has taken hold is tight and tough and frequently becomes ulcerated".

We lost contact with Fiona and her family when they moved but last year Fiona read an article and decided to get in touch with us. We were delighted to hear from her after knowing how poorly she was as a young girl and to hear how she is now.

Fiona wrote: "I'm almost 19 now and have never felt better. I saw your address in the 'Take A Break' magazine and thought you would like to know that I am now a Mummy! I had a baby girl, Danielle Louise, on 13th August 1991. Having Danielle has done me the world of good. Throughout my pregnancy I had only one ulcer on my finger and during my pregnancy all my treatment was stopped. Since Danielle's birth I haven't suffered severely in any way (touch wood). My hands still get painful during the cold weather but I don't go out unless I really have to. I recently saw my doctor at the hospital and he told me that my scleroderma was not active at the moment".

You don't look ill!

My wife's eighteen years with Raynaud's

Around eighteen years ago my wife Janet was diagnosed as having Raynaud's Disease. Raynaud's? Never heard of it. "You're a bit of a rarity" the G.P. said to her. She suffered from either 'dead' or painful blue fingers which subsequently affected her feet and even her knees. "Nothing we can do about it" said the G.P. "You'll just have to live with it or move to California' he said half jokingly. Janet felt very alone with Raynaud's from that day because nobody seemed to know what Raynaud's was and nobody really understood how she was feeling. After all, she didn't look ill! By chance she saw an item on TV about this woman who also suffered from Raynaud's and had decided to start a self-help group. Of course that woman was Anne Mawdsley.

Janet wrote to her and became one of the very early members of the Raynaud's Association as it was called then. We helped to raise funds for the Association in a variety of ways including holding a stall at the local Flower Show. Since then Janet has been to the Raynaud's Research Unit in Dulwich for various tests including a course of plasma pheresis. This involved putting her blood through a machine to 'cleanse' it, getting rid of all the antibodies. Unfortunately they built up again straight away. Eventually she was asked to try a new drug but with no guarantee of success - only bad side effects. Janet wouldn't try this as she has always been anti-drugs of any sort. She also spent a month in Mile End Hospital, London undergoing all sorts of tests, but with no concrete outcome. Since then she has tried all sorts of alternatives including homeopathy. She now sees a Reflexologist fairly regularly mainly to help relax painful shoulders and arms caused by muscle wastage, which in turn is caused by her poor circulation. Recently Janet mentioned to the Reflexologist that prior to a trip to America 19 years ago, she had a smallpox vaccination to which she reacted very badly. She had an infected arm for a month. As a very young child she had severe eczema and he told her that because of the eczema she should never have been vaccinated, as it upsets the antibodies in the blood. This has been referred to as Vaccinosis in homeopathic literature. Meanwhile Janet soldiers on with her Raynaud's (she has also been diagnosed as having lupus). She is determined to only use 'natural' methods to help herself, i.e. walking and other exercise, eating sensibly, dressing warmly, but no drugs. Sometimes she feels very down about it all but mostly she keeps a cheerful outlook. Her thinking is that nobody wants to know you if you are miserable all the time. She always looks forward to the Raynaud's newsletters as the main source of information - indeed almost the only source. The most unfortunate thing, maybe, about Raynaud's is that YOU DON'T LOOK ILL!

Brian Roberts

Honour for Anne and The Association

Anne Mawdsley MBE

Anne Mawdsley was awarded an MBE in the Queen's Birthday Honours List in June 1993. Anne founded the Raynaud's Association in 1982 (later to become the Raynaud's & Scleroderma Association), and has run it with great success since then. Her energy and enthusiasm have been prodigious and she has enabled the Association to become a powerful force at both national and international level. Her efforts have ensured that both Raynaud's and scleroderma are now much better known and understood and she has helped facilitate much current research. All of us are delighted with the award which is a tribute both to Anne and the Association she created.

Alan Golding, Chairman Trustee

Awareness Campaign 1993

In July we decided to send out a press release called 'Search For Sufferers' with an amazing response. More than 60 newspapers printed the article and Anne took part in 16 live BBC radio interviews and several independent radio stations also gave air time, many with 'phone-ins' to the programme. By far the greatest response came following an interview with Anne and Dr. Hilary Jones on GMTV in August. Although there was not time to get across all we would have wished, at least both Raynaud's and scleroderma were described and seen by millions of people across the country. Anne's hands performed brilliantly by turning bright blue in front of the cameras. The Association received over 2,000 enquiries in the next two weeks and these are still arriving at a rate of 50-70 daily. We have enrolled 300 new members to date as a result of this publicity. In November, Carol Black and Anne were interviewed by Jenni Murray on Woman's Hour on Radio 4.

Mrs Ann Winterton MP for Congleton came to launch the Awareness Week at the office with the release of hundreds of balloons. Ann Winterton accompanied Anne and Dr. Black when they visited Mr Tom Sackville MP, Junior Minister for Health. The meeting was to discuss issues relevant to Raynaud's and scleroderma sufferers.

I'm positive but realistic

In September 1986 we moved to Wales, to run our own hotel. Over the next few months I noticed that my fingers were turning blue at the slightest change of temperature, and I was getting quite a lot of septic fingers, even having to have nails removed. It was not until June of 1987 whilst having my gall bladder removed, that I was told I had Raynaud's! Soon after this I fell pregnant with my first child - I was twenty-nine years old. The pregnancy went well and I had a normal delivery at thirty-seven weeks after just four hours labour. Our lovely baby boy, Richard arrived on the 27th April 1988, weighing 5lbs 3ozs. In June 1988, we decided to move to Torquay and continue our business there. It was a hot summer and I noticed I had a rash on my lower arms and hands. The rash persisted and I went to my doctor. After many blood tests I was diagnosed as having systemic sclerosis. As you can imagine, I had never heard of it let alone knew what was going to happen over the next few years. I was referred to a Professor in Leeds who put me on Prednisolone and basically said I had nothing to worry about.

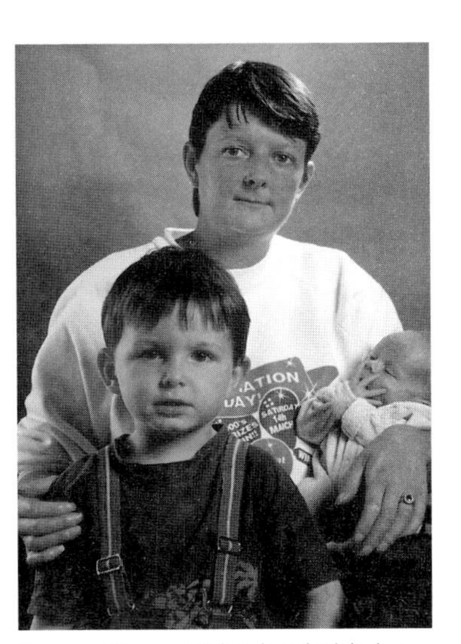

Susan with sons Richard and Nicholas

In 1991 I noticed two scaley patches of skin on my upper arms. I asked my local specialist if I could have a second opinion and was referred to a hospital in London where I was given infusions of prostacyciin, and was advised to come off the steroids. At this time I asked what the situation would be if I wanted another child. I was told the only problem would be a greater chance of early miscarriage but apart from that, all should be fine. In January of 1992, I was taken in for another infusion of prostacyclin. Not long after this I found out that I was pregnant again and they told me I was due in September, but due to the falling off of the baby's growth, they induced me in August. So on August 21st after a caesarian section, we had another boy weighing in at 4lbs 2ozs. After a shaky start due to a minor infection and a minor operation on his tummy, Nicholas was fine. It was about 4 weeks after his birth that I began to realise that I was having difficulty reaching objects on higher shelves and that picking Nicholas up and dressing him was becoming more difficult than usual. By November of the same year all the skin on my arms and across the top of my back and chest had hardened considerably, to the extent that I could no longer straighten my arms or turn my hands enough to pick Nicholas up. Also the pain in my joints was increasing. I contacted Anne Mawdsley at the Association for advice and was referred to another hospital in London. I was seen quickly in view of the rapid spread of the disease, and I have undergone various treatments. It was also established that since the birth, it has spread to my lungs. This was naturally very distressing. My hands were not good before the birth but I could manage to do some cooking and a little ironing and at least personal hygiene was no problem. However now I have to rely on other people to help me dress and wash my hair and assist me in and out of the bath. It is often the silly things that annoy me such as being unable to clean my teeth or brush my hair but possibly worst of all is the inability to do all the things for my baby that a mother wants to do.

I am very lucky because I live with my partner Keith and his parents, who are very supportive. Keith's mother does everything for Nicholas whilst Keith does as much as he can for me. My eldest son Richard understands my limitations, and often tries to help even though he is only five. My parents also try to help but they live in London. They do come down to help as much as possible. I must add that both sets of parents are in their seventies and therefore it is no joke to have a five year-old, a nine month-old and a thirty-four year old to clean up and look after. I have been very fortunate with my family for without them I would need twenty four hour help, but even though they are good, I still sometimes feel resentful that I can't cuddle my baby or play simple games with the older one like most mothers. Anyway, we have been told the prognosis is unsure but my partner and I are positive that I will still be here to see my grandchildren, although there are times when you can't help but wonder. I think the most important thing is to be positive, but also realistic. Having scleroderma could make it too easy to spend the rest of my life as a spectator but I am determined to participate as much as possible.

Susan Churcher

We Are No Longer Alone

As a new member of the Raynaud's & Scleroderma Association, I write with gratitude and thanks for the help that I was desperately seeking for my four year old son Robert. Robert was diagnosed as having scleroderma after seeing many different kinds of doctors. Because these doctors did not know much about this disease, they could only tell me the basic facts. This evoked a number of emotions in me which I could not cope with. I needed help but had no one to turn to. I went from denial to despair. After exhausting local libraries, my last hope was to contact my local paper which runs a 'helpline' page. My prayers were answered! A man in the next town replied, sending me some information and also an address to contact for more information (and at last someone to talk to!). This turned out to be Mrs Irene Tredgett, a member of the Association. She was so kind, helpful and understanding and put me in touch with Anne Mawdsley, who in turn gave us her immediate help and support. My sincere thanks to Mrs. Tredgett and her son Gary for taking us out of our isolated situation and putting us on the road to hope. It is such a relief to know that we will never be alone with this again. The heavy weight that I have carried is now lifting from me and I feel I can do something constructive at last. My first efforts are underway with local firms for used postage stamps, to try to help the Association to raise funds for the much needed research. Robert was in his first School Sports Day last Monday and he won his first ever race. I was so proud of him - considering his problems he raced to glory. He knew he had done well and shouted out to me "See I can run fast can't I Mum?" The tears just rolled down my face. As you can imagine I will treasure that moment for ever.

Robert playing happily in his garden

Jill Newman

Help for Nicola

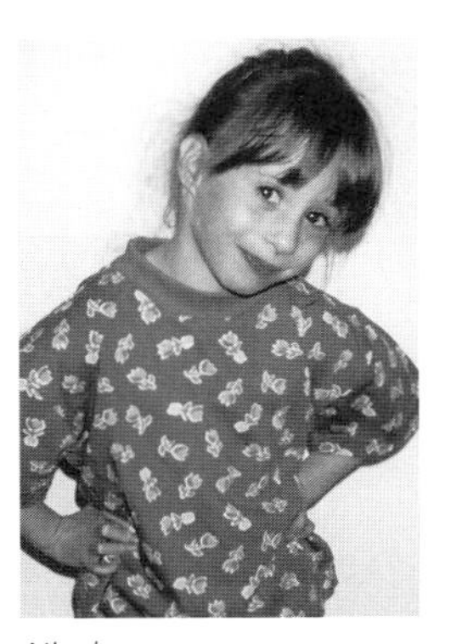

Nicola

Nicola Blears is just four years old and has many problems of which Raynaud's is just one. We heard about Nicola through Professor Jayson at Hope Hospital, who wrote to ask if we could help. Nicola's Mum, Glenys, has a problem in finding warm clothing which is small yet not babyish. Nicola is very small, eats very little, is on a liquid diet and is soon to be fed intravenously. She starts school in September and it is proving difficult to find a school uniform which is small enough. Glenys would love to hear from anyone who knows a shop where she could buy small, suitable clothing. Her shoes are made specially for her at Bolton General Hospital as her feet are very narrow.

Welfare Fund

Through our Welfare Fund we have been able to help several members in various ways. Unfortunately, we are not in a position to make payments towards heating bills. This is for obvious reasons - mainly due to the number of requests we receive.

The following extracts have been taken from letters received from some of the members we have been able to help:

"I am writing to thank you for my Mangar bath lift. It really has made a wonderful difference to my day as I have to bathe several times a day and it was becoming increasingly impossible for me to do this for my own safety. Many thanks again.'

Barbara Eastwood

"I am writing to let you know that I have had the intercom fitted and it has made things very much easier for me. I would like to thank the Association for the generosity you have shown to me - I will be forever in your debt."

R. Wright

"Many thanks for helping me to have the best holiday of my life. It really helped me to 'Break Free' in Southport's 'Sandpipers', where Bob and all the staff and helpers made our holiday one big happy family. We had lovely outings, great evenings, ending with a boat sail on the River Dee at night, on 'The Lady Diana', where we had a big party and disco, lots of fun and food. We all exchanged addresses to keep in touch. You have helped me to overcome my own problems and even to forget them with the great excitement, happiness and relaxation of being with many other people (friends) who all, like me, 'Broke Free' in beautiful Southport at 'Sandpipers'. Thank you again".

N. Stewart

Susan Edwards received a specially adapted cooker with help from the Association and the Florence Nightingale Aid in Sickness Trust.

The Association would like to thank Roger Jefcoate for the wonderful contribution which he has made towards both our research and welfare funds. Roger has been instrumental in giving advice on Trust Funds, Charitable Organisations and Companies who the Association could approach for support. Many of these contacts have proved to be fruitful. He introduced us to BT, British Gas, Lazards, The Florence Nightingale Aid in Sickness Trust to name but a few and has himself recently donated a much needed word processor to the Association. Thank you Roger for your encouragement and practical help whenever needed. It really is appreciated.

A Candlelight Supper

What a surprise we had during Awareness Week when we received a cheque for £9,500 from Eileen and Dennis Nicholson.

On 16th October, at Hadley Memorial Club, a Candlelight Supper took place and was a roaring success, thanks to Eileen, Dennis and the Hadley Memorial Club Social Committee. They had all worked very hard in order to raise funds for Awareness Week.

Apart from an excellent supper, there was a presentation by actor Anthony Slinn on Vincent Van Gogh with illustrated slides and six masters from Merchant Taylor's School provided entertainment with Barber Shop songs. Eileen ran the raffle - not just an ordinary raffle but a really big one. There were 20 prizes including a Jeroboam of champagne and £100 voucher from Marks & Spencer. The chef from Merchant Taylor's School made a cake in the Association's colours and together with all the other prizes which Eileen had managed to persuade people to donate, a total of £650 was raised on the raffle alone. The whole evening raised £1,293 and the rest of the £9,500 was made up with very generous donations from Mr and Mrs Newton, The Childwick Trust, The Thornton Foundation, The W. T. J. Griffin Charitable Settlement, J. A. Dick and The Barnet Recreational Trust.

Our sincere thanks to Eileen and Dennis for this very special effort which is greatly appreciated.

Pam's daily struggle to get to grips with a painful problem

Pam Fruer, from Billericay, is one of millions of people in this country suffering from Raynaud's syndrome. She also has an associated condition, scleroderma, which causes hardening of the skin and sometimes the internal organs. When Pam burnt her fingers on a match as she tried to light her gas fire she felt no pain. It was only when she saw her scarred skin that she realised what she had done. She struggles to get to grips with taps, door handles and getting her key in the lock. She is used to insensitive people remarking on her florid cheeks and her 'boozer's' nose. She dreads the winter when even going out by car can make her extreme sensitivity to cold, impossible to manage. Even in the most tropical of British heat waves her hands are icy. Pam explained how Raynaud's disease causes a lack of blood to the extremities causing them to go numb. She said: "But they still hurt, and are like painful lumps which do not do what you want them to. I lose my sense of balance and have to walk with a stick because I cannot control my legs." Cut fingers are a regular injury as Pam tries to manipulate kitchen knives. And she frequently drops things from her grasp. She said: "Coins are the worst. I cannot pick them up again". She has had to give up driving her car once the temperature dips because she can no longer operate the pedals. The skin on her feet frequently breaks down and she has to be careful ulcers do not develop. Attacks can also be triggered by stress. Scleroderma is a complex rheumatic disease in which the body produces too much collagen or connective tissue. It affects Pam's digestion and facial muscles. She said: "Sometimes my mouth does not work as I want it to and I know I am slurring words." She had always put down her problems to bad circulation caused by arthritis until a chiropodist came up with the diagnosis about 10 years ago. Now any outing has to be carefully planned and her winter wardrobe is stocked with thermal

Pam Fruer

underwear, thick socks, body warmers, gloves and snug tracksuits. Her two adoring spaniels and an electric over-blanket keep her warm in bed. She had to give up her librarian's job and now has only her reduced pension to meet soaring heating bills. Pam said: "I keep thinking there is only one more winter to get through until I get my old age pension. I am never really warm and the pain can be excruciating. But I have had a tremendous amount of help from the Association and am a lot luckier than some sufferers. But you have to learn to live with it and concentrate on what you can do rather than what you can't. At least my red cheeks make everyone say how well I look, which automatically makes me feel better".

The above article appeared in the Basildon Evening Echo

I'm not alone any more

Jed Malins

Since joining the Raynaud's & Scleroderma Association two years ago I have not ceased to gain new friends throughout England, Scotland and Wales. At the conference held in Alsager in September I gained even more. Last year I attended the conference knowing only two people but this year I felt I knew everyone. I suppose we all have a common bond, in dealing with our illness. It was heartening to know that the Medical Profession is striving to find the answer and to me, that was the theme of the conference - to discuss how far research has gone in the last year towards seeking this goal. Even though I don't always understand the technicalities, I do understand the positive approach generated in no small way by our fund-raising efforts. It wasn't all serious and a great deal of warmth and humour developed throughout the weekend. I shall never forget seeing the large audience responding to Bridget Ferguson's session, exercising and singing "pack up your troubles in your old kit bag and smile, smile, smile" and everyone did smile. Mind you I was worried that Bridget would fall off the desk top in her enthusiasm!

I also stayed on the Saturday night this year and I'm very glad that I did. After the buffet, Kelsey taught us a few simple folk dances and I was persuaded to drag Bridget onto the dance floor to do an impromptu 'Lambada'. There were bits moving that haven't moved for a few years. (I hope nobody misconstrues this!). On Sunday morning some of the stragglers ended up at HQ, filling envelopes with newsletters and folding leaflets. There were thousands and Anne kept producing box after box, like the magician she is. We really had fun helping. Then it was a long drive home to Dorset reflecting on a spiritually uplifting conference weekend where the time had flown by. They say "time flies when you are enjoying yourself". Finally I think we must all commend Anne and her staff, not forgetting her Mum, for all the time and effort put into organising such a super conference but like you said last year Anne, "How do I follow that?" You will, I have no doubt.

Jed Malins

I can dance again!

This photograph of Ray Patterson and Kelsey was taken during the conference weekend in 1993, and shows the joy which Kelsey experienced at being able to dance again.

Kelsey Blundell, who has had both legs amputated during recent years, has shown tremendous courage in overcoming her problems and gave a most interesting talk at our conference in 1991.

Earlier this year Kelsey decided that she wanted to participate in her love of folk dancing - her aim being to dance again (preferably without a man on both sides for support!). The video which Kelsey had made in time for the conference shows how she went about achieving this aim by writing to the limb fitting centre. Her problem involved not being able to rotate her right leg which was causing problems when she tried to dance. Her case was treated very sympathetically and a new limb was created. The video took place over a period of several months from the first consultation to the final fitting of the limb. It ends with Kelsey dancing. Members and friends who stayed on the Saturday night spent a most enjoyable evening. Following the buffet supper Kelsey was anxious to show us her folk dancing skills using this new leg. Everyone joined in but found it difficult to keep up with the speed and intricacy of the steps which were involved in the dances, which Kelsey had mastered so magnificently on her two artificial limbs. She was the life and soul of the party and an inspiration to all who have had the pleasure of knowing her.

Fond memories

Just before the above article was published in our newsletter, we heard the very sad news that Kelsey Blundell had died suddenly at her home on 7th November 1993. Knowing that it would have been her wish, the articles referring to Kelsey at the conference have not been changed. Anyone who knew Kelsey could not fail to be inspired by her personality and courage to live life to the full in spite of the many problems which she fought to conquer. The video showing the making of her new leg which was shown at our conference was entitled 'I Want to Dance Again'. This she did with staggering determination and was an inspiration to all who tried to keep up with her, on the Saturday evening following the conference. I can honestly say that it was one of the most enjoyable evenings I can remember. Kelsey was so full of life and fun and we were all so happy.

Kelsey and Anne

It is wonderful to have such memories and to have shared so many years of friendship with such a remarkable lady. Kelsey never complained but just got on with life, facing and coping with problems as they arose. She will always have a place in our hearts and I feel very privileged to have known her.

Anne Mawdsley

What do we do all day?

People often ask what I do as a job. I usually say that I work for a charity and watch as their eyes glaze over! It struck me today that perhaps some of you may wonder what goes on at the place simply known as 'the office' and the easiest way to explain is to describe a day. Today is Thursday 4th November 1993, the fourth day of Awareness Week. As you know we try to obtain maximum publicity for this week each year and many members are able to help by sending our Press Release to their local newspapers and radio stations for inclusion in this week's editions. However, this year we seem to have excelled ourselves, with items in most of the weekly and monthly women's magazines together with two of the national daily newspapers. The Daily Telegraph printed a small item and instructed readers to send a large SAE for information and the Daily Mail published a wonderful full page article about the Association on their Health Page, giving our address and telephone number, but unfortunately there was no request for an SAE! Given this information you will not be surprised to learn that the first job of the day is to open the mail of which there were 380 enquiries today. It is vitally important to open the mail daily and to answer as much as possible on that same day in order to avoid a backlog. May slits the mail, emptying any packages of stamps into a bag as she goes along. Jan begins to do the typed letters required from yesterday's mail on the word processor, pausing every couple of minutes to answer the telephone. The callers usually request information and are asked to send an SAE or maybe they wish to talk to someone. Anne is replying to letters which need her attention and sorting out items that need to be typed, which will be done this afternoon, time permitting!! Andrew, who is a regular volunteer, is putting together the information packs which will then be sent out. I have started to put together the orders which have accumulated over the last few days and so we begin. The phone rings and so does the front door bell!

The phone continues to ring. All enquirers are happy to send an SAE when asked, they simply had not thought of doing so before. The telephone is constantly engaged and so it is not possible for us to make any outgoing calls. I suppose it is one way to reduce the phone bill! Anne has a radio broadcast to do soon. The radio station telephone the office and the interview is done over the line. There have been many interviews this week and today is Radio Derby's turn but first we have to arrange for the line to be clear! Eventually they get through and the call goes out live. Meanwhile the orders are complete and the envelopes are all slit. May and I do a swap - she lists the parcels on a postal certificate, so that we can claim if any of them are lost in the post and I begin to open the letters. Many of the letters are requests for information and so the SAEs start to pile up for May to fill later with the information packs. There are also stock orders with cheques which need to be listed, various official letters which will go to Anne, letters from members - we all like to get to these letters amongst the seemingly endless requests for information - then there are those without an SAE! It is not only the cost of the stamp and envelope that is the problem, it is the time it takes to decipher the name and address and write it onto an envelope. Second post arrives! The radio broadcast went well and the phone is now ringing again with new enquiries. Tomorrow Anne and I are going to Cannock Chase Hospital where Dr. Sheeran has arranged an Open Day for Raynaud's and scleroderma patients. We are going to have a stand from where we can talk to sufferers, telling them about the Association and how we can help. The display boards and stock items have to be put together today ready for us to take in the morning.

The majority of the mail is completed by 3 pm - in fact we are now left with just three piles, one has official letters, one containing letters from members which will soon be answered but may be a little delayed this week, and the final pile of cheques which are for stock items, payment of membership, the proceeds of fund-raising events and some donations to our Research Fund. The official letters go directly to Anne. Your letters are answered either by Anne or myself and I take the cheques to list them for banking. These are then sorted again into the various sections i.e. memberships which I keep to send out with the membership package, donations and stock orders which are put aside for another day! Meanwhile the phone rings. We now have a lovely information room where people can call to talk to one of us or to see what heating aids are available and we also have a supply of Christmas items for sale. Our photocopying and fax service helps to generate income and involves many callers throughout the day. It is now five o'clock and we have almost caught up with ourselves. I am afraid that there is a growing pile of members letters but they will all be answered very soon I promise! I am going home now, the others have gone except, of course, Anne is still behind the small mountain on her desk trying to sort it all into some sort of order so she is going to be here for some time yet!

So what do we do all day? Well, we just work for a charity!

Raynor Lancaster

Evaluating and Treating Raynaud's Phenomenon

An article by Dr. Jill Belch entitled 'Evaluating and Treating Raynaud's Phenomenon' was published in the Prescriber Journal dated 19th January 1994. The following is a brief summary of this article:

It is only recently that studies have been carried out into the origin and causes of Raynaud's and this lack of knowledge has led to difficulties in the treatment and prognosis of the condition. It is not now considered essential for the three colour changes for a diagnosis - in some patients only two of these changes may occur. Other triggers are emotion, hormones, chemicals (especially those in tobacco smoke) and trauma, particularly in the form of pressure such as is produced by carrying shopping bags. We know that it is not only the fingers and toes which are affected but also the tip of the nose, tongue and ear lobes. The link between migraine headaches and Raynaud's is now well recognised.

Syndrome or disease?

Raynaud's phenomenon is subdivided into secondary Raynaud's syndrome where there is an associated disorder and primary Raynaud's disease where there is no underlying condition. However, long term studies have shown that Raynaud's phenomenon may be an early symptom of a systemic illness and may be present for more than 20 years before it becomes evident that it is not simply primary Raynaud's. Recent laboratory procedures have shown that more than one half of patients referred to hospital have an associated systemic disease such as systemic sclerosis (scleroderma), mixed connective tissue disease, systemic lupus erythematosus, polymyositis, dermatomyositis and Sjögren's syndrome. Raynaud's also occurs in 10% of patients with rheumatoid arthritis, which is similar to that seen in the normal population but with a higher degree of severity.

Raynaud's phenomenon of occupational origin is seen in workers exposed to poly vinyl chloride and those who work with vibrating machines such as chain saws, pneumatic drills and buffs, when the condition is called vibration white finger. Although estimates show that between 40% and 90% of all workers using vibratory equipment will have Raynaud's, their symptoms may resolve in 25% of cases if their job is changed early on in the disease.

Primary Raynaud's disease versus secondary Raynaud's syndrome

Patients with Raynaud's phenomenon attending hospital are far more likely to have a secondary condition than those in the general population who have Raynaud's phenomenon. It is vital to detect which patients with Raynaud's phenomenon will develop a connective tissue disease such as scleroderma. This is not an easy task but there are some clearly defined abnormalities which have been linked with secondary Raynaud's syndrome. These are:

- *certain clinical features*
- *abnormal nail-fold vessels*
- *abnormal immunological tests*

One should be aware of any suspicious clinical symptoms which may be indicative of connective tissue disease. For example thin, shiny and leathery looking skin (sclerodactyly) and finger ulceration which does not normally occur in primary Raynaud's disease. Pitting scars found over the pulp of the fingers are strongly associated with later connective tissue disease development. Patients who suffer from Raynaud's attacks all the year round should also be considered for investigation. The age of onset of Raynaud's is important, being most common in young women in their teens and 20's, most of whom have primary Raynaud's. Patients who show symptoms for the first time during their 30's or 40's are at risk of developing Raynaud's syndrome, whereas 80% of patients who develop Raynaud's at the age of 60 years or more will have an associated disorder which is mainly atherosclerosis. Alternatively, when Raynaud's occurs in young children although rare, it is usually due to an underlying connective tissue disease. It was mentioned earlier that Raynaud's can precede scleroderma by many years and in these patients it is more likely that they will develop the limited form of the condition (CREST syndrome), whereas those presenting with systemic sclerosis within one year of onset of the Raynaud's tend to develop diffuse systemic sclerosis. Other clinical symptoms which may be suspicious of secondary Raynaud's syndrome are the recurrence of chilblains in adults and spasm affecting only one or two fingers on each hand initially. Treatment should be adapted to each individual patient and the detection of an associated disorder in a patient with Raynaud's phenomenon is an important step in the management of that particular patient.

History of Scleroderma

We are often asked if scleroderma is something new. According to an article found in the Annals of International Medicine the earliest descriptions of skin similar to scleroderma skin date back to the days of Hippocrates (370 B.C.) and Galen (131 A.D.). However the first clear case report was by Dr. Carlo Curzio in Naples in 1753. He described a woman, Patrizia Galiera, aged 17, who complained of 'excessive tension and hardness of skin all over her body, by which she found herself so bound that she could hardly move her limbs". She was treated with warm milk and vapour baths, bleeding from the foot, (they report that her skin was so hard that it was difficult to find a vein to bleed her from), and with small doses of quicksilver. Within 11 months she had improved to the point where her skin was 'perfectly soft and flexible, being capable of being moved". Doctors today are very sceptical about this case and doubt whether in fact this lady did have scleroderma.

The next case reports occur around 1847 independently by Grislie, Forget and Thirial. By 1895 more than 500 cases of the skin disease had been reported and the name scleroderma was given to the condition. There was now a well defined clinical picture of scleroderma, diagnosis and categorisation of patients became possible and attention could be given to the features associated with this illness. In 1878 calcinosis was first noted when a woman complained of hard concretions in her skin that then discharged to the outside. This was initially thought to be gouty deposits but analysis revealed calcium. This lead to speculation that abnormal metabolism might be responsible for scleroderma. Raynaud's phenomenon was noted to be present in most patients, an observation reported by Maurice Raynaud. In 1899, Dr. Monro calculated that 13 out of 188 patients with Raynaud's also had scleroderma. Soon localised forms of scleroderma such as morphea and linear were distinguished from the more diffuse skin involvement in generalised scleroderma. In the early part of the 20th Century, several researchers began to notice the association of organ abnormalities with scleroderma. Joints, heart, lungs, kidneys and gastrointestinal problems were all individually described by multiple researchers. Pathological study of skin and organ sections revealed that scleroderma was was in fact a systemic illness rather than a local skin disease and in 1945 Dr. Goetz suggested that the name be revised to progressive systemic sclerosis (PSS).

During the second half of the 20th Century much activity has taken place to help researchers understand the complexity of scleroderma. The defining of CREST syndrome by Drs. Victor and Winterbauer in 1964 coupled with the discovery of a specific antibody to the centromere of chromosomes (anti-centromere antibody) in patients with CREST and systemic sclerosis. Probably the most satisfying discovery of the last 20 years has been the improved treatments which have led to increased survival and improved quality of life for scleroderma patients. Antihypertensive medication, particularly ACE inhibitors such as captopril, have dramatically reduced the mortality associated with renal disease in systemic sclerosis. Calcium channel blockers such as nifedipine have significantly improved symptoms in patients with Raynaud's phenomenon, and the drug omeprazole has greatly improved the suffering associated with reflux oesophagitis in scleroderma patients. Antibiotic treatment of bowel malabsorbtion has helped the nutrition of patients with intestinal involvement. Studies of treatment response in the lung are encouraging and it is no longer accepted that there is no treatment for lung disease in scleroderma. HLA typing, computed tomography and DTPA studies have confirmed that it is now possible to predict more precisely which patients are more likely to have a future lung problem. It has been suggested that the drug D-penicillamine may slow the progression of scleroderma, particularly the skin disease.

We keep in close contact with doctors and researchers both in the U.K. and overseas in order to keep abreast of any new developments. Patients groups such as ours are of tremendous importance not only to the patient and their families but also to the dedicated doctors who are working towards better treatments and eventually a cure. It is through newsletters such as this that information can be disseminated and we are appreciative for any articles or news items from doctors/research workers who specialise in this field of medicine.

G.P. Booklet

An informative booklet for G.P.s called 'A new look at Raynaud's and Systemic Sclerosis (Scleroderma)', has been written by Dr. Carol Black and distributed to all G.P.s in the U.K.

Lucy Irvine

Castaway - Lucy Irvine

Even as a schoolgirl Lucy Irvine - now an internationally known author - was always aware of suffering more than others with cold hands and feet. Lucy had heard the word Raynaud's many years ago although she was not diagnosed as having the condition until she reached her late 20's. Her first book 'Castaway' was a best seller in the 1980's and told the true story of her spending more than a year with a stranger on a tropical island. The real life adventure was made into a film of the same name. During her time on the island of Tuin, off the coast of Australia, she was blissfully free of Raynaud's, that is apart from one episode when she and her companion were fishing on rocks and were cut off from the island itself by sharks. It was then that Lucy became very cold and had to do exercises to try and maintain her body temperature. These days she is the mother of three lively boys aged 4, 6 and 8 and is still managing to write articles. She has also started to work on her latest novel. For someone with Raynaud's, Lucy does not live in the most ideal spot. She and her sons have made their home in a remote cottage in the Scottish Highlands where winter really does mean extreme temperatures, hard frosts and deep snow. The family love it so much there that they do not want to leave, so Lucy, now 38, has totally accepted the fact she has Raynaud's and has adapted her life accordingly.

Her message to other Raynaud's sufferers is quite straightforward - "don't let it get you down - don't allow it to depress you". From October to the height of summer Lucy wears a minimum of three pairs of tights and a pair of socks. The colours of trousers, tops and sweaters are toned in and complimented by hats, scarves and gloves. For someone who likes to feel free physically it is all very restrictive but she is determined not to look bulky and dowdy and urges fellow Raynaud's sufferers to think the same way and to shamelessly make their own fashion statement. Having accepted that she has Raynaud's she tries very hard not to allow it to restrict her life or those of her children. She makes herself face the outside world and enjoys taking the boys on treks and outings in the surrounding countryside.

"It is a matter of accepting the situation, adapting and thinking ahead', says Lucy. She strongly recommends silk thermal underwear. She also wears silk glove and sock liners. Her hands are dry and her fingers are stiff, cold and numb. If they start to crack it takes along time for them to heal. Lucy wears rubber gloves for any household chores, even for peeling vegetables. She takes nifedipine every day during winter and says the benefits outweigh any side effects such as headaches. Raynaud's obviously affects Lucy's writing. She finds it a great effort to write legible long hand and says it is awkward writing with fingerless mittens on. She types albeit with difficulty, as her work nears completion. When she is writing Lucy sits close to her Rayburn with a blanket over her legs and a heater at her back. She feels the cold and the pain of cold in her feet more than her hands. At night she wears cotton socks under a pair of bigger socks which are doubly insulated in the toes and heels. She has suffered from chilblains and frostbite. Keeping her core temperature up is one of her biggest problems. She can thoroughly recommend chopping logs or walking quickly as great ways of keeping warm! Her own experience leaves her in no doubt that stress exacerbates Raynaud's. In her case stress did not cause her condition but if she has an emotional, stressful event in her life she is more likely to suffer an attack of Raynaud's. One of the most distressing aspects of the disease is when Lucy touches her children. If her hands are stiff she feels clumsy but she makes a joke about it with the boys and goes in for big body hugs instead. Lucy has become a member of the Association and wants to help in raising awareness of the condition amongst members of the public. In her own way she is already doing that. As a victim of Raynaud's she obviously has difficulty getting money out of her purse while wearing gloves. Checkout assistants are used to her by now - she tells them she has the condition which makes your hands and feet cold. Lucy also urges members to tell family and friends to buy them lots of fabulous gloves and nighties.

I'm Winning!

"In 1988 when I was in my 30s I had a very speedy diagnosis of systemic sclerosis but although to me the 8 months were long and frightening, I have since heard many horror stories where diagnosis takes much longer. In July 1988 I had extensive skin involvement and found walking, sitting, eating, dressing and mobility in general very awkward and painful. In November 1987 my doctor first told me I had Raynaud's so without stopping to think twice, I gave up smoking and from then on it was downhill so to speak. It was very tempting to associate this with my lack of nicotine but I persevered and possibly wouldn't be here today if I hadn't stopped at that time. I was referred to Dr. Black in July 1988, when she was at the West Middlesex Hospital. I devoured every piece of literature to be found on systemic sclerosis which were few and far between. Since then much more literature has become available to patients published by the Raynaud's & Scleroderma Association. I joined the self help group and tried to get on with my life as best I could. Needless to say there had already been some dramatic changes like being forced to give up work and my social life which had been pretty active was now zero. I was devastated but tried to make the best of my situation. I realised that I had more energy during the day so I started a counselling course and quickly discovered that I needed counselling myself as I hadn't quite come to terms with what having systemic sclerosis meant to me or my family. I also went back to school part-time and tried to get to grips with 'O' level maths and 'A' level sociology with other students. I was thoroughly enjoying myself and then one day woke up in the Royal Free Hospital to learn, albeit slowly, that I had just woken up from a three day coma, having had the odd fit along the way and that the next worry was controlling my blood pressure and kidneys.

To cut a long story short, I ended up on peritoneal dialysis. I have dialysed since March 1991 and my kidneys have recovered sufficiently to allow me to stop dialysing. However, although I still have some obvious systemic sclerosis problems, my quality of life has so improved that I am able to work two days a week at The Royal Free and participate socially back in the real world. One of the awful things about being a sick person is the inevitable role changes that go on around you. For example, my boyfriend Paul became my carer, my Mum who is over 60 started looking after me as though I was a small, precious child again and for a while I was totally dependent on everyone around me. Recently we went to Olympia to the Good Food Exhibition and although we were both exhausted by the evening it was Mum who was struggling to hobble back home because her osteo arthritis was playing up. Not so good for Mum but for me things are getting back into some semblance of order. Paul, who was too scared to leave me alone at home for the first year of my kidney failure, is now a Globe trotter and as I write this article he is unexpectedly working in New York. Due to better awareness and vigilance by the medical profession and perhaps ourselves, better drugs and dialysis means that renal crisis is no longer the greatest cause of death in systemic sclerosis patients. However, renal crisis is still rare even within a rare disease".

Kim Fligelstone

International Scleroderma Conference - Sydney, Australia 1994

In February while the U.K. was snowed up and freezing cold I was sizzling in 30°C in the Australian Summer where I had been invited to attend and speak at The International Conference on Scleroderma in Sydney. This proved to be a valuable experience in terms of knowledge gained and communication with people from around the world.

The Conference programme was designed to extend from basic science to applied research as well as incorporating clinical issues. Allied health and community based programmes ran concurrently with the scientific programme giving the lay person and workers in the field of medicine the opportunity not only to hear from each other but also to listen to the experts. Most of my time was spent with the allied health professionals and community groups programme but I was fortunate in being able to hear Dr. Jill Belch, Dr. Carol Black and Professor Alan Silman from the U.K. present their work. More than 50 speakers from around the world presented papers and generally discussed scleroderma. It was encouraging to know that so much interesting work is taking place and that so many experts are collaborating and disseminating information about their findings.

London member Kim Fligelstone attended the Conference and it gave me a good opportunity to illustrate just how medical advances have improved, particularly with regard to renal problems in scleroderma. Kim had renal failure in both kidneys, was on dialysis and critically ill, (see previous page). She has since made a remarkable recovery enabling her to live a reasonably active life and travel as far as Australia. I attended a meeting of patient groups from the various Australian states. It was no real surprise to hear that we all share the problems, particularly with regard to diagnosis. It was stated that on average it took between 3 and 4 years for a scleroderma patient to get a correct diagnosis. Raynaud's of course is common in all scleroderma patients but Primary Raynaud's is nowhere near as prevalent in Australia as it is in the U.K. due mainly to the climate.

Communication

Communication between patients and doctors and the lack of information given to patients was a major concern. Each group spoke about the relief shown by patients who had contacted them and the joy of being able to share their problems with others who understood.

It was wonderful to make new friends and meet old acquaintances, such as Julie McMahon from Adelaide and Niels Bo Sorensen from Denmark, who have both attended our Annual Conferences in Alsager in the past. I was pleased to meet member Kathleen Flanagan from Victoria who has been a member for many years and I enjoyed sharing experiences with other patients and representatives of self help groups. Sadly there were no representatives from the American patient groups who I had been looking forward to meeting, having corresponded with several people during the past twelve years. It was however lovely to meet at last with Irene Case, who was on the organising committee for the Conference and who had been regularly in touch with our Association since 1982. I stayed with Irene and we talked for hours about the running of our two respective organisations.

Almost every aspect of scleroderma one could imagine was covered at this Conference and although I took notes at each session it would take a book to write it all down. However, most of the sessions were recorded on video. There were many lectures on learning to cope with the various aspects of scleroderma. Dr. Carol Black gave the keynote address - Scleroderma into the 21st Century - which gave a general overview of scleroderma ending on a positive note for the future.

Management

A review of medications used for scleroderma was given by Clinical Pharmacologist, Professor Richard Day. He described the various symptoms with regard to both early and late diffuse scleroderma, how different drugs helped with the many complex problems and the drug options which are available to patients, together with non-drug therapies. An excellent talk on psycho social aspects by Julie Dunsmore was appreciated particularly by the sufferers present. She discussed the stages one may experience in coping with a diagnosis such as denial, avoidance, intellectualism and regression. How one copes in a crisis, the crisis cycle, uncertainty, issues of support, betrayal, coping with new realities and the role of supporters. She stressed the importance of maintaining one's own identity and setting realistic goals for yourself. Maybe not the same goals as before you developed scleroderma but new ones which can be equally important. Finally Julie stated "we cannot prevent the birds of sorrow flying overhead but we can prevent them from nesting in our hair". Two patients, Scott Harding who developed linear scleroderma as a young child, leaving him with a scar on his head, and Kylie Powell who was diagnosed initially as having lupus, gave a positive talk on the way in which scleroderma had affected their lives.

A most interesting and informative talk on incontinence was given by Wendy Bower who is an Incontinence Promotion Officer. She stated that this topic is often avoided by patients who are too embarrassed to tell their doctor that they have this problem. It is however quite common in scleroderma patients and can affect either the bladder or the bowel; 20-60% of patients have abnormalities in small bowel function and 10-50% have abnormal large bowel functions. A few tips which she gave on self help for the problem are:- To drink plenty of fluids (6-8 glasses a day); retrain bladder storage if toileting frequently day and night; include food high in soluble fibre in your diet; use stool bulking if necessary; consider using enemas if no stool is passed for several days; adopt optimal defection habits. Exercise, especially swimming, stimulates bowel activity. So why do patients not ask for help? She suggests that people with scleroderma may not realise that leaking is normal, they feel a threat to their self esteem, a fear of surgery, shame or embarrassment, think there is no effective treatment and are not aware that the problem may be manageable.

A Variety of Topics

Dr. Rosemary Swift talked about new developments in plastic surgery and Dr. Michael Tonkin discussed options for hand surgery; Rosemary Stanton discussed diet and Sue Buckle gave advice on caring for ulcers; Jill Fogarty gave an excellent talk on foot care and Pauline Brooks presented 'Activity vs Inactivity', which stimulated the audience into a very lively session; Col. Robert Sjogren spoke on surgical intervention in gastrointestinal disease; Raynaud's syndrome was discussed by Dr. Sam Breit and Dr. Katherine Ellard talked on gastrointestinal disease which affects 90% of scleroderma patients. Like many of the speakers, Dr. Ellard recommended the drug Losec for reflux problems, in some cases combined with cisapride to assist motility. Finally, the spectrum of connective tissue disorders and an update on research was given by Dr. Thomas Medsger Jr.

The Role of Support Groups

On the last day representatives of groups gave a short presentation of their work. I spoke about the role of our Association in Great Britain and the importance of all groups working together, each doing a little towards an ultimate goal of finding a cure for scleroderma in the future. At the end of this session the chairperson asked if there were any people present from other countries who would like to say a few words. At this point Niels Bo Sorensen from Denmark talked about his group, a lady from New Zealand talked about her newly formed group of patients and Dawn Raphaely from South Africa, who has since become a member of our Association, gave her feelings of frustration at being so alone in a country where very little help is available and she has to work in order to pay for her drug therapy. There is no help from the Government towards prescription costs as we have here.

In Conclusion

It was a long journey but well worth it for the knowledge gained and friends made. I returned with renewed enthusiasm for the task ahead in finding a cure for Raynaud's and scleroderma. Together we must work towards this goal. My thanks to Irene Case and Professor Ron Penny for their initiative and efforts in organising this Conference and for the hospitality which I received during my stay. Thanks also to Therakos for paying my Air Fare. The world is not so big after all, strong friendships can be formed and hurdles overcome through common interests, ideals and goals.

Anne Mawdsley

Exercise Tips in Scleroderma

Exercising in a warm environment helps avoid problems with Raynaud's, facilitates collagen stretch and helps make you feel more comfortable and relaxed.

Avoiding positions that trigger reflux and indigestion means adapting exercises and finding alternatives.

Avoiding exercises that trigger continence problems again means looking at what you are doing, how you are doing it and adapting the exercise accordingly.

Analyse your fatigue! Is fatigue because of the disease, depression or general lack of fitness? Pace yourself and your programmes.

Reducing tension and inducing relaxation will make exercise easier and more effective. Use relaxation techniques before you exercise and appropriate music and tapes to work with while you exercise.

Monitoring pain is essential as a guide to the amount and type of exercise that you do. Learn to recognise your pain and discomfort levels and how far you can extend them.

Pacing yourself is vital to your enjoyment and long term maintenance of your programmes.

Dressing for success in your exercise programme means wearing non restrictive clothes that are layered to keep you warm but of appropriate materials to keep any sweat away from you.

Set Realistic Goals

Have some idea of what you would like to achieve through your exercise e.g. walk further, be fitter, maintain better hand function, remain active. Work towards your longer term goals by breaking them up into smaller components with their own shorter term goals.

Build Slowly

Little and often will make sure that you don't overdo it and put yourself off. Your exercise programme is a lifetime friend and companion so there is no rush to success! Learn to listen to your body and to stop before you pay a negative price.

Record Your Progress

Keeping an exercise diary reminds you of where you have come from and helps you to see where you are going. Remember how easy it is to focus on the "what has not been achieved" and forget what has been.

Make Your Programme Convenient and Varied

Be sure your programme fits in with your routines and lifestyle but make sure that you value it enough to give it the time and the place in your life that it needs. Add variety and remember the whole picture. Remember to use stretching, strengthening and fitness exercises and try something different.

Keep Positive and Value Yourself

Affirm the benefits of your exercise programme and of your goal. Remember that keeping in control will positively affect the long term outcomes of your disease and the quality of your life. Valuing yourself and caring for and about yourself will in turn affect your belief in yourself and your ability to succeed.

The above article was taken from a talk by Pauline Brookes at the Scleroderma International Conference in Sydney in 1994.

Capital Woman

Anne with Anneka Rice

On January 6th 1994, I was invited to take part in a programme on Carlton Television called 'CAPITAL WOMAN'. The theme of the programme was 'Keeping warm in the Capital' and the programme went out on 10th January. The interviewer was Anneka Rice whose warm and vivacious personality helped to make me feel very relaxed. Before we went on air we talked about the problems of keeping warm and she showed a genuine interest in the work of the Association. She explained that she had problems herself, especially in cold, wet conditions, which are inevitable when making programmes such as 'Challenge Anneka'. Like many Raynaud's sufferers she has one finger in particular which constantly goes white, numb and dead-looking and her hands are always cold. It must be a real problem for someone in the public eye who always has to smile and look one's best. Knowing how I feel when I'm cold I think she does a marvellous job. Having expected to be interviewed in a television studio, I was quite surprised to find that the 'studio' was in fact the middle of Whiteley's Shopping Centre, with shoppers walking back and forth and others watching from the level above. One amusing incident happened as Anneka was reading from an autocue camera, walking towards the bench where she was to interview me, when an elderly lady sat herself next to me with her shopping bag. She was completely oblivious to the fact that she was on the T.V. set in spite of all the cameras and the fact that Anneka Rice was standing a few feet away from her! Take 3!

At this point I should add that the 'bench' was made of marbled stone and was freezing cold. From here I showed Anneka and the viewers various items of warm clothing, two small portable heat packs and a jacket potato wrapped in tin foil. Unfortunately there wasn't time to go into too much detail about Raynaud's but one day we will have to persuade someone to do a documentary. However it is all good publicity and we hope that through television programmes such as this, we can reach many more people who were previously unaware of our existence.

Anne Mawdsley

Matthew Corbett and Sooty lend a hand by launching our new Helping Hand pin badge when they visited the office in Alsager.

Lending a Hand

Matthew and Sooty have certainly been busy on our behalf with newspaper articles, radio and television coverage. Anne Mawdsley took part in a television interview during which Matthew stated that although he and Sooty only have a mild form of Raynaud's, he is really glad that he found us because when he was first diagnosed three years ago he thought he was the only one in the world with cold hands. Sooty showed his gratitude by aiming his water pistol at Anne on live television!

The Association were allocated a 5 minute slot on Central Television's Lifeline programme. The filming took place at two venues, firstly at the home of scleroderma sufferer Helen Birtles in Newcastle, and secondly at our office in Alsager, where Matthew Corbett and Sooty joined members Sandra Baddeley and Wayne Partington, as well as our office staff.

Matthew with Wayne Partington and Sandra Baddeley

The Hand Collection continues to grow

It all started with two or three delicate pottery hands and then I became totally fascinated by ornamental hands of all shapes and sizes. Such is my addiction to the 'Hands on' hobby that our headquarters in Alsager boasts a collection of well over 300 hands made from a wide range of materials. The link with hands isn't totally unexpected of course, since Raynaud's sufferers know only too well how the condition affects the circulation in their hands. My interest in collecting the ornaments began when the Association moved from the landing in my house to our headquarters in Crewe Road, Alsager seven years ago. I started to collect hands because they were the Association's symbol. We now have ornaments from all over the world, not just from this country. I scour car boot sales (when I manage to find the time) for hands and also look for them when speaking at conferences in towns and cities around the country and abroad. While in Dublin at a meeting in April, I was taken into Dublin by my host who asked was there anything particular I would like to look for in the shops. "Yes 'hands'," I said. Nicky said that I wouldn't find any in Dublin but in the first shop we went into I spotted at least four different ones and she was amazed. We have had many 'hands' donated by companies and our members have contributed greatly to the collection by spotting items in their own area or while they are on holiday. We get very excited when a parcel arrives containing a new addition to our collection. I am really fixated by hands now and the collection is growing so fast that I have to go to car boot sales to find shelves and display cases to house the umpteen ornaments! I recently approached The Sunday Times who were offering a Dali print of 'Apparatus and the Hand'. They kindly donated a framed print which now has pride of place in our office.

Anne Mawdsley

Erythromelalgia

Erythromelalgia (EM) is a condition characterised by intense burning pain, increased temperature and redness of the skin, particularly of the lower limbs.

The symptoms are precipitated by exposure to heat, exercise and sitting while the legs are dependent. The attacks can last from minutes to days. It is often experienced under bedclothes at night, near heaters and after a bath. Symptoms are experienced in these situations because there is an increase in the critical skin temperature. Temporary relief is often obtained by lowering the temperature of the skin, thus patients often expose their extremities or immerse them in cool or ice water. Extreme cases have been reported whereby patients sleep with their feet out of the window or in the fridge.

Primary and Secondary Erythromelalgia

There are two types of EM. In the primary form there is no associated disorder. It is often seen in a younger age group, which is predominantly male, there may be a family history of the condition, and both arms and legs can be equally affected. The secondary form is associated with a number of disorders, for example; diabetes and systemic lupus erythematosus (SLE). This tends to present in middle age, both men and women being equally affected and there is often no recognisable family history.

Investigations

Our own EM investigations unit at Ninewells, Dundee is a tertiary referral centre in which we see only cases where a previous hospital consultant has failed to determine a cause for the EM.

The vascular tests developed and implemented are part of a six-year part-time PhD studentship, which is currently in its second year. As the condition is dependent on temperature for its symptoms, the main aim of the investigations is to assess the adaptation of the circulation to both cold and hot environments. The investigative programme (two three-hour sessions) takes place in a temperature-controlled room. At the first session the room is cool to induce vasoconstriction, whereas at the second the room is very warm (28°C) to induce vasodilation. Thermographic monitoring is carried out using a camera which measures skin temperature. The toes, feet and lower limbs are observed for asymmetry of temperatures between the limbs and to determine if there is any link between skin temperature and symptoms. A laser Doppler flow meter (donated by the Raynaud's & Scleroderma Association) is used to measure skin blood flow at various points on the foot and lower limb, and to assess the local reaction to direct heating.

Complex reflex reactions are also monitored by laser Doppler to establish nerve damage. Burning nerve pain is similar to the pain described by EM sufferers.

Preliminary Results and Therapy

The combinations of the tests highlight three possible causes for EM:

1. Vasodilatory mechanism, those patients who have high blood flow velocity and stay too warm for too long in a cool environment. Normally primary EM treatment includes vasoconstrictors like the B-blocker propranolol.

2. Vasoconstrictive mechanism, those patients who have low blood flow velocity and stay too cool for too long in a warm environment. Normally secondary EM treatment includes vasodilators like praxilene combined with amitriptylene. Amitriptylene is an antidepressant, but it is used here because it has powerful pain relieving effects.
3. Neural mechanism, where some neural trauma resulted in both pain and localised hyperaemia. Treatment includes amitriptylene and transcutaneous electrical nerve stimulation (TENS).

Future Work

Further analysis has shown which specific tests are required to ascertain the mechanism responsible. Thus all future referrals will be assessed using these abridged tests in a cool environment only. The techniques of iontophoresis and capillary microscopy, both kindly donated by the Raynaud's & Scleroderma Association, will be used to further develop EM tests. In recent years it has become clear that the lining of blood vessel walls, the endothelium, plays a major role in regulation of vascular tone. Iontophoresis provides a simple and convenient method for producing a quantifiable stimulus to the endothelium. This technique may highlight for the first time any problems of the endothelium in EM. Capillary microscopy allows direct observation of the capillaries at the toe or finger nailfolds. Specific capillary patterns can be used to aid the diagnosis of certain conditions, like systemic sclerosis. A full assessment of EM capillary patterns and their change over time may indicate further the underlying mechanisms responsible for the symptoms of EM. As micro vascular tests become more specific it is more likely we can screen and treat sufferers earlier, thus dramatically reducing the distress and pain in EM.

Dr. Jill Belch

I wish I had wrinkles!

"I was 47 when I first noticed something was wrong. I had hot flushes and my joints started to ache. I thought it was the menopause and my doctor put me on HRT. But while hormone treatment stopped the hot flushes, the pain in my joints got worse. I began to feel like an old lady. My fingers and toes swelled up like sausages. I couldn't walk properly or lift anything. Simple tasks became impossible - opening a tin, peeling vegetables or cleaning the house were all too painful. My hands and feet always felt cold - I just couldn't seem to keep warm. Then my skin started itching and a 3 inch pinky-mauve mark appeared on the inside of my thigh. It felt as if the skin all over my body was shrinking. So I covered myself with moisturising cream, which helped a bit. My husband, Mike, a production supervisor with the Ford Motor Company thought a holiday might help, so he booked a week in Jersey. While we were there my hands and feet swelled enormously. I couldn't wear shoes and I had to force off my wedding and engagement rings with soap. When I came home my feet were so swollen I had to wear flip-flops to work. I still managed my part-time job as an administration clerk for an insurance firm - but I was always tired. I still had no idea what was wrong. In June 1990 my G.P. referred me to a consultant rheumatologist and an expert on joints.

Kathy Allen

Although it was a warm day, I was wearing trousers and a jumper. "Do you usually wear so many clothes?" he asked. I told him I was cold. The consultant examined my discoloured skin and told me that he thought I had scleroderma. I'd never heard of it, and even the consultant said he'd only ever seen four cases.

Afterwards, I went to the library and looked it up in the medical books but they only gave me an impression of what could happen if the disease went untreated, and I was more frightened than ever. I then went to the Royal Free Hospital in London and for the first time, someone actually explained what was happening to me. By then my skin had become very tight and I couldn't bend my knees. I had to go up and down stairs sideways with my legs straight, and the skin discolouration, which was like an uneven suntan, had spread across my stomach. There were some benefits, however. The cellulite on my thighs disappeared and my legs looked lovely and smooth. I also used to have drooping eyelids, but the skin became really tight and smooth - as if I'd had an eye-lift. The crow's feet were less prominent too. Although my skin will always be like this, I was very lucky the scleroderma was diagnosed early - before I'd suffered any internal damage. My condition is now under control with drugs. I do get a lot of indigestion, but I'm coping with that and if I try to open my mouth really wide, it still feels as if my skin is tearing and my lips feel tight. I am a lot better though, and I can lead a normal life again. I may have a smooth unlined skin, but this isn't something I'd wish on anybody".

Kathy Allen

You Need a Good Physician

Valerie Evans

"I will begin my story three years ago, April 1991 in the lobby of a lovely old hotel in Caerleon, Gwent (although it had begun sometime before then). I was saying farewell to relatives and friends after the wedding of a niece. I had enjoyed it very much but had been unwell at times, having to withdraw from the photo calls because we were in thin clothes and there was a cold wind which had provoked chest pain and other symptoms. Relatives who had not seen me for some time were concerned at how ill I looked. I had been a bonny eleven stone some years before. I was saying goodbye to my son, a doctor. He was examining my hands and he said "Mum, you need a good physician, I think you have a connective tissue disorder." Since (even allowing for a mother's pride) one of the finest physicians in the land was looking at me, I knew then that whatever was wrong with me was very complicated and difficult to diagnose. It was at that time I was seeing a very eminent cardiologist, who had diagnosed angina, due to coronary artery spasm and rhythm irregularities but he could not tell me what caused it. He did not seem to think it was serious. It was to be eighteen months and a lot of problems later before I was to find that good physician, who I found through the help and advice of the Raynaud's & Scleroderma Association. During that eighteen months my symptoms, chest pain, palpitations, high blood pressure and bouts of great weakness went on and new symptoms developed including Raynaud's, dry eyes, dry mouth and intestinal problems. I was told that it was due to anxiety as a result of my husband's sudden death a couple of years before, then depression, viruses, overactive thyroid, irritable bowel syndrome and many other conditions were queried.

I was almost operated on during a ten day spell in hospital with a bout of what I now know was severe vasculitis. I changed my cardiologist and the new one did more tests. During this time I was given tablets that made the symptoms worse. I took to keeping my own record to avoid this as some were prescribed the second time around! It appears to me that some very eminent specialists in their own fields are not aware of the situation when it comes to connective tissue disorders, especially if they cannot find markers in the blood, or very visible signs in the skin etc. We are passed from one to another (often with great relief on their part) as they decide we are not in their field of medicine. I experienced this in at least three specialties - cardiac, gastroenterology and even rheumatology! In the NHS as it is at present, each specialist can take up to three months to see a patient. Add to that a busy and sceptical G.P. and we are left in a non-observation, non-treatment situation. The illness itself is variable, we have good days and bad days. We often look very well - no wonder the doctors think we are neurotic! It is a strange, puzzling, distressing illness. We learn the hard way to manage ourselves, what to avoid - temperature changes, damp, stress, certain foods, smoking, scented soap etc. After a great battle, mostly with my G.P., help came to me when I saw Dr. Black at The Royal Free Hospital in August 1993. To see the words Scleroderma Unit over the door of the department and to know that I was in the hands of experts brought an overwhelming sense of relief. They did a whole lot of tests and I now know the nature of my illness and that is more than half of the battle. As yet I am lucky. Whilst it never goes away I am better at times and feel able to cope with my symptoms, or at least understand them. However, if it were not for my doctor son initially and then The Raynaud's & Scleroderma Association and Dr. Black, I would have gone under in the last few years, unable to understand what was happening to me.

I find the newsletters the greatest of help, other people's stories and the sharing of knowledge are reassuring. I no longer feel so odd or alone and wanted to relate my experience to other members. It is my intention to help the Association in every way I can to further their work".

Valerie Evans

New Trustee

Jo Kaddish

Jo Kaddish, who has been a member of the Association since 1985, became a Trustee in January of this year. Jo trained as a nurse at the Westminster and Westminster Children's Hospitals, London and qualified as SRN and RSCN in 1968. After completing her training she travelled to Africa, spending a year working in the children's intensive care cardiac unit in Cape Town with Professor Christian Barnard. She then moved on to Zimbabwe and for several years arranged and held medical clinics seeing patients with a variety of conditions including eye disease, TB and Leprosy, in rural areas throughout the country. After returning to the U.K. in 1977 Jo joined the Sales Department of Van den Bergh Foods (makers of Flora) in Sussex. This involved a complete change of career, but after attending several Management courses, she now holds the position of Sales Administration Manager in the Sales Operations Department. Jo has raised substantial amounts of money for the Association, and has taken part in several local radio interviews.

Computer Thanks

Emma with her computer

Some members will remember a photograph in our newsletter of little Emma Vaughan when she was 2 years old, sitting in her pushchair wearing electrically heated gloves. Emma, who still has Raynaud's, is now 7 years old. Her mother Jane wrote to us because she was anxious for Emma to have a computer as she had to stay indoors so much. Through the Association we put Emma's Mum, Jane in touch with Roger Jefcoate, an adviser on technology for people with disabilities, and he came to her rescue. Roger has always been very supportive of the work of our Association particularly because his wife Jean is a sufferer.

We later received this letter:

"Roger Jefcoate did a wonderful job in raising funds for my daughter Emma's computer and printer. She has to spend a lot of time indoors, especially during the winter months, and she can now switch it on and 'away she goes'. She might not be expert yet but is learning fast. She not only plays games, but can use it to help with her school work. She has just moved to a new school, and hopefully will settle in and manage just like all the other 7 year olds. She is very independent, always smiles even when in pain and I'm very proud of her.'

Jane Vaughan

Scleroderma - It's More than Skin Deep

Due to the success of our first video on Raynaud's, 'Back in Circulation', the Association decided to make another video focussing this time on scleroderma. The video was launched at our Annual Conference in September 1994. It has been produced mainly for patients, their relatives and friends, in addition to giving the general public an insight into how scleroderma can affect individuals. Scleroderma was first described over two centuries ago, in 1753 by Curzio of Naples. The current term scleroderma was named by Gintrac in 1847 and was then recognised as a skin disorder. The word scleroderma comes from two Greek words, 'sclero' meaning hard and 'derma' meaning skin. Scleroderma is a very heterogeneous disease - it is not all one type. It may be diffuse scleroderma where the thickening of the skin is spreading up the body and onto the trunk, or limited scleroderma, where the skin thickening is affecting only the hands, lower arms, face and feet but often accompanied by poor circulation. Almost all scleroderma patients also have Raynaud's.

Professor Carol Black introduces four of her patients, Kathryn Thomas, Yunwah Wan, Susan Churcher and Jed Malins. The video illustrates how they have coped with the physical and emotional problems that have arisen as a result of developing scleroderma and describes the treatments which are available to stabilise and improve the condition. Professor Black emphasises the importance of bringing one's problems out into the open by talking about them.

Kathryn is 16 years old and was diagnosed as having scleroderma four years ago. She had great difficulties at school. She felt different, looked different, was losing weight and couldn't join in things with her friends. She was depressed and tearful. Her hands were swollen, she developed ulcers on her fingers, her skin had tightened and the tightening extended up her arms onto her body. It involved her legs, she had very bad Raynaud's and a lot of problems swallowing. Kathryn still has to go to hospital regularly to have her oesophagus dilated but she is gaining weight and eating better since taking the drug omeprazole (Losec). Kathryn now tells us that she doesn't mind going into hospital as she has made many friends there. She copes well with her illness and is now continuing all the activities she enjoyed before developing scleroderma. She has just started college and is doing 'A' Levels. She enjoys going out with her friends, playing badminton and going swimming when possible. Kathryn tries not to let her illness restrict her life more than necessary. She enjoyed making the video and hopes that it will help more people come to terms with their condition. Overall she is now a much happier person.

Yunwah is 22 and has had scleroderma since the age of 15. She has recently graduated from University and plans to be a teacher. She has a mild form of diffuse scleroderma with dreadful contractions in her hands, making writing very difficult. Her circulation has been very poor and she has had to make sure that she kept warm as much as possible. She lost weight and as well as her skin being painful, she was tired all the time. Yunwah found the most difficult period was when she didn't understand what was happening to her. With current treatment she feels much better and says that "everything is alright now".

A patient who has the diffuse form of scleroderma is Susan Churcher. She is 36 years old and has two young children. In Susan's case (see page 91), the skin thickening has progressed quite rapidly and she has quite severe deformities to cope with. Professor Black states that she has coped quite magnificently. The skin has thickened on her arms, face, neck, upper chest and back. Her hands are clawed and her mouth has shrunk. Her whole life has changed and for someone who was very independent she finds it difficult to have to ask for help all the time. She can't bath herself, wash her hair, brush her teeth, prepare food etc. She says that she never feels well, is in pain most of the time and her hands and joints are extremely painful and she feels constantly tired. She says you have good days and bad days. You have days when you think "Ugh I can't get out of bed but you do get out of bed because if you didn't get out of bed, you would give into that disease and you can't do that, you can't let it beat you in any way". Her eldest son is five years old and understands but she hasn't been able to pick up her youngest son since he was ten weeks old - he doesn't even know who she is. Most people in this situation would understandably give up but not Susan. On the video she shows her strength of character and Professor Black describes the treatments which have helped her to cope. Susan's positive attitude has helped her to come to terms with scleroderma.

Jed Malins (see page 96), is 52 years old and has been a patient of Professor Black for four years. He has limited scleroderma, his main problems being finger ulcers and shortening of the fingers, together with severe Raynaud's. In addition he has scleroderma of the heart. He had always been a talented man, a skilled artist and ballroom dancer. Scleroderma meant that he was unable to hold a brush properly and could not find the energy to dance. He was withdrawn, depressed, had ulcers on his fingers and his heart was not functioning very well. He had begun to think that life was not worthwhile. Now he is back doing all his favourite activities, drawing and travelling. He travels abroad and is ballroom dancing once again. He now feels happier, more confident and is really beginning to enjoy life. The video takes Jed through his treatments, particularly the effects of Iloprost. His ulcers have now healed and he is a totally different person.

Our sincere thanks to Professor Carol Black and her patients for their contribution to this video. We hope that it will help to inform both patients and medical professionals, as well as the general public, just what it feels like to live with scleroderma.

We are most grateful to Astra Pharmaceuticals, The Three Oaks Trust and The Summerfield Charitable Trust for sponsoring this production.

Morphea

(from the Greek word morphe, meaning form)

Morphea is the name given to localised patches of hardening (sclerosis) which can affect the skin. So why is it not called scleroderma - which as you probably know means hardening of the skin!! It could be, but it probably helps to have a different name to distinguish morphea from the more generalised sclerosis affecting both skin and other organs that occurs in progressive systemic sclerosis or scleroderma. Although there is some overlap, morphea and systemic sclerosis are better regarded as separate entities. Morphea usually appears spontaneously, as asymptomatic hard patches in the skin. These have a faint purplish colour initially, fading centrally to develop a waxy ivory appearance with lilac-coloured edges. The patches are round or oval, and may be multiple, affecting almost any part of the body. Rarely, morphea may become generalised. Sometimes lesions are deeper, involving tissue beneath the skin. One well known but uncommon deep form affects the face and scalp and is called 'en coup de sabre" (a blow from a sword). A characteristic linear depressed groove of scarring extends from the forehead back into the scalp and sometimes down onto the face. Morphea is three times more common in women than men. It most frequently occurs between ages 20-40 years but 15% of cases occur in children. The lesions usually appear without any apparent cause. Patches rarely may be provoked at sites of physical trauma, vaccination, radiotherapy, or after infections, for example measles. Most lesions of morphea improve with time - typically 3-5 years - and eventually clear almost completely. Residual pigmentation may persist. Generally treatment is not indicated, although local steroid applications may be used to hasten clearance.

Dr. Susan Morley,
Consultant Dermatologist Ninewells Hospital, Dundee

Over half a million pounds committed to research

The Raynaud's & Scleroderma Association is committed to £520,592 for research during the next three years. This takes into account all present commitments in addition to newly awarded grants. This would not be possible without the support of our members who spend hours thinking up ideas, organising fund-raising events and persuading their friends and relatives to help; people who collect used postage stamps and petrol coupons; donations which come from individuals, companies, organisations and Charitable Trusts; legacies and donations which are sent to us in lieu of flowers in memory of loved ones; in fact everyone deserves a special thank you for helping in any way towards the funding of our research projects. This money has not been raised by large donations but by many people raising small amounts, which when put together make all the difference in the world. Your support could help towards finding a cure for Raynaud's and scleroderma. This is a very exciting time as many interesting new theories and ideas are coming forward. We should all feel positive and hopeful for the future.

Why me?

Have you ever asked "Why Me?" My advice is to conserve your precious energy and use it to cope with your condition, because at present, Why Me? is an unanswerable question. Leave it to the medical researchers to look for the answer, while you learn to deal with your condition, readjust your lifestyle and your attitude to what has happened to your body. The medical profession can only help so far. We have to develop the right mental and physical conditions to assist the healing. Don't leave it to the doctors, join in, because it's your body and they need to know how you feel. This sort of co-operation can only help to find the solution and being involved will help your attitude to the condition. Also it has been my experience that positive thinking can help to lessen the suffering. My condition was brought on by emotional stress in 1974 and then taken a stage further in 1991 by further stress. My heart, lungs and, to a lesser degree, my kidneys became involved, which meant admission to The Royal Free Hospital in London, under the care of Professor Black. This was the turning point for me as I was at last in the care of physicians who knew what scleroderma was. They brought me under control from a near fatal heart condition and I am now more stable. I experienced more stress when I returned from hospital but nothing was as bad as what I had just been through.

I went through bankruptcy, house repossession, finger amputation, and then a marriage split followed by divorce. I ended up on my own, and after visiting my sister in Canada, who helped me reassess my situation, I returned home ready to stand on my own two feet. I found myself in control of my life with a good deal less pressure and it suited me. With six monthly visits to hospital all my ulcers healed up, I put on weight, my heart strengthened and I had a new experience - no pain! I had forgotten what it was like. Before this change occurred I used to play little games, mostly mental ones, to pretend the pain was Mother Nature nudging me to "get hold of myself". I was working too hard with little reward, trying to please everyone with a self destructive attitude. One game I played was to expect pain whenever I did any task, and if it didn't happen, it was a bonus. It was amazing how many times it didn't happen, and also how much better I felt when it didn't. In my case, as I cheered up my condition became more bearable. It seemed that once my condition had been switched on, worrying didn't help. I almost believed I was doing this to myself, but if that was the case then I should be able to reverse the whole process. It may not work, but I certainly feel more optimistic and positive, resulting in a more active and fulfiling life.

Jed Malins

This is a brief account of Jed's talk given at our Annual Conference in 1994. (See also page 90).

New Patrons

Sir Donald Wilson, is best known as Chairman of the former Mersey Regional Health Authority, which he served for 12 years until the new North West Authority was established in 1994. He is currently a Deputy Lord Lieutenant of Cheshire. Commenting on our invitation to serve as a patron of the Raynaud's & Scleroderma Associatiuon, Sir Donald said: "I am more than happy to become a Patron and will do all I can to be fully supportive".

Sir Donald Wilson

Sir Robin David

His Honour Judge Sir Robin David recently became a Patron to the Association. Sir Robin has had a distinguished career as Crown Court Judge on the Cheshire and North Wales circuit and earlier this year he received a knighthood in recognition of his outstanding contribution to the legal system. In response to our invitation Sir Robin said "I am delighted and honoured to become a Patron of your Association".

Stories from members

Brenda

Brenda first realised there was something wrong with her hands at the age of 16, when they started turning blue. Over the next few years Brenda, who started her working life as a typist, found her fingers becoming increasingly stiff, cold and painful. Twenty seven years on from developing the first symptoms of the condition known as Raynaud's, the Kidderminster speech therapist assistant, now finds some of the simplest household tasks difficult and painful. If she touches metal stands in the cold, or goes near the fridge, her hands can seize up and become

Brenda Preston

Photograph by kind permission of the Worcester Evening News

lifeless. When the condition is at its height, Brenda says, "it is like having frostbite. I have to always keep warm and avoid activities which might bring it on', says 43 year old Brenda. I get a lot of ulcers and cuts, which makes it very painful. I often can't do simple things, like sewing or picking up small objects". Brenda says one doctor has diagnosed her as suffering from the more serious condition, scleroderma, which can develop from Raynaud's and can affect major organs such as the heart, lungs, kidney and digestive system. Again, there is no cure. "I don't know if I've got anything more than severe Raynaud's', Brenda says. "I'm just determined to keep going and live my life as normally as possible".

Extracted from an article in the Worcester Evening News

Jenny

Jenny Bush

"The other day I was out shopping near my home in Nottingham. I bumped into someone I hadn't seen for a long time "Jenny" she cried, "You haven't changed a bit. How do you stay so young?" A few years ago I would have been delighted at the compliment, like most women. I used to be so proud of my smooth, ageless skin. Now those few words cut through me like a knife. You see unlike most women of 52 I'd love to look my age. Every day I study my reflection in the mirror, hoping that I might see some lines, some signs of aging. Until two years ago I could never have imagined I'd have an illness like this. My husband Derek and I have always been so active. We had a big house in the country, two grown up children and plenty of animals to look after. I worked a couple of days a week in a nearby shoe shop. One day in March 1993, while I was gardening I felt a stabbing pain in my hand and two of my fingers started to swell up. Within a couple of weeks the swelling had got worse and my fingers became quite hard and rigid. I was sent to hospital for tests and referred to a dermatologist. I'll never forget the dermatologist saying that what I had wasn't just a mild complaint that would clear up in a few days. "You've got something called scleroderma" she told me. She went on to explain that it was a rare disease which affects people who produce too much collagen - the substance which gives the skin a plump, smooth appearance. When I went home and told Derek and our daughter Amanda what the doctor had said, I was my usual joking self. I laughed off any suggestion that I should be concerned and the truth was I wasn't really worried. The dermatologist had recommended I try steroid treatment and I was convinced that would make me normal again. As the weeks passed and numbness slowly crept into both hands and arms, it became harder to shrug off the pain and to ignore the fear that had begun to gnaw at me. Every day my skin seemed to be stretching tighter and tighter, taking on a translucent, marble-like sheen. After a while I was in constant pain. Even dosed up with a constant supply of painkillers, the slightest contact on the rock hard surface of my hands was excruciating. The greatest comfort was that the dermatologist told me that the disease was containable. Even though I could feel the rigidity spreading I clung to the belief that I could be treated and that it may not get any worse. As far as the family were concerned I was still good old Jenny, the life and soul of the party. I tried to keep up the facade. I know how important it is to think positively but sometimes when I'd spent two hours trying to put on my make-up with inflexible fingers that fumbled and smudged, I'd sob with frustration.

It's the lack of independence that really gets to me. I've always been so headstrong, so self-sufficient. After two years my hands had become claw-like and my arms rigid. I'm in constant pain and any kind of physical contact is unbearable. A while ago Derek had to cut off all my rings because my fingers had swollen so much. Now when I see women with nice hands and lovely jewellery, I feel a pang of jealousy. "Why me?" I think, but it doesn't help to think like that and I don't like myself for it. So I just keep trying to smile, hoping against hope that one day I'll look in the mirror and find a line. Derek and the children have been marvellous but it's difficult for them to reconcile me, with the energetic person they used to know. For their sakes, I try to laugh off my fears and we talk constantly about a brighter future. I am determined not to give in, so try to think positive thoughts".

Jenny Bush

Lillian

"In 1983 I started to find it difficult to swallow food, and my stomach started to blow up. After quite a long time of going back and forth to the doctor he diagnosed a hiatus hernia. This I put up with for a few years and then my muscles started to pain when I walked, my fingers started to turn blue and I found that I felt cold all the time. So many things happened to my body I cannot remember in which order it followed. My bowel and stomach gave me my biggest problem. If I did manage to get food down I would soon start vomiting and this went on for some time. My doctor sent me to a specialist who, after tests, discovered I had pancreatitis but he did not know what was causing it. I started to vomit again and another doctor was passing, so the nurse called him over, and he asked how long had my skin been tight on my face. I never noticed this before, so was referred to Hope Hospital where they diagnosed scleroderma. My lungs, gullet, bowel and kidneys are affected. In 1993 I had to have an ileostomy as the large colon had stopped working. Since my operation I eat a lot better and although I am still sick it is not as often, so it was well worth having the operation. I have worked full time at C & A in Wigan for 17 years and for the last 5 years have only worked 3 days a week. Some days I find it difficult, and some days there seems to be nothing wrong. I am not ready to finish work yet because I really enjoy my job. All the girls that I work with are fantastic, they are so considerate and supportive they keep me going. I know the time will come when I cannot work any more but hopefully it will not be for a while. It does you good to be positive and keep going as long as you can".

Lillian Williams

Yvonne

Yvonne Grayson, aged 48 from Wilmslow, has had Raynaud's since she was a child and has learned to cope with the pain and discomfort it can cause. Yvonne, whose younger sister Michelle also suffers from Raynaud's, leads as normal a life as possible. Yvonne says "It can be very painful but I am a positive person and I try not to let it rule my life. I am always cold whether I am in the office or outside. At home I have the central heating on as well as the gas fire. People at work don't realise that I have Raynaud's, they just know my hands are always freezing!" Yvonne has worked as a district manager with the Cheshire Building Society for 20 years. She says "I always wear suits to work because then I can keep my jacket on without looking as though I am wearing a coat! If I'm going to a meeting I always try to sit next to a radiator to keep warm, and when I get home from work the first thing I do is have a hot bath to warm me up. Raynaud's does affect my life but I refuse to let it spoil things so I don't think of it as a problem.'

Eleanor Clark

My friends don't understand

"My name is Eleanor Clark and I live in Wolverhampton. I am 8 years old and was told I had Raynaud's when I was only 4. I have bad Raynaud's in my feet and sometimes in my hands. During playtime at school I never go outside in the winter. The teachers know that I have to stay in and they let me have a friend to play with me. This winter I have suffered from chilblains on my feet which were very sore. The doctor said that if the chilblains burst my feet would be very bad. (Luckily they didn't burst because of my medicine.) I find it difficult to do PE in the winter but my doctors says I must do exercise to keep my circulation going. I do not like hospitals but my doctor at New Cross Hospital is very nice and looks after me. They do tests on me that I don't like but I know they have to be done and my mum and dad are always with me. At school the other children think that I am the teacher's favourite because I can stay in during the cold weather - they do not understand that I cannot go outside as it would make my feet very, very sore - and they also do not understand that I would like to be outside with them and play games with them. I do not like to talk about my Raynaud's to other children as I feel embarrassed that they think I am different from them".

Eleanor Clark

Laura O'Connor

A positive lass!

"I am 10 years old and I have linear morphea on my right leg. It has affected the growth of my leg and I wear a specially made raised boot. I go to Great Ormond Street Hospital and when I am 14 my doctor is going to straighten my foot as much as possible. Due to this complaint I have now only got one artery supplying my foot, therefore it makes an operation very difficult and I cannot have plastic surgery. I can only wait at present to see what will happen"(see pages 189-190 for update).

Laura O'Connor

Helen

Helen with her son, Ryan

Last December, Helen Birtles, 26, a sufferer from both Raynaud's and scleroderma, was taken into hospital knowing she might need her thumb amputated. She was put on an antibiotic drip, which saved her thumb, and was discharged a few days before Christmas. Helen's first symptoms of Raynaud's showed up when she got a hand infection - a reaction, she thought, to the chemicals she used in her work as a hairdresser. However, the hospital diagnosed Raynaud's and told her to stop working in the salon. She was referred to a hospital where specialists diagnosed scleroderma. She took drugs which reduced, but did not stop, the symptoms. Then she became pregnant and felt great. All the symptoms disappeared - until she had Ryan and they came back worse than ever. Helen now suffers from nagging pains, ulcers and tight skin on her fingers.

Helen says "I first started with symptoms of Raynaud's when I was 18 years old. It began with chilblains on the ends of my fingers. The local doctors were not concerned but when the symptoms got worse I arranged to see a specialist at the local BUPA hospital. He recommended a cream to use to improve the circulation. After about a year of this treatment I heard about the Association and contacted Anne Mawdsley. She suggested that I asked to be referred to a hospital which specialised in Raynaud's. The local BUPA doctor was happy for me to change and told me to mention that I also had scleroderma. This was the first time I had heard of scleroderma, let alone knew I had it, but what was it?

I attended Hope Hospital and was seen by Professor Jayson who carried out lots of tests and X-rays and I was told that I would be admitted for a few days at a later date. I will never forget the first time I went into hospital. I had a telephone call one Friday at work saying there was a bed for me on the Monday. I was told I would be having several tests and would be in for three days. All that weekend I was very nervous and my stomach kept churning over. Everything was going through my mind and although everyone was telling me not to worry, it wasn't them going into hospital. Monday arrived very quickly and I arrived in the afternoon. Everyone seemed to be staring at me and I couldn't see any other patients of my age. I kept telling myself "it's only for three days". I was shown to my bed which had a locker by the side which made it rather cramped and I could guarantee every time I went into it I knocked my fingers. I was asked to put on my night clothes and told I was going to another part of the hospital for some skin tests. I was taken by a porter all along corridors which were freezing cold and I remember the porter saying I should have been given a blanket. The bathroom on the ward was old fashioned and very cold. The top windows were open but as I was a new patient I was too nervous to ask for someone to shut them. The meals I found very hard to swallow as it was a set menu so it was that or nothing. My family used to bring in food which I could eat. After I had been in for three days my father rang the hospital to see when I could come home and he was told I would be in for another week. I couldn't believe it. I have been in hospital three times since then and feel more confident to ask for more blankets and the food has improved a little. I really hate going into hospital and leaving Ryan behind but at the end of the day I know that the doctors and nurses are there for my benefit and I cannot thank them enough for what they have done for me.'

Helen Birtles

Lindsay and Dave with baby Thomas

Lindsay

"I was in my early teens when I was diagnosed as having Raynaud's but in common with many other people I was told that it would be no more than an inconvenience and to wrap up warmly. Over the years the white and dead-looking finger ends degenerated into more severe and painful spasms when the whole of my hands and feet turned a dark blue but, fortunately, got no worse than that. In the early eighties, when I was approaching my final University exams, I began to suffer paralysing pains in my chest which were extremely frightening. I was diagnosed with mixed connective tissue disease involving the left lung. Never having been warned of the possibility of this, I was dumbfounded, but looking back I realise how lucky I am. The lung problems have not recurred and after several years of excessive lethargy, even this has now improved and I have been told that at present the disease is not active. I am very grateful for this as, after many years of trying for a baby, our son Thomas was born in March after I.V.F. treatment, and I need all my energy for him! Both the rheumatologists and gynaecologists were non-committal on whether there could be a connection between my infertility and Raynaud's/MCTD. Ironically I sailed through the pregnancy and my Raynaud's was much improved. In fact most of the time I was complaining of being too hot! My circulation now seems to be slowly returning to its 'normal' state but it's too early yet to say how it will settle. I just need to wait and see and concentrate on enjoying the new addition to our family".

Lindsay Profitt

Rita

"I thought that other sufferers might be interested in what I must admit is a very shortened account of my illness. In 1942, when I was 11 years old, I became ill with what I now know to be Raynaud's, scleroderma and calcinosis but this was never diagnosed until having spoken to Anne at the Naidex Exhibition in Manchester, when she told me about Professor Jayson. I asked my doctor to refer me and after many tests I finally had a name for my condition, 48 years after it began. All the years with what I now know were all the classic symptoms of the complaint, I had to struggle without any help. I saw many doctors and had endless examinations and tests, mainly X-rays, in fact there is not one bit of me which has not been X-rayed but still no treatment. I was determined to lead as normal a life as possible including working, getting married and having a perfectly healthy daughter. Possibly one of the worst things to happen began in 1961 when my throat muscles started to be affected. Since then I have never had a solid meal. To start with I lived on Complan but for the last few years Fresubin has been added to my diet. Losec has been a great help but nothing can be done for all the muscular weakness that affects me - I have to accept that. I am writing this in the hope that young people newly diagnosed will realise that it's not the end of everything for them. I have had a happy life despite everything and at 64 I hope to carry on for a while yet".

Rita Hardman

The Jimmy Young Show

Dr. Mike Smith has been supportive once again by giving us a plug on the Jimmy Young Show and several newspapers and magazines have published articles about both Raynaud's and scleroderma including TV Quick and Best magazine. These conditions are getting much better known and it is only through sufferers talking about their experiences that people will begin to understand.

NHS Handout

A donation of £2,000 was given by the South & East Cheshire Health Authority to make our Headquarters more accessible to both wheelchair guests and visitors. In the photograph is Mr. Simon Cousins, Chairman of the Health Authority, with Anne Mawdsley and Carol Holland, one of our volunteers.

The use of heparin in Raynaud's and Scleroderma

Some time ago I spoke at the Annual Conference in Alsager, describing a trial of heparin therapy for patients with Raynaud's and scleroderma which we were about to start at the Royal Free Hospital in London. I am pleased to report that the study has now been completed, and I can outline some of our preliminary findings.

Heparin is a drug which was discovered 'by accident' at the turn of the century by a medical student undertaking a period of research. The student unintentionally left some of his samples out on his laboratory bench over the weekend. Instead of throwing them away on Monday morning, as a more diligent scientist might have done, he continued to use them for his experiments the next week. Surprisingly he found that the properties of his test substance had changed, so that it could now prevent blood from clotting (i.e. he had discovered an anti-coagulant). Although clotting of the blood is generally a good thing, for instance when you cut yourself, there are many medical conditions in which blood clots at the wrong time, or in the wrong place. Examples of such disorders include common life-threatening conditions such as heart attacks (coronary thromboses), pulmonary embolism (blood clots on the lung) and some forms of stroke (cerebral thrombosis). Heparin has proved remarkably effective for both the treatment and prevention of these conditions, and has been in widespread medical use for the past 60 years. One of its few drawbacks has been the necessity to give it either by continuous intravenous infusion (drip) or by injection several times every day. More recently new preparations of heparin, called low molecular weight (LMW) heparin, have become available with some advantages over the traditional forms, notably a longer duration of effect which allows them to be injected less frequently.

Our interest in heparin stemmed from an observation that some patients with scleroderma and Raynaud's who were put on LMW heparin for other medical conditions noticed an improvement in their Raynaud's severity. This was accompanied by apparent changes in some of the specialised Raynaud's tests, such as finger nailbed capillaroscopy. This unexpected observation, which illustrates how important it is to listen to what patients tell doctors about their disease, led us to examine the scientific literature to look for an explanation as to how heparin might be helping these patients. We were intrigued to read research papers suggesting that heparin might have a number of effects on blood vessels which could be helpful in Raynaud's. For example it stimulates the lining cells of blood vessels to make prostacyclin (the agent some of you may be familiar with as iloprost), and reduces production of a chemical called endothelin which may cause blood vessel spasm. Heparin also interacts with some of the chemical products of the immune system and alters the properties of cells called fibroblasts which are thought to be central to the scleroderma disease process. With this background we designed a study to test whether heparin treatment, given by injection under the skin three times a week, would be safe in Raynaud's and scleroderma and to see if it might help a significant number of patients. Having decided to set up and run the trial, we were delighted when so many patients volunteered to receive the treatment.

We enrolled 31 patients into the study, some with Raynaud's and some suffering from both Raynaud's and scleroderma. The trial involved regular visits to the Royal Free for medical assessment, blood tests and the 'non-invasive blood flow studies' which some readers who have visited the Royal Free may have undergone. These include thermal images taken before and after a 'cold challenge' (when the hand is placed in some cool water), video recordings of the small blood vessels around the finger nails and a new approach called laser Doppler flowmetry which uses a laser probe to measure the flow of blood in the fingertips. Although patients participating were observed for 12 months they only received heparin for half this time so that we could accurately determine its benefit by comparing the patients condition 'on' and 'off' therapy. Our study has now finished and some of the initial results are available. In time these will be prepared for formal publication in a medical journal, and for presentation at scientific meetings so that other doctors will become aware of our work, and can discuss it with us. We were reassured that heparin appears to be as safe in Raynaud's and scleroderma as in other disorders, and were impressed how easily most patients learnt to give their own injections. As with all new therapies we must be cautious in interpreting the results, but a significant number of patients did notice an improvement in their Raynaud's attack severity whilst on heparin. More persuasively, when the skin blood flow results from laser Doppler flowmetry were analysed, we found that recovery time after the standard cold challenge was significantly shortened by heparin treatment. So far though we have not found any differences in levels of the blood markers which were taken regularly during the study.

In conclusion, we feel that the results of our small pilot study suggest that heparin may indeed have a role in the treatment of Raynaud's, although a larger study will be needed to confirm this. At the moment we would consider its use only for those individuals not helped by more conventional therapies. We are particularly grateful to all of the patients who volunteered for the study, including several members of the Raynaud's & Scleroderma Association.

Dr. Chris Denton, Research Fellow,
Royal Free Academic Rheumatology and Connective Tissue Disease Unit

Grant to Northern Ireland

The Trustees approved a grant to Dr. Aubrey Bell at Musgrave Hospital in Belfast, 'Constitutive nitric oxide synthase and endothelin-1 genetics in Primary Raynaud's Phenomenon'. The project is described below:

Most people with Raynaud's know that the painful symptoms and colour changes which occur in their hands and feet are due to closing down of the small blood vessels (i.e. increased vessel tone or vasoconstriction). Research suggests that this effect could result from excessive action of a chemical released from the blood vessel (endothelin-1) which causes vasoconstriction. However, Raynaud's phenomenon could also arise by deficient action of another recently-described chemical, nitric oxide, also known as endothelial-derived relaxing factor (EDRF), which acts to relax the blood vessel wall thus sustaining patency and precluding vasoconstriction. A proper balance between these two molecules appears to be very important in maintaining normal tone of blood vessels when temperature changes occur, hence preventing disorders such as Raynaud's phenomenon.

Primary Raynaud's phenomenon tends to run in families implying hereditary predisposition to developing the disease. It is possible that an abnormality of the genes responsible for the production of nitric oxide and/or endothelin-1 may contribute to the development of Raynaud's in these patients. Our study will identify 100 patients with primary Raynaud's phenomenon including family members from whom we will take blood samples. From these samples the genetic material (DNA) and the genes responsible for nitric oxide and endothelin-1 production will be examined by molecular genetic techniques for abnormalities and compared with the findings in a group of normal subjects who do not have Raynaud's phenomenon. This will enable us to determine whether the genes responsible for the production of nitric oxide and endothelin-1, and therefore ultimately the control of blood vessel tone, are abnormal in people who develop Raynaud's phenomenon. If successful, establishing genetic abnormalities in nitric oxide or endothelin-1 will not only shed new light on the underlying cause of primary Raynaud's phenomenon but will also provide a rational basis for the development of new treatments. It may also reveal mechanisms relevant to other kinds of Raynaud's such as that which occurs in scleroderma.

Dr. Aubrey Bell, Senior Lecturer and Consultant Rheumatologist and Anita Smyth, Research Fellow in Rheumatology

Genetics of Scleroderma

Over the past year we at the Oxford Transplant Centre and the Royal Free Hospital have been collecting and storing samples from over 500 U.K. scleroderma patients. This represents the largest collection of samples in Europe and forms a solid basis for a genetic study in this disease.

The cause of scleroderma is unknown, however some people are more prone to develop the disease than others and the disease undoubtedly has a strong autoimmune component. The basis why some people are susceptible is connected to the characteristics we are born with i.e. the genes that are passed onto us by our parents. At the Oxford Transplant Centre we test for the genes which influence our immune response as these may be important in scleroderma. These immune genes are situated on chromosome 6. Chromosomes contain genes and also areas which are called VNTR's (this stands for Variable Numbers of Tandem repeats). These are sequences between the genes and these sequences can be changed and affect the function of nearby genes. In work we have already carried out we have shown that patients with SSc have changes in these chromosomes. In the last few months I have been looking at samples of blood from 500 SSc patients. The purpose of this study is to define the genes and gene variation that are common among scleroderma patients and scleroderma patients with particular organ involvement (e.g. lung fibrosis). Eventually these findings may lead to the genetic screening of Raynaud's patients to determine those individuals who will go on to develop the disease and what the likely outcome will be. We are making real progress and have analysed 200 patients so far and preliminary results suggest that genetic screening along with the more traditional signs and symptoms will be useful in disease prediction and may facilitate the early treatment of patients.

My grateful thanks to The Raynaud's & Scleroderma Association for funding this important work which may in the future influence patient management.

Greg Fanning, Oxford Transplant Centre

The Management of Scleroderma

The cure for systemic sclerosis is still not known but there are many treatments which can help to alleviate, stabilise and improve the condition.

Professor Carol Black and Dr. Chris Denton at the Royal Free Hospital suggest that five elements are important in managing the condition effectively. Firstly, it is necessary to determine which subset of the disease the patient has, for example, whether it is diffuse (spread over the body) or limited involvement. There are four main subsets - a 'prescleroderma' phase; diffuse involvement; limited involvement and a rarer subset where the skin never thickens but internal organs are affected. It is important to determine what stage the disease has reached. An early diagnosis of internal involvement and the extent of the involvement is crucial. Keeping up to date with current medical thinking on how the disease develops will help ensure that patients receive the most appropriate treatment for their specific condition. Scleroderma is a disease where the body's own immune system, for some reason which is unclear, begins to attack itself. It is usually characterised by several pathological alterations in the body's normal processes. These include changes in the blood vessels and in the number of white blood cells and an increased deposit of collagen. Collagen is the major protein of the white fibres of connective tissue, cartilage and bone, which builds up in the skin and internal organs. These processes are closely related and perhaps directly linked but researchers are still not sure exactly how.

Effective therapies for systemic sclerosis should take into account three factors: what is happening to the vascular system, the immune system and the reaction that leads to an over-production of fibrous tissue. Only when all these factors are taken into account can the best combination of available drugs be found for any individual patient. Once permanent changes occur in the vascular system, the skin or the internal organs, patients can be divided into different groups, not only according to physical characteristics but also based on readings from blood and serum tests. Each group or subset has a distinct pattern of how the disease has presented and the course it is taking. At that point physicians can treat each patient according to the particular pattern in which the condition has manifested in their case. Usually within the first year of observing a patient it is possible to tell whether the pattern of skin involvement indicates diffuse or limited forms of the disease. Limited scleroderma, where skin involvement is restricted to arms, legs and face, is usually preceded by a lengthy period of Raynaud's phenomenon and the aspects of the disease that relate to changes in the blood vessels, are especially prominent. When making a decision on treatment and when designing trials to test particular therapies, not only is the subset group important but also the duration or length of time the patient has had the condition. Patients with late stage diffuse systemic sclerosis are not usually good subjects for trials of therapies that act by suppressing the immune system. This is because measurable improvement in a relatively short time frame cannot be expected when the disease has entered the phase of advanced fibrosis and vascular damage. Trial results with such patients could therefore be misleading about the drug's possible value. Similarly, patients with limited involvement are not good subjects in trials to test major antifibrosing agents, as these patients' problem is mainly concerned with the vascular system and not with excess production of fibrous tissue.

As an aid to managing the spectrum of scleroderma disorders, it is important to be able to recognise patients with a 'prescleroderma' status before the disease is fully expressed. Between five and ten percent of those who develop Raynaud's phenomenon will progress to a connective tissue disease, of which scleroderma is the most common. There are two good 'markers' whose presence is a good predictor that Raynaud's will eventually develop into scleroderma. One being abnormal nailfold capillaries and the other anti-nuclear antibodies. Some studies suggest that over 90 percent of patients with both 'markers' will develop systemic sclerosis, therefore identifying such patients early will mean they can be carefully monitored and given appropriate drug therapy at the earliest possible stage. The same approach should be applied to achieve the earliest possible detection of internal organ involvement, to enhance the chances of containing the involvement without further damage. Lung involvement, either from fibrosis or vascular disease, is now the major life threatening complication in scleroderma patients. Various scanning methods can now provide a much earlier diagnosis of lung disease and regular measurement of its progression. Such tools for diagnosis and serial monitoring make it easier to accurately evaluate the effectiveness of steroids and cyclophosphamide and other therapies for lung disease. That in turn increases the likelihood of determining the most appropriately effective therapy. Pulmonary hypertension is still a particularly serious problem. However, detection in the early stages, especially in those patients who are otherwise quite well, makes it possible to begin early with therapies such as long-term anti clotting agents or repeated or continuous infusions of Iloprost, which have been found to be useful.

In controlled trials no single drug or combination of drugs has proved satisfactory in the treatment of systemic sclerosis. This is understandable since recognition of the cause and mechanisms of the disease are still evolving. Systemic sclerosis may represent more than one disease. Limited scleroderma, for example, could represent a separate vascular condition or at least something far removed from diffuse involvement. There are several factors which give rise to these conditions and they may occur simultaneously or sequentially. The ultimate therapy for systemic sclerosis and its subsets may well be varied. In the diffuse form of the disease it may be appropriate to direct initial treatment toward the immune system and later add anti-fibrotic and vascular therapies. On the other hand, the best therapy for the localised form may turn out to be primarily vascular. The best way to evaluate potential new therapies for a disease which is uncommon is for multicentre, multinational trials. As yet there are no targeted therapies in effect but instead an approach using non-specific immunosuppressive, anti-fibrotic and vascular drugs. The use of drugs that are currently available can be optimised if the therapy takes into account the specifics of each patient's subset grouping, duration and stage of disease and degree of internal organ involvement.

There is much hope for the future as the level of interest and active research into the condition is increasing and increased knowledge should quickly translate into rational therapy delivered at the earliest possible stage.

This article, which was written by Professor Carol Black and Dr. Chris Denton for the British Journal of Rheumatology, January 1995 has been adapted for the lay person.

Life is a Challenge

(taken from Anne Mawdsley's talk at the 1995 Conference)

Twenty years ago almost to the day my life changed dramatically. Following an operation I suddenly developed Raynaud's. I think the most frightening part was not knowing what was happening to my body and the fact that no one seemed interested or understood the condition. I felt so isolated. My sons were very young at that time and coping with their everyday needs was difficult, painful and frustrating. Now when I think back over that time and what has happened since, I can honestly say that despite the bad times with ulcerated fingers and other problems, having Raynaud's and scleroderma may have changed my life but has given me a challenge bigger than anything I could ever have imagined. Had I not looked upon it as a challenge, twenty years of my life could have been wasted instead of being fulfiled. I am a great believer in looking on the positive side of life and trying to turn negatives into positives.

Raising funds and producing literature are of vital importance but we feel the most important aspect of our work is to provide both emotional and practical support for sufferers. We are constantly busy in the office but when the phone rings, the person at the other end of the line is of sole importance. Just a few words on the telephone, a letter or a visit can be reassurance that someone cares. One message at meetings throughout the country has been to encourage members to visit others in hospital and this has met with a positive response. It is particularly important when a member is in hospital a long way from home. You will have read in the newsletters about members who have benefited from equipment such as electric wheelchairs, car conversions, portable oxygen machines, wheelchairs, special beds, a microwave oven and more recently a stair lift. We have been able to help members who needed respite care to give both themselves and their families a rest. We are most appreciative for the support given to our Welfare Fund by The Florence Nightingale Aid in Sickness Trust. Until a cure can be found it is vitally important that we as an Association try to support each other so that no one feels alone. I only wish we could do more. Sadly it is often those who need help who don't ask for it.

We should never give up on our goals in life even if sometimes we have to move the goal posts. We may not be able to achieve the ultimate but together we can make a significant contribution to research and to the well being of patients. It is incredible just how much money has been raised in the 13 years which the Association has been in existence. The total now exceeds over two and a half million pounds, the majority of which has been used to support research at 20 hospitals around the country. Our commitment at this present time is £585,440 which is a substantial sum when you consider that the biggest single donation which we have received from a company or Charitable Trust is £13,000. My heartfelt thanks to everyone in the Association who has helped to raise money in whatever way. Without your efforts we could not support research and welfare projects.

Another of our main objectives has been to get publicity for Raynaud's and scleroderma which has entailed sending out many Press Releases to the media. This is Jan's speciality and she is wonderful with her ideas and enthusiasm. Jan has helped in the design and publishing of all the new leaflets which as you can imagine saves a great deal of money when it comes to printing costs. All our literature is sponsored and we are grateful to the companies who so willingly support us in this way. On the subject of publicity, during probably the hottest day of the year I was contacted by Best magazine. I had put them in touch with Helen Birtles, who although she has scleroderma, is always bright and cheerful. They wanted us to send a selection of heating aids to be photographed for the magazine. I suddenly realised that this was the day that their photographer was at Helen's house in Newcastle and suggested that he came to the office to take the photos to save us time and effort. This they agreed, so I asked Karen if she could pop home and get a thick sweater, hat and scarf. I didn't say what it was for. This she did and the photographer arrived, not too happy because I had said we were just down the road and he thought it was walking distance. I explained that it was local terminology and 15 miles was just down the road! I called Karen and asked if she could pop these garments on together with a hot water bottle, leg warmers, slippers and a knitted blanket, while she was placed on a couch and given a magazine to read in about 90 degrees, while the photographer took what seemed like dozens of photographs. Poor Karen, who doesn't feel the cold anyway, almost melted. I don't think she will ever forgive me, especially as they didn't use the photographs in the magazine article anyway! However, we did get a good response from the article.

Much has been achieved and although there is still a long way to go we can look forward to the future with great hope.

Anne Mawdsley

Persevere for Diagnosis

I guess with hindsight that my mother always had Raynaud's. Swimming in the sea, hanging out washing, her fingers always went extremely white and lifeless. The major problems started post menopause. My mother was diagnosed as having diverticulitis. However, the treatment for this made her much worse. She was admitted to another hospital where they said that she didn't have diverticulitis but irritable bowel syndrome. She continued to live with this, becoming progressively worse for a decade when burning in the feet commenced. Unbeknown to us my mother had been sleeping with her feet outside the bedcovers even in winter and was putting ice in her shoes (a very dangerous thing to do). Her doctor allegedly had no idea what was wrong with her. When we discovered this series of events we bought her multiple office fans for each room in order to keep her feet out of water and we asked her G.P. if she could see a vascular consultant. At this stage my mother had been housebound for months and presented with swollen, burning hands and feet to the sockline. Her nails were discoloured and her legs speckled. However, the local consultant told me that my mother did not have any circulation problems, "not my department" were his words, and he prescribed another drug. This of course made her sleep at night but did not affect the underlying symptoms. We were surprised by this diagnosis so we took her privately to see a neurologist, to eliminate peripheral neuropathy. He confirmed our diagnosis that she had Raynaud's and had a very long history of Raynaud's-type symptoms and prescribed a drug which made her worse. I then began to research published papers on this subject and telephoned Ninewells Hospital in Dundee to seek advice. With the G.P.s help we went to Dundee where the consultant took one look at my mother's hands and feet and diagnosed severe Raynaud's. Tests carried out in their vascular laboratory confirmed a vaso-constrictive element and diagnosed erythromelalgia. She was treated with Iloprost and subsequently discharged on Praxilene. Her condition is now being controlled with this treatment by the Royal Free Hospital in London which is nearer to her home in Kent. My mother's quality of life is now vastly improved. She can now wear clothes and recently went to the local village to do her own shopping. As an artist, she is even able to paint again! She was housebound for well over a year and eventually bedbound before we could obtain the correct treatment. My advice is to persevere as several times I had been told that these symptoms were psychosomatic.

Lynne Ramsey

Amy's Story

Amy Best

I have recently become a member of the Raynaud's & Scleroderma Association. My name is Amy and I am 4 years old. I have just found out that I am suffering from Raynaud's and scleroderma. My legs have been painful for a year and a half, but we were told by doctors that it was just growing pains. My Mum and Dad were not happy with that and knew it had to be more than growing pains. We went to see the consultant at our hospital, who mentioned scleroderma and told us it was very rare. They also said they had never come across a case of it as it was so rare. We were then referred to Great Ormond Street Hospital where they had come across it. Both my legs are affected but my right leg is very bad. I have a lot of scarring on my leg, also my skin is very tight and shiny. My joints are stiff and I walk with a bad limp. My muscles in my right leg are wasting away so I have to do lots of physio to try to make them stronger. I wake up several times a night with pain in my legs and I am forever falling over. I was admitted into Great Ormond Street for a week and they took me over to the Royal Free Hospital to have colour pictures taken of my legs. I am on tablets at the moment and have to have regular blood tests. I am always very cold. Even in the summer I would have a thick blanket around me in the evenings. My feet also turn blue. I am due back in Great Ormond Street in January.

Julie Best (on behalf of Amy)

No One Can Tell

Mrs Ann Benson,who suffers from Raynaud's and scleroderma, believes she began suffering from Raynaud's when she was a little girl, but it wasn't until she was 54 that it was diagnosed. She says: "When I was young I would go swimming and my hands would be so cold they would turn white but it was when I was in my mid-50s that it really got bad. I used to type and my fingers got so sore that they all had to be bandaged up. I got ulcers on the ends of my fingers and had to retire a year early. Now I have to wear gloves in the winter months and even during the cooler summer days. The house has to be warm all of the time and I even use electric gloves and socks to heat myself up when it gets really bad. Winters for me are agony but the disease is not properly recognised so we get no financial help to pay our heating bills. One of the problems is that the disease is not immediately obvious and although I can be in pain, no one else can tell. People are not sympathetic because they cannot see what is wrong, and that is one of the benefits of the Association. It gives us the chance to share experiences and to talk about what we are going through with people who understand".

The above was taken from an article in The Bolton Evening News.

Awareness Week 1995

Once again Awareness Week was very successful thanks to all members who helped by contacting their local papers or radio stations. As a result personal stories about members appeared in newspapers around the country and several members took part in radio interviews. Thanks in particular to Kathryn Thomas and Sally Warr who joined Anne Mawdsley and Matthew Corbett on Radio 1's programme 'Newsbeat'. As a result of this publicity the Association published a new leaflet for teenagers entitled 'You don't have to be old to be cold'. Radio interviews totalled 13 around the country and became very hectic when Anne was asked to do two at the same time! She explained the problem but when giving a live interview on BBC Radio Humberside which was only expected to take a few minutes, the staff were coming in holding up notices saying that she was wanted live on BBC Radio Norfolk. It was just impossible to break with one programme and go to the other phone to do another, so sadly we ran out of time for Radio Norfolk. They were not too pleased but an item on Raynaud's did go out thanks to member Pat George but sadly there was no mention of the Association as had been planned. Women's magazines featured articles on Raynaud's and scleroderma, with Sue Churcher's story being portrayed in TV Quick. Jo Kaddish was the focus of an article in Woman magazine and The Independent newspaper helped with further publicity.

On the left, Brenda Kerslake who nominated Anne seen above with Anne and Esther Rantzen.

Carol Smilie, Anne & Esther Rantzen

It's official! Anne has a Heart of Gold

I can now reveal that 'Tales of Hope', the documentary the BBC were filming about the work of the Association, was no more than a cover story for Esther Rantzen's programme 'Hearts of Gold'. Member Brenda Kerslake from New Milton nominated Anne earlier this year and had forgotten all about it until the BBC contacted her in August. It has been a real cloak and dagger adventure keeping the secret from Anne. Congratulations Brenda - it is the first time anyone has got one over on Anne.

Well done Anne, you deserve it!

Jan Scott

A Knight to remember for Golden Hand Appeal

In the photograph Sir Cliff Richard is seen pointing to our new pin badge held by Anne Mawdsley. He autographed the card at a recent concert in which the Association was presented with a cheque for £500 by Sir Cliff. In the centre of the photograph is member Marion Lewis from Wisley who was instrumental in arranging for the Association to receive a donation from this concert. We are most grateful to Sir Cliff who gave his valuable time in order to support ours and other local charities on this very special occasion. It was certainly a night to remember.

Sir Cliff Richard, Marion Lewis and Ann

Mr. Kevin Lafferty

Newly appointed Trustee

We are delighted to announce that Mr. Kevin Lafferty, Consultant Surgeon at Basildon and Orsett Hospitals, has been appointed a Trustee. Mr. Lafferty has been involved with the Association since the very beginning and wrote the book, 'Raynaud's - A Better Understanding'. Mr. Lafferty was the first doctor to be supported as a researcher by the Association when he was at Dulwich Hospital in 1983.

Living with Raynaud's

Being a sufferer of both Raynaud's and scleroderma, Anne decided to write this book in order to promote a greater understanding of the problems experienced by Raynaud's patients. It was intended to guide both patients and their relatives through some of the trials and tribulations which they may encounter.

Oral and Dental Aspects of Scleroderma

A new booklet has been written for the Association by Dr. Stephen Porter, Senior Lecturer/Honorary Consultant in Oral Medicine at Eastman Dental Hospital, and Sarah Bain, Tutor Hygenist at Bris6ol Dental School. Although intended for dentists, this booklet has been written so clearly that it is easily understandable to the lay person as well as to health professionals.

A study of the prevalence of macrovascular disease in Systemic Sclerosis

Dr. Meilien Ho

We have previously reported a pilot study which showed that higher numbers than expected of our systemic sclerosis (SSc) patients appear to have evidence of obstruction to their large blood vessels/arteries supplying their legs. This causes ischaemia, i.e. a lack of oxygen, which manifests as a cramping pain in the legs on exercise (intermittent claudication), and non-healing ulcers, and may progress to a critical state requiring surgery. This pilot study was done by recording symptoms of intermittent claudication using the Edinburgh Claudication Questionnaire devised by Professor Fowkes to detect and differentiate symptoms of intermittent claudication from other causes of leg pains. However, although it is very useful, not all patients with peripheral arterial disease (PAD) have symptoms and also some people with other rhematological conditions may be incorrectly identified as having PAD. In order to validate our findings therefore, we have to obtain more information about the state of our patients' large arteries and compare our findings with those found in a 'normal' healthy population of a similar age who do not have SSc. Our new study protocol expands on the question of large vessel (macrovascular) disease by investigating other large vessels, namely the carotid and vertebral arteries which supply the brain, the coronary vessels supplying the heart and the pulmonary arteries supplying the lungs. The study is progressing well and we are keeping up with our target numbers of SSc patients and controls. We hope that by showing a true increased prevalence of large vessel disease, we can target the patients who would benefit most from early preventative treatment with e.g. aspirin which we would not normally prescribe freely to SSc patients who have a high incidence of inflammation in the oesophagus. The benefit may ultimately be a reduction in strokes, heart disease like angina and heart attacks and peripheral arterial disease.

Dr. Meilien Ho, Ninewells Hospital

Kevin Howell

Blood Flow Studies

1995 was a busy year in Blood Flow Studies, and a lot of progress has been made, especially in the field of research. In December I was awarded my MSc. degree in Medical Electronics and Physics from St. Bartholomew's Hospital Medical College. This was a successful conclusion to two years of part-time study. Practical project work was performed at the Royal Free on laser-Doppler flowmetry. Our research into blood flow in the small bowel in scleroderma patients is continuing. For this study we use laser Doppler flowmetry to measure bowel blood flow during an endoscopy. In September I presented our results to date to the inaugural meeting of the Institution of Physics and Engineering in Medicine and Biology. The presentation was well received by the meeting, and for me it was excellent experience in addressing a large audience. Thermographic and capillaroscopy studies have continued to be of importance in our research. In 1995 we used thermography to assess the response of patients taking part in our comparative trial of nifedipine and probucol treatments. Currently we are comparing the effectiveness of infusions of iloprost and CGRP (calcitonin gene-related peptide) using thermography. Capillaroscopy results are often requested by our Research Laboratory staff, who have a current interest in the capillary state of the primary Raynaud's patients they have found to be antibody positive. With regard to the routine clinical testing of patients we are, as usual, very busy. The Department has developed a computerised patient database over the past year. Results of patient testing can now be logged on a single computer and analysed quickly and easily. Information from Blood Flow Studies forms a part of this database, so now it is easier to get access to capillaroscopy results and compare them with other tests. In 1996 the computers in the Department are to be networked, which will mean every member of staff who requires this data will have it available on their desktop.

Kevin Howell, MSc. Blood Flow Studies,
Rheumatology Department, Royal Free Hospital

A study of oral iloprost in Raynaud's Phenomenon, secondary to Systemic Sclerosis

Last year a study using orally administered iloprost as a treatment for Raynaud's phenomenon was carried out in 7 centres in the UK, Holland and Denmark. 103 patients kindly participated, 13 of whom were recruited by the University Department of Medicine at Ninewells Hospital, Dundee. All patients were required to complete diaries throughout the course of the Study (14 weeks). Each day the patient was required to record each Raynaud's attack, how long it lasted and, at the end of each day, how severe they felt their Raynaud's had been for that day on a scale from 0 - 10.

Patients were recruited on the basis that they had a minimum of 6 attacks per week in the pre-treatment phase (Week 1 and 2). Patients were then allocated to one of three groups:

a) those to receive 100 micrograms oral iloprost (high dose) twice per day

b) those to receive 50 micrograms twice per day (low dose) and

c) those to receive a placebo (dummy drug) twice per day

Neither the investigator nor the patients were aware of which dose, if any, they were taking. Medication was given for 6 weeks and patients continued to document their Raynaud's attacks for a further 6 weeks after treatment had stopped. Side effects were also recorded at each visit.

Results

The effectiveness of treatment was assessed by looking at changes in:

a) the number of attacks experienced

b) the duration of these attacks

c) how patients assessed the severity of these attacks

In both high and low dose groups the average number of attacks was reduced by one third while on treatment. At week 12 (6 weeks after treatment had been completed) patients continued to show an improvement with attacks being reduced by almost one half. With regard to duration of attacks, both high and low dose groups showed a reduction in duration of attacks of more than a half. The most significant difference found between high and low dose groups was reflected in how patients rated the severity of their Raynaud's during and after treatment. Low dose patients rated their condition as having reduced in severity by one third, whilst those on higher doses rated severity as having decreased by a half. Those patients receiving placebo showed no significant reduction in either number, duration and severity of attacks.

During treatment various mild side effects were reported in all groups, the most common being flushing, headache and nausea. Nine per cent of placebo patients discontinued treatment as compared with 30% in the low dose group and 51% in the high dose group i.e. the high dose drug seemed poorly tolerated by over half the group.

Conclusion

In conclusion, oral iloprost does appear to be effective in reducing symptoms of Raynaud's secondary to systemic sclerosis but the lower dose may be preferred due to its greater tolerability. Obviously these results are encouraging and we are most grateful to all the patients who helped us with the Study. The success of this early Study has led to the development of a major programme, which took place last winter, to gather data together for possible submission of the drug for registration.

Sisters Jean Bancroft, Ros Robb & Dr. R. McCollum
University Department of Medicine, Ninewells Hospital, Dundee, August 1996

Calcinosis Problems

I am 64 years old and have suffered from Raynaud's and scleroderma since 1983. I am writing mainly about my calcinosis which has caused me a lot of trouble since it first raised its ugly head. At first only my hands were involved. The middle finger of my left hand has a large collection of calcium which has caused the finger to become badly deformed and virtually useless. Fortunately this has never turned septic but smaller areas on my other fingers have. After one particularly bad night with a throbbing finger I arrived at my doctors next morning only to be told that the finger needed lancing. He said he would not touch it because I had scleroderma and to go to the hospital. As my consultant had a clinic that morning I decided to visit her rather than going to casualty. She agreed that I had done the right thing.

Five years ago I discovered a lump in my left buttock. My doctor contacted a surgeon and within three days I had been operated on. The lump proved to be an accumulation of calcium. Three years after this, calcium started to appear in my right buttock and the consultant said that as we knew what it was, she did not advise surgery. The calcium spread rapidly and became very uncomfortable so I asked if I could have it removed. I was told that it now covered too large an area for surgery to be performed. I continued in this state until one morning when I awoke to find my right buttock hot, burning and very red. My doctor had me admitted to hospital where I remained for a month before being allowed home. 1995 was a bad year for me as I was in hospital a further three times with the same problem. My consultant finally decided that the calcium would have to be removed and I was referred to a plastic surgeon. The day before the operation the surgeon explained that a skin graft would not suffice and that a large area of flesh would have to be removed from my thigh. Imagine my delight when I awoke after the operation to find that my thighs had not been touched and that the calcium had been removed with the skin skillfully pulled together to make a very neat operation. I remained in hospital for a further three weeks during which time I was not allowed to sit down or even lie on my right side. The calcium which had been removed had been very deep, going into the muscle. Today I have to avoid sitting on a hard surface but it is lovely to have a normal bottom again!

Audrey Wileman

Child of Achievement

Eileen Pott with her son Jason

Eileen Pott from South Wales has had systemic sclerosis for four years. Since the onset of her condition she has become a single parent and has an only child, Jason, who is twelve. Since the early stages of her illness, when Jason was eight, Eileen has been very dependent on him. He had to grow up very quickly to deal with her problems, which could not have been easy for him to understand. Last year, unbeknown to Jason or Eileen, a close friend nominated Jason for a Child of Achievement Award and in February, Jason received his award from the Prime Minister at the ceremony in London. Jason's citation reads: 'Jason provides marvellous care and practical help in enabling his mother to live a relatively normal life. He accompanies her to the shops, reaching and lifting things on display, helps with the housework and on occasions has prevented her being hospitalised due to his mature care for her at home. Jason helps his mother get up in the mornings and assists with dressing. He is ready and willing to help his mother when most other children are playing, and is a credit to her". Eileen said "He is a wonderful child and keeps me going when I am low. He does practically everything around the house, even decorating. In spite of this he is achieving well at school, plays the violin and shares interests with his friends".

Before the announcement of his Award, very few people knew of Eileen's health problems and Jason's devotion to her needs. His school is now planning to acknowledge Jason's Award in their Hall of Fame.

Fond memories of champion fund raiser

Members will have read about the tremendous fund raising achievements of Marion Robinson and her husband Mike. Since joining the Association in 1985 Marion raised the incredible sum of £30,000. This was achieved mainly by selling used clothing and bric-a-brac on market stalls at Tring and Wendover in addition to other activities which included whist and bridge drives. Marion suffered for many years with Raynaud's, scleroderma and rheumatoid arthritis. In spite of her personal health problems, she never let these conditions interfere with her zest for life and her ambition to raise funds to help others with similar problems. Even though she fought a courageous battle, surviving two major operations, in February we heard the sad news that Marion had passed away. The support which she gave to the Association will always be remembered and we are most grateful to Mike for giving Marion such tremendous help, particularly during the past couple of years when she was not able to be as active as she would have wished.

Marion and Mike Robinson

Sarah

Sarah Cleaver

My name is Sarah Cleaver and I am 10 years old. I have had Raynaud's symptoms since I was 8. Living with Raynaud's is hard at times. I hate being cold so much of the time. When my fingers go white and dead, on recovering they are painful and tingle. During the winter it has stopped me from being able to write when my fingers go dead. I like staying in at playtimes with my friend in the winter. I don't like missing sports but I have to as I am not allowed out when it is cold. I am looking forward to the summer when I can play with my friends at playtime. I also miss not being able to play my recorder as holding my hands in one position can trigger an attack.

Sarah Cleaver

I became an outcast

Nicola Barnett

Like every child when I was 7, I just wanted to be normal and liked. This is hard enough but when you suddenly find some of your fingers going white and being in a lot of pain, it's a different story. I became an outcast, not knowing what was wrong with me, walking around the playground alone and in pain. It must have been when I was about 10 that my Mum read something about Raynaud's. It has now spread to both my hands and feet. Trying to keep me warm for 24 hours started to take its toll, not just on my life but my family. By the time I was 12 I was really fed up. I had to do jobs at lunchtime so that I didn't have to go out in the cold, which made my social life suffer. I started reading anything I could about the condition. My Mum sent away for books and between us I learnt about other people and the Raynaud's & Scleroderma Association. I was so happy that I now had answers to so many of my questions and have accepted that what I have is part of me, as it controls most things I do or can't do (like the school ski trips which a lot of my friends went on). At 17 I am now in my first year of A levels and having to deal with the fear and ignorance people have about me all over again. It still upsets me sometimes but at least I know that I am not the only one out there. I have done fundraising to raise awareness and have talked my college into donating some of their money to the Trust. The main reason I have written this letter is to share my experience, frustrations and to say how great it is to read about people that have the same problems. I hope that through this letter I can meet sufferers of my own age and hear if they have the same hassles as me.

Nicola Barnett

Artistic Shirley

Shirley Roe

About five years ago I was pondering on how to make more money for the Association when I thought about selling cards or notelets. I am an artist working in silk dyes, fabrics and threads. The dyes are very much like watercolours so the work involves some painting embellished with various kinds of embroidery. From these processes I create wall hangings and pictures. They are mainly of flowers or landscapes and they sell surprisingly well and I thought that perhaps cards based on these pictures would find a market. I went ahead and had some photographs taken and then had cards produced. In the first year I sold one thousand and more were called for so I continued the process using a new picture each year. When I first started my work I used my hands a lot for working threads and coarse fibres but as the pain in them has increased I have had to find other ways of working. I use less stitchery now and the results have been different, but equally effective from an artistic point of view. Now I have just had a long spell in hospital and my sight has been damaged. I wonder how I shall deal with this new impediment to my work?

Shirley Roe

Shirley has raised thousands of pounds by selling her very attractive cards.

Raynaud's and Scleroderma Research in Belfast

Studies aimed at giving a clear understanding of the basic pathophysiology involved in Raynaud's phenomenon with particular emphasis on the role of the endothelins in vascular spasm are ongoing in the Department of Rheumatology in Belfast. The initial study involves patients with the primary form of this condition, however while recruiting patients who were felt to have Primary Raynaud's phenomenon we have found that a number of individuals have an associated underlying tissue disease. We know that Raynaud's phenomenon may be the first symptom of connective tissue diseases such as scleroderma and may predate the onset of other symptoms by many years and it is therefore desirable to identify patients who are likely to evolve into a connective tissue disease at an early stage. As a result of a project grant from the Raynaud's & Scleroderma Association UK, our department now has the facilities to perform nailfold capillary microscopy and therefore enable early diagnosis of those patients with connective tissue disease. While this is a research tool at present we have plans to introduce it into our clinical practice.

Various research centres in recent years have provided evidence that substances released from endothelial cells that line our blood vessels may provide part of the explanation as to why people develop Raynaud's phenomenon. As part of our research study we are examining the role of the vasoconstricting molecule known as endothelin-1 which has been shown to be elevated in patients with scleroderma and in some studies in patients with Primary Raynaud's phenomenon. We are looking at changes in the level of this molecule during an episode of Raynaud's phenomenon. Drugs are being developed that effectively block this molecule and therefore the role that endothelin-1 plays in Raynaud's phenomenon must be clearly defined through studies such as our own. Many people with Primary Raynaud's phenomenon have other family members with this condition; they are therefore genetically predisposed to developing this condition. We are examining the genes that control the release of these vasoactive molecules to establish if certain forms of the gene are associated with the development of the disease.

Senior Lecturer and Consultant Rheumatologist
Dr. Anita Smyth, Research Fellow in Rheumatology and
Dr. Aubrey Bell, Musgrave Park Hospital, Belfast

Annual Conference 1996

The following are extracts from talks given at our Annual Conference in Alsager

Clinical Nurse Specialist

Helen Wilson

I initially started working in the Department of Rheumatology at the Royal Free Hospital 5 years ago, running a research project looking at the incidence of Raynaud's phenomenon in families. That was a three year project and when it finished I took over the running of the clinical trials. I also now work as what is known as a nurse specialist.

The textbook definition of a Clinical Nurse Specialist is: an academically prepared nurse with significant clinical experience in a specialised area of nursing practice, but I feel the job involves much more than that. By creating the position of Rheumatology Nurse Specialist in the department we felt we could offer a more holistic approach to the care of the individual patient. It is an emerging and exciting role which has developed out of patient need. As the name suggests, I am a clinical specialist. I tend to work closely alongside the doctors when they are in clinic helping to assess and monitor patients and also evaluate their care. There are many kinds of drugs that people take for Raynaud's and scleroderma. Many of these drugs are slow acting and can have side-effects and so they must be monitored carefully. Much of this monitoring will be done by your Primary Health Care Team, that is your G.P. and Practice Nurses. We are now trying to provide clear monitoring guidelines and support to these teams and many of you will be given a shared care card for your G.P. or nurse to use. The card contains your details, a list of your medication, and a space for your doctor or nurse to fill in the results of the blood tests. Plans are underway to further extend my role by my learning how to do IV cannulation which means, for example, putting up iloprost infusions and also joint injections.

Another major part of my role is as an educator. There is an increasing tendency for all patients to want to know more about their diseases and treatment. At the Royal Free, the Scleroderma unit attempts not only to treat scleroderma medically and investigate it scientifically, but to teach you the sufferers about your disease and how to live with it. This education is particularly important in chronic diseases such as scleroderma as both the disease and its treatment may last for years. However long a medical consultation may be, there are usually many more facts and questions which patients may wish to discuss. The need for information is not fully satisfied by a single educational visit but extends through the lifetime of the disease. There is, therefore, a requirement for readily available expertise whenever it is needed. I spend a lot of time educating patients and their families, developing education packages and specialised information leaflets and attending ward rounds to pick up gaps in patient education there.

Patient advocate/Emotional support

As health professionals we can sometimes be in danger of assuming that only we know what is best for the patient. By providing clear information we can help patients, particularly those who are vulnerable and without the support of family and friends, to feel confident to make their own decisions. Because of the chronic and deforming nature of many rheumatological conditions, many patients need a lot of emotional support and reassurance. I often find that while patients like to be given their diagnosis and discuss their medication with a doctor, they often find it easier to discuss other aspects of their condition with a nurse. As a Rheumatology Nurse Specialist you are often the individual most able to co-ordinate and support the patients both in the hospital and the community, by networking and linking with all the multidisciplinary team. I also liaise with the ward - answering pre admission and post discharge queries - and liaise with the Primary Health Care Team. Due to the impact of the chronic disease process and often anxiety about the treatment that has been instigated by the multi-disciplinary team, we felt that patients needed a point of contact when they felt ill, anxious or depressed so I also run a helpline.

The Rheumatology Helpline is available to:

1. Patients and Carers
2. General Practitioners
3. Practice and District Nurses
4. General Public
5. Health Care Colleagues

The availability of a 'helpline' telephone number provides direct access to the department for patients, carers, primary health care teams, other professionals and anyone who wants information regarding the rheumatic diseases. It allows quick access to information for queries on drug and disease management. Many patients live a long way away and this helpline will hopefully give you an easy way to talk to someone without having to come down in person.

Finally, I am involved in undertaking clinical audit, running clinical trials and research projects. Because scleroderma is currently still incurable we are continually working within our own laboratory and with outside pharmaceutical companies to find new drugs and to improve established therapies to treat this condition. Laboratory work is to uncover the malfunctions in the body which cause the disease and clinical trials help us to find drugs to prevent them.

A clinical trial might test:

- a new drug (many trials of new drugs compare the drug with a placebo)
- a new formulation of a current drug
- one drug versus another
- different doses of the same drug
- another kind of non-drug therapy such as acupuncture or hand warmers

Only after extensive preliminary safety checks are drugs tested on patients and such testing is what we call a clinical trial. The design of the trial is usually submitted for approval to the hospital ethics committee which is comprised not only of physicians and surgeons but also of clergymen, lawyers and scientists. However, you may still be wondering why you should participate in a trial. Well, firstly, of course, if no-one volunteered we would never have any new treatments. Without laboratory work to uncover the mechanisms by which a disease develops and advances, no progress in treating it would be possible; we should have no idea what processes we are trying to remedy. Once a disease mechanism has been identified drug treatment can be used to attempt to reverse or at least halt its progress. You may find that the new treatments you try will help your disease and if not they may still be of benefit for others with the same disease. Of course new treatments may not always work but by trying them out in a carefully controlled situation you will help doctors and drug companies to identify potential problems and side-effects more rapidly. Without your help as volunteers we will never be able to find out what causes this disease and prevent it happening to others, so on behalf of everyone in the unit I'd like to thank you for giving us bits of your skin and your blood and for being patient in clinic when we seem to ask you endless repetitive questions.

Helen Wilson,
Clinical Nurse Specialist Royal Free Hospital

Psychosocial aspects of Raynaud's and Scleroderma

Jennie Iliffe

I work as part of a multi disciplinary team at The Royal Brompton Hospital in London, where the care and management of patients is carried out by a group of different professionals, each contributing their special skills. The philosophy behind this is that any type of chronic illness involves not just the body, but the whole person, body, mind and spirit. It might seem like a journey with stops, starts, plateaus, highs, lows, losses and gains, and may involve people having to make constant adjustments to their lifestyle, relationships, goals and expectations. Once a week there is a group for scleroderma patients on the ward when a physiotherapist talks about physical exercises, a nurse talks about skin care and facial exercises, an occupational therapist talks about relaxation, self pacing, and demonstrates useful gadgets and aids. Finally, I join the group for what one man describes as 'The Hearts and Minds' bit. This, of course, seems the right order.

More than many other illnesses, Raynaud's and scleroderma are manifestly physical illnesses which can affect appearance, sensation (feeling cold), energy levels and mobility, and consequently have great impact on the way patients experience their bodies and on the quality of their lives. Whilst this process is observable and can be monitored and measured, there is another process going on which is often harder to understand and acknowledge and that, in some cases, may threaten the basic assumptions that underpin identity, and the way people experience themselves. Attention to this 'inner world' can be every bit as important as attention to the outer physical symptoms of illness. Being in a group with others with whom you have something in common, like an illness, can be a very effective way of enabling people to identify and express their feelings, and just as importantly to know that other people have similar feelings and needs. Listening to people and reading the vivid personal testimonies in the Association's Newsletters, it is possible to make some observations about the core needs and feelings people experience, and to suggest ways of responding to them. Our need for life to be logical, fair and under our control is challenged when living with discomfort, disability and awareness of losses incurred by illness. The questions "what if?', "why me?', "why now?', and "what next?" are all part of a search for meaning.

Most people with systemic sclerosis will have experienced an acute period in their illness before reaching a plateau, others may have had crisis times, when jobs, hobbies and ambitions may have had to be changed. Some live with the experience of a changing appearance and the continual uncertainty of 'good' days and 'bad' days. One part of a social worker's job is to help patients and their families to recognise their strengths, their resources, and to help them remember previous survival tactics and strategies. Many people are surprised at the resources they find within themselves to adapt and accommodate change and transition. Another part of the job is to help them through the transition to a revised model of the world. There is often a need for reassurance that strong and conflicting feelings are normal. Feelings like anger, guilt, regret, fear, lack of self-esteem, and that it is legitimate to acknowledge and express them. This is difficult for a lot of people who may not want to own such feelings or to protect their partner and family from them. Such feelings can seem very powerful and destructive, and there is a fantasy that they will be as destructive to others as they seem to you. We live in a culture which idealises and promotes the heroic notion of achievement against the odds. We applaud people who fight and show survival skills. I have no argument with that (we all want to show grace under fire), but I do have a problem when this is presented as the only credible response to illness. It takes a different sort of courage to live with feeling disfigured, being unable to have children, with peoples' ignorance, prejudice, and owning the negative feelings that illness can cause. A lot of people communicate a sense of simply not being able to translate their feelings in a way that can be understood and received by others. This inability seems to isolate people in a private world of their own experience, and this sense of isolation can be compounded by being cut off from normal social life and meaningful roles and activities.

Mark Flapan, founder of the American Scleroderma Society, said in one of his articles: "You wish somebody could live inside your body for a week, or even a day, just so they know what life is like for you". Well, I don't know what life is like for you, but that doesn't mean that you can't try to tell me, even if you can't get it all across. Sometimes, in wanting to say everything, some people can say absolutely nothing. There are times when somebody's physical and emotional energy is used in coping with illness, and being withdrawn and uncommunicative is rationalised as 'not wanting to worry others', whereas in reality, it may create more distress and cause distance between people, just when they most need to feel close. Sometimes it is hard for partners and carers to admit that they too have negative feelings and a need for support. They too may have been required to take on a different role and, perhaps, responsibility for the family, and they may feel helpless in watching the suffering of somebody they love. A significant chronic illness involves the whole person, not just their body but the total self. It will also almost certainly involve those closest to them. The same illness can have different meanings for different people. It may result in a change in a person's role in their family and in society. Relationships, lifestyle and their own sense of identity may alter accordingly. For many, there is little real choice about these changes, and they are experienced as loss, and loss over which we have no control can raise some primitive and strong feelings. A lot of people speak about feeling isolated, feeling different, and about the ignorance and lack of understanding of others. Many people have also told me what they have gained from illness. They have had to dig deep and find hitherto unrealised qualities in themselves and their families. If, for whatever reason, it is not possible to talk, you could always write about it, or paint it, or perhaps as one lady did, talk to her dog about it - apparently he was a marvellous listener! Anything is better than just putting the lid on it.

I want to end by quoting something written by someone who had come through an acute but protracted episode of systemic sclerosis. She said, "When I told my eldest son I was writing this, he said he thought I would want to forget it all - why? The last two years have had a big influence on us all. It has been distressing and difficult but not all bad. We have changed a lot, learnt a lot, and some good things have come of it".

I hope for all of you who have changed a lot, learnt a lot and taught a lot to people like me, that some good will come of it for you.

Jennie Iliffe, Senior Social Worker, Royal Brompton Hospital

Jo Kaddish

My Role as a Trustee

When I was first invited to become a Trustee 3 years ago, I was very honoured, and then I thought to myself - what does this involve?! I quickly sent for documents from the charity commission and after studying those decided that for a well run charity such as ours, it would be a very interesting venture.

The Association has three trustees and we have many responsibilities. The main ones relate to the administration of the Association's finances, ensuring audited accounts are produced annually, and that all funds received by the Association are properly invested and used wisely. As trustees we also have the general duty of protecting the charity's property and are accountable for its solvency and effectiveness. We are responsible for making sure proper controls are in place to ensure that the way in which the charity is administered is not open to abuse.

We also have the responsibility for considering all requests for funding and awarding grants accordingly. Requests for funding mainly fall into two categories, welfare and research. In the case of research grant applications, with the exception of Kevin Lafferty, we do not have the medical knowledge necessary to assess the clinical value of each project, and therefore all applications are peer reviewed by experts in the field, who report back to us on the medical value of the research suggested, and whether the sum requested constitutes value for money. The trustees then re-consider the applications and make the final decision. One important factor that we always adhere to is that we never award a grant unless there are sufficient funds available to cover it. We are very aware of the hard work put in by members, who are out in all sorts of weather conditions, and employ a vast variety of innovative methods in order to raise funds, and we want to ensure it is put to the best possible use.

The trustees have responsibilities for the Association's administration and management and although Anne and her staff deal with everything involved in the day to day running of the Association, we trustees are there at the end of a phone ready to offer help and advice whenever needed. We hold four regular trustee meetings per year, which are organised with great efficiency by Anne, and we are therefore able to get through a great deal of business at each meeting.

The trustees act on a voluntary basis, receiving no payment other than actual travel expenses. I find that being a trustee of the Association is extremely interesting, rewarding and challenging, and I hope to be able to continue for some years to come.

Jo Kaddish

House of Commons Talk

Anne Mawdsley was invited to speak about the work of the Association to the All Party Parliamentary Group on Skin at the House of Commons on February 5th 1997. This gave her the opportunity to spread the word to a wide range of people including several MP's. As a result the Association has had offers of support from representatives of pharmaceutical companies who were present. Support to the meeting was given by local MP Mrs. Ann Winterton, who has always shown a great interest in our work.

More stories of members

A story of courage and determination

Olive Kent

"Just over halfway through March of this year I attended a hospital clinic to be told 'you are going nowhere you're staying right where you are". Even though the toes on my left foot had started to become discoloured, this remark rather shook me. I was to be shaken still further when some two weeks later I was transferred to a London hospital and on Easter Saturday morning underwent an urgent by-pass operation on my left leg. The next day, Easter Sunday, I was advised that the bypass had proved unsuccessful and that an emergency operation would be necessary that same afternoon for the amputation of my left leg, just below the knee. At that particular moment I thought "this is the end." For several days I felt I was having an extended nightmare and that I would eventually wake up to find that it was all untrue. After the initial shock and trauma I began to realise that this was not the end but rather the beginning of a different way of life in which I would learn to walk again. I have a number of long-standing friends in different areas of the country and I was constantly assured that the churches to which they are attached were praying for me. Since that time I have been amazed at how quickly I have progressed. The physiotherapist under whom I was placed was tremendously helpful and encouraging, as have been my family and friends. After having my artificial leg for just three months I found myself able to walk around our ground floor maisonette unaided by sticks. As the days go by I get quite excited when I find I can accomplish something more, the latest being the climbing and descending of a flight of stairs in a friend's house. When I originally asked how long it would take to learn to walk about on my artificial limb I was told six to nine months but with a great deal of determination and hard work I have managed to reach that stage of mobility in just over four months.

If any readers have been unfortunate enough to undergo a similar experience then be encouraged - you can do it!".

Olive Kent

I couldn't feel my fingers and toes

Lyndsey Harrison

"I have been a member of the Association for three years and your regular newsletters have given me a lot of useful information about the condition and helpful advice on how to cope. It is also reassuring to know that there are other people who suffer the same problems as I do and who understand what it is like during the cold winter months. I am now 20 years old and have suffered from Raynaud's for as long as I can remember, so I can appreciate how difficult and at times disabling the condition can be, especially when people around you don't understand. All they see is a young, fit, healthy person which I am, but for the problems on cold days. When I was at school, I was told that I was just 'soft'. I hated going out on cold days because I couldn't feel my fingers and toes. People always thought I was clumsy because I couldn't catch a ball and I was always dropping things and fumbling about, as my hands were so numb that I couldn't grip or hold anything properly.

My symptoms got gradually worse as I entered my teens, and I encountered more problems at school. I was forced to take part in games outside during winter when we were made to go out wearing shorts and T-shirts in freezing cold weather. At times I virtually lost the use of my hands and feet and it was often so painful and extremely uncomfortable. It was embarrassing too, going into lessons afterwards as my hands were still so stiff and numb that it was difficult to write, but people found it difficult to understand as I was a competitive dancer and a very fit, active person. As I got older, I learnt how to cope with the problems that the cold weather brings and although my symptoms can still be quite severe at times, most people who know me are very understanding and helpful.

It can still be hard, though people don't realise and look at me strangely because I have difficulty with simple things like getting money out of a purse or signing cheques or separating carrier bags in the supermarket, as they don't expect people of my age to have problems like that. After all, I'm a perfectly fit, healthy 20 year old and most of the time I'm fine! I just have problems on cold days".

Lyndsey Harrison

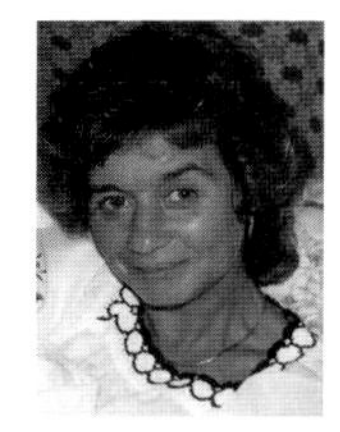

Christine Griffith

A Lonely Experience

"Twenty years ago I was found to be suffering from Raynaud's, and was dismayed to be told there was no cure. My G.P. was very good but, at that time, there was no publicity about possible treatments and it was a case of grin and bear it. Having just experienced a bitter divorce, I had two children to support and it was quite a struggle to run a home and hold down a secretarial job. Many times I was in tears because of the pain in my fingers and toes. Winters were particularly difficult and, on cold mornings, I was often physically sick when I arrived at work. Constant tiredness was also a problem. Fortunately, I managed to cope for several years, the children grew up and I remarried. Then, seven years ago, the reality of ill health really caused a dramatic effect on my life. I suffered months of continual pain when one severe infection caused a finger nail to turn green and lift off. Eventually, the nail had to be surgically removed before the infection cleared. Shortly after that, I began to experience difficulties with swallowing and was restricted to a diet of milk and soup. To add to these problems my joints began swelling, causing stiffness and restricted movement. I was referred to a rheumatologist and had several tests, including a barium swallow, but diagnosis was elusive and a conclusion was reached that I must be suffering with nerves. I couldn't quite believe this, but had no choice but to accept what I was told.

Luckily, a breakthrough came in the guise of my husband's teeth! While sitting in a dentists' waiting room reading a magazine, he came across an article about the Raynaud's Association. He made a note of the telephone number and later that day we rang and made enquiries. The lady we spoke to was most helpful and sympathetic and sent us information regarding the Association, and a specialist unit at the Royal Free Hospital. I notified my G.P. who requested a consultation for me and, one month later I arrived at the hospital for my first out-patients appointment. As soon as the Consultant saw my hands and skin, she confirmed that I had Raynaud's and scleroderma. I was admitted to hospital for tests and the swallowing problem was discovered to be caused by involvement of the oesophagus. When I was discharged two weeks later, the symptoms were mostly under the control of medication. I came off my miserable diet of milk and soup and was able to eat properly again. Not only did I feel better physically, but knowing I had medical back-up gave me and my poor worried husband, a completely different outlook on life. At least we knew what we were up against and how to cope.

Over the years, the illness has progressed to bowel involvement and formation of calcium lumps, but with the combined support of the hospital and the Association, I manage to stay cheerful and live a relatively normal life. Coping with a chronic illness is a lonely experience for both patient and carers, and adjustments to lifestyle have to be made. Early diagnosis is imperative and I for one, will be celebrating the 15th Anniversary of the Raynaud's & Scleroderma Association with thanks for giving me my life back. I shudder to think of the consequences had I gone on much longer without treatment, and will be forever indebted to the Association, and all those other people involved, who have done so much to make my life more bearable than it otherwise would have been".

Christine Griffith

I have been very fortunate

"Having found many letters from various members so helpful and encouraging in the newsletters, I decided I ought to write with my own experiences. I began having trouble with my circulation when I was 17 with dead fingers and toes. Doctors didn't seem to know very much or what to do then, apart from one doctor telling me to plunge my hands into hot and cold water alternately, which made no difference. When I began my nurse's training I was told that after I had been nursing for a few months I would find my circulation improving. I began cycling to work but had to give up in the winter as my hands were so painful. One doctor then put 'query Raynaud's' on a form and that was all. I just learned to live with it, keeping as warm as possible. When my two children were small it was agony taking them out in a pram in the winter. I then began to get spots or blemishes on my hands and face which I now know was part of the Crest syndrome, and I later began to get a lot of heartburn and difficulty in swallowing. I was sent for a Barium Meal and was told I had a hiatus hernia plus a mechanical obstruction. I was given charcoal biscuits to eat which made things worse. That was in the 60's. I coped for about 20 years, never being free of the heartburn, but learning that when I had trouble swallowing during a meal, if I took a big gulp of water, I could feel my food going through and could carry on with the meal. It was too embarrassing ever to eat out! I also found that propping up with pillows in bed was a great help.

One day in 1991 I was having trouble with my shoulder and arm and went to my G.P. I play the organ in Church and was unable to continue because of the pain. My G.P. sent me for x-rays and then to the Rheumatology Department of my local hospital. I had to undress for an examination and although the weather was not particularly cold, my feet were white and the doctor remarked on it and then began to ask a lot of questions. He then said - "your shoulder is OK - you've had a trapped nerve but you have a condition known as scleroderma' and he began to explain it all to me. I had a number of different tests, blood, lung function, ECG etc. and also an endoscopy which revealed a badly scarred oesophagus. I was put on Losec which healed it completely and I still take one daily. My swallowing is normal now. I have been very fortunate as, so far, no other internal organ is affected and I go every six months to have repeat tests. My general health is fairly good".

Mary Ward

Spare a thought for erythro sufferers!

"Summer's hot sunny days gladden the hearts of Raynaud's sufferers. But for those of us with erythromelalgia (EM for short) summer puts dread into our hearts. The hot weather brings on intense burning pain in our feet - so we have to hide away indoors behind closed curtains! Warm summer nights are terrible because our fiery feet prevent any sleep unless we use cold fans, or sleeping tablets to 'knock us out' for a few hours. Many of us also have Raynaud's to varying degrees which can mean painful feet all year round. EM is rare - rarer than scleroderma - so most people, including doctors, have never heard of it. We remain a very isolated misunderstood group. We long that research will find a cure for us too".

So what is EM?

This awkward Greek word literally means 'red painful extremities'. Some of you with Raynaud's experience temporary fiery pain in your toes when they are re-warmed. This is the pain we experience, but for us burning persists for hours or even days. For me the pain pounds on constantly day and night during hot summers. I've had very severe EM for three and a half years, and mild Raynaud's for most of my life. At any time a few degrees rise in temperature can trigger off burning symptoms within minutes e.g. moving into a warmer room or car, even just walking. I must avoid all heaters and radiators. Even the sun scalds my feet within minutes! On hot days I can barely stand on my hot swollen feet, never mind walk. I welcome cool cloudy days so I can leave my home by car. Then in winter Raynaud's 'cold' pain takes over. I've had to abandon my job and a normal social life and become a recluse in the summer.

I was diagnosed as having erythromelalgia in 1994 by a dermatologist and was later referred to a consultant in Dundee. I was prescribed praxilene, which began to ease my pain each morning. In November 1995 I had an iloprost infusion and watched my feet improve. Back home I could walk in proper shoes again. The improvement continued until March but by May the EM worsened. I was anxious to receive iloprost locally, which I did in June, but alas this time it gave me no relief. I now feel abandoned medically but thankfully through the Raynaud's & Scleroderma Association I have made contact with other sufferers. So I would now like to make a plea for help from anyone with EM who has had relief from iloprost or any other treatment.

Jean Jeffery

43 years with Scleroderma

"August Bank Holiday Monday 1954, at the age of 12, I was out with my parents, brothers and sisters. My Dad noticed that I was not turning my head properly so he took me to the doctor who was at the Village Carnival. The doctor told my Dad to get me straight home and he would follow. On Wednesday he visited me and referred me to a Specialist; on Friday, I was admitted to hospital. Little did I know then what was in front of me. Within a very short time the skin on my face, neck, arms, hands and the top part of my body was solid. I spent 1954 - 1956 in hospital and in 1956 moved to an Orthopaedic Hospital. I don't know what drugs I was given as I had so many tablets and injections. One thing I do remember is that a lot of my hair fell out. The physiotherapist worked very hard giving me heat treatment, massaging oil into my skin, and wax. One of the physios used to hold my shoulder down on the bed while the other pulled my arms to try and get them to move - slowly but surely we did make progress.

Later in 1956 I came out of hospital and was allowed to go to school if I felt up to it. It was my last year at school anyway. In 1958 I managed to find work - it was very hard for me to cope but I did - I would not let anything beat me. In 1962 I married Peter who still puts up with me. Our sons Christopher and David were born in 1967 and 1974. In 1979 I took a part-time job but in October 1995 I had to finish as I was having problems with my legs. I couldn't cope with the stairs as there were three flights and was having such awful nights. Some nights I had very little sleep as it felt as if my legs were on fire. The Doctor has now put me on Amitriptyline which keeps them fairly well under control".

Josephine Woolley

Enjoying the outdoors

Pam Deards

"About 35 years ago I was diagnosed as having Raynaud's Disease. I had a sympathectomy operation on my left side - it was not completely successful so the other side was not operated on. From then on I had a great deal of trouble with my hands and feet, also my whole body had a problem, and the specialists told me I would have to live in trousers or long shirts or boots. I did not believe this but it soon happened and I stopped buying dresses and skirts as any draught would affect my whole body. When my illness was first diagnosed I was advised to go to a warmer climate which we decided to do. My husband, two young sons and myself decided to live in Australia but were refused entry due to my having had a serious breakdown twenty years previously! We then moved to Southampton as it was warmer there but the problem stayed with me.

In 1989 my husband took early retirement, as specialists at the Hants and Southampton General Hospital told me that if I lived in a temperature of 70-80 degrees and no wind, if possible, I would live almost a normal life. The 'no wind' is not possible where we live now in Spain but as I still live in trousers for eight months of the year this is not a worry. We do quite a lot of walking as we do not have a car and find this is very good for me in the cooler weather. The specialists were quite correct, I do live nearly a normal life. We do miss our family and friends but they phone and visit at various times. Before we moved we made sure that we had central heating in the complex.

To anyone who has a similar problem - do think about moving, discuss it very well with relatives and friends - maybe stay in the area where you think you may like to go. We consider our move very worthwhile and it has made a difference to our lives and has given me a chance to enjoy outdoor life again".

Pam Deards - Spain

Why Worry?

Tricia Howland

"If you have recently been diagnosed with this condition, it is more than likely that previously you had never even heard of it. It is this lack of knowledge of scleroderma, and more importantly what it will mean for you, which makes it particularly frightening. As a sufferer myself, I hope you will read my story and take heart from it - you may be as lucky as I am and actually benefit from the condition.

Three years ago, feeling more than unusually tired over a long period of time and nursing an ulcerated finger, I visited my family doctor who suspected scleroderma. I was seen by a consultant at our local hospital for confirmation of the condition. Once confirmed, I was advised that there was no cure, it could be disfiguring, disabling and even fatal. However, symptoms could be relieved if necessary, but it would be my attitude to the condition which was paramount. I left the outpatients department feeling devastated, confused and not really knowing what scleroderma was. I felt I had no future and everything I was looking forward to was over. I was fifty - more settled financially than I had ever been, the children were grown-up and settled with their respective partners, and it was time to enjoy life myself. Suddenly, there seemed nothing - I pictured myself as ugly, maimed and a trial to everyone around me. I became frightened to wake up in the morning in case I found movement in my extremities more restricted than when I had gone to bed! I cried for a week until I was sick, although I was tremendously supported by my husband who hardly left my side. However, human nature being what it is, I soon became bored with being miserable and realised that in fact my condition had not deteriorated in any way. I could still move freely, although the skin round my eyes was tighter, it was not uncomfortable and in fact, if anything, made me look younger than I had previously! I regretted wasting so many days in misery - days I would never see again and which could have been spent in a much more positive way. Suddenly, it was not going to be allowed to beat me! So what could I do to help myself?

The first positive step I took was to track down the Raynaud's & Scleroderma Association. Everyone reading this article will know how wonderful it is to find Anne and her marvellous team who are always there to deal with queries, questions and anxieties. They have a useful number of books and leaflets which offer practical advice and keep one informed of progress in research. For the first time, I began to understand what scleroderma was all about. The second step I took was to look at my whole lifestyle and see if there were improvements I could make to keep my general health in good condition, the better to fight scleroderma. This meant re-assessing lifestyle, diet and stress. My husband and I own and run a small country house hotel in Herefordshire - a tremendously hard job, starting work at 7.30 a.m. each day and not finishing until about 11 p.m., seven days a week, nonstop. We immediately decided that although there was no harm in being tired at the end of the day but to be totally exhausted, as we often felt, was definitely foolish. Then and there we decided to open the hotel for five weeks and close every sixth week thus allowing ourselves a complete week in which to rest and recover.

Diet was the next item to come under the microscope. Much has been made of the Mediterranean diet and its beneficial properties so we altered our eating habits to take in fish dishes at least three times a week, plenty of fresh salads dressed in olive oil, fresh vegetables, fruit, rice, pasta and potatoes and last, but by no means least, red wine! I restricted tea and coffee to one cup a day and drank plenty of fresh fruit juice, milk and sparkling mineral water. From that day to this I have avoided manufactured foods just in case additives could be in any way detrimental. To make absolutely sure my diet was not deficient in vitamins or minerals, I took daily supplements of anti-oxidants, in particular Vitamin E, primrose oil, cod liver oil and garlic oil and, of course, ginkgo biloba to help with the circulation. The effect of this dietary change was dramatic. From childhood I had been underweight and self consciously thin. When diagnosed with scleroderma I weighed just over 7 stone, but gradually over the course of the next year, I began slowly and evenly to gain weight - the first time in my life. I now weigh a healthy 8.5 stone - I feel much fitter and much more confident, and, of course, a lot warmer! I still maintain this diet.

The third step, and probably the hardest to deal with, was stress. I was one of those people who was always bothered about something, most of it absolutely trivial and certainly not worth becoming tense about. If I was to slow down the progress of scleroderma, I felt sure that mental attitude and frame of mind would be helpful. I became determined that I would not worry about the minutiae of life at all, and as for the big things - if I could do something about a problem, I would get on and do it. If I could do nothing, then worrying would be pointless. Better to face it with a smile. This I managed by switching off if something small had gone wrong, changing the subject in my mind and forgetting about it. I found I could change my mood entirely by listening to a favourite piece of music, reading a much loved poem, buying a new paperback or just looking at a photograph album of holidays I had enjoyed in the past. It is said that 97% of all we worry about never happens - what a lot of time we all waste in worry then. How much more relaxing it is to put life in perspective!

Three years on, I am really well. Yes, I do have stiffness in my feet, hands and face which is uncomfortable rather than painful. I have no deformity, no calluses, no calcium deposits, no problem swallowing, and no problems with my internal organs. I work full-time and look and feel better than I have ever done in my life. Scleroderma affects each and every sufferer differently and I shall never know whether the steps I have taken really had any effect on the progress of the condition or whether it would have taken the same course in any event. It helped me to take some kind of action to help myself and not be at the mercy of the condition. I do know that facing scleroderma and an uncertain future has made me re-assess my values and what really matters. I no longer take for granted the gift of health which I continue to enjoy each day and all the wonderful things I am still able to do, which I thought I would be deprived of when first diagnosed. Time is no longer wasted on worrying about trivia and no opportunities are lost to go out there and grab life. Please don't despair if you have recently been diagnosed. You may be as lucky as I am".

Tricia Howland

Maidenhead Support Group raises over £2,000

Marilyn Williams

"I first started the group in May of last year so this event was for us, in many ways, a celebration of a very successful first year as a support group to the Association. During the year we have begged and borrowed all that we could to make our day as effective as possible. The loft in my home had been filled to capacity with boxes of clothing, bric-à-brac etc. until the overflow spread throughout the entire household! The big day arrived. Tables were set up and soon filled with sale items and the kitchen ladies prepared a wonderful layout of homemade cakes. 2pm. arrived all too soon. I was told that the deputy mayor had arrived. 'Swanking' with my Raynaud's sweatshirt I went to greet him and his wife and daughter who were a very warm-hearted family and cared so much about our Association and the conditions from which we suffer. The raffle prizes were donated by local companies and our thanks go to them for their generosity. The event was well supported by the public, having been widely publicised and supported by a special feature for the children. The Raynaud's video was shown throughout the event. It only leaves me now to thank with deep gratitude all members of our Support Group, for their encouragement and loyal support, and all friends who so willingly gave their time to help us to raise the magnificent sum of £2,095.02 which is more than we could have dreamt of. It was fun, hard work, but we worked in total harmony and all enjoyed just being together - a truly happy and worthwhile day".

Marilyn Williams

I am determined

Pat Edwards

"Some time ago Anne asked me to write a short piece about myself for the newsletter. I was a little reluctant at first as I had had a rough time during the last couple of years with Raynaud's and scleroderma. I have had both conditions for about 27 years but never let my illness stop me from doing what I wanted to do. I am now 55 years old. At 40 I decided to study for a degree and after passing that went on to gain a post graduate degree in Housing Management. About 3 years ago the illness seemed to go berserk and I developed bad leg ulcers which were very difficult to heal. I was in constant pain and at a very low ebb. The result of all this was that I had both legs amputated within a year. It was such a shock and I wondered how I was going to cope after being such an independent person, having to rely on other people and most of all getting used to being in a wheelchair.

I am still coming to terms with this after being home for just over 18 months but feel I have coped pretty well. One thing for sure is that the pain has gone and I am no longer in and out of hospital. I still have problems with my hands as I have had a couple of fingers amputated and ulcers do recur but otherwise I am feeling much better. My first goal after coming home was to obtain a powered wheelchair which gives me a lot of independence. The second was adapting to a new lifestyle, which meant carers and an invasion into my privacy. My two carers, are not only my carers but my very good friends. After I started to feel better I began to get bored so I am now a member of the University of the Third Age (USA) and I am studying Spanish. I go to Tai Chi classes which I find very rewarding but also humbling as most of the people there have MS and are in a far worse position than I am.

Earlier this year I went to Majorca on holiday which was very enjoyable and my next goal is to get back driving my car. During the past few months I held two charity stalls in Barnsley and would like to take this opportunity to thank everyone who helped me. We raised a total of £320 and I am planning to do a third one before the winter sets in. So as you can see, Raynaud's and scleroderma have limited me and I now live a different lifestyle but I am determined that it will not stop me from doing what I want to do".

Pat Edwards

My Dream

"Hi, my name is Michele, I am twenty three years old and have suffered from Raynaud's for the past four or five years. It actually started when I was abroad in a hot country and I noticed my hands in the cool evenings started to go white and numb. I ignored the problem for about a year as at the time it was little more than a nuisance. However, as the time went on it started to affect my day to day living as well as my job. I read an article in the Daily Mail about Raynaud's and recognised my symptoms. I then went to see my doctor and after many months he referred me

Michele Noble

to a specialist. The doctors at the hospital did several tests, diagnosed Raynaud's and put me on several types of vasodilator tablets. After several months there was still no change in my condition, my fingers were permanently purple and sores had begun to develop. The doctors for some reason were very reluctant to admit me into hospital for any intravenous treatment, but eventually after my fingers had been constantly purple for several weeks and after many phone calls and pleas for help, I was admitted and given Iloprost. In all I spent seven weeks in hospital where I was also given six large amounts of steroid treatment twice a week for three weeks (intravenously). After all the treatment my hands returned to their normal colour and the sores healed but the frequency of my Raynaud's attacks continued.

I attended the Raynaud's & Scleroderma Annual Conference last year, where I was introduced to Professor Black. I then realised that I needed to be referred to the Royal Free where there is much experience and understanding of the condition. My first appointment with Professor Black was last October, when I had many tests done. I now go into the Royal Free for treatment twice a year for five days rather than the gruelling seven weeks which I previously endured. I do feel that I am very unlucky to have developed Raynaud's disease as when I left school I chose a career with horses, that is training young and experienced horses to do Dressage. Unfortunately, all this was brought to a sudden end when I realised the reality of it all, that is working outside in the winter in such cold conditions was just impossible with Raynaud's. The excruciating pain often left me in tears and I became very depressed about the thought of giving up what was my whole life. I eventually stopped feeling sorry for myself and I am now half way through doing my N.N.E.B. child care diploma. I am doing very well passing every module with distinction, but I still miss working full time with my horses. The weather this summer has been fairly good and through my summer holidays I have been able to compete my horse 'Inform' in quite a few dressage competitions, where we have been placed either first, second or third every time we have competed.

It may appear that I have moaned on about my condition but I am fully aware that there are people who are far worse off than I am and I also realise that at least I am able to do some competing and riding in the summer. Maybe one day there will be a cure for Raynaud's and I will be able to fulfil my ambition of working full-time with my horses and my dream of representing Great Britain on my horse 'Inform' will come true!".

Michele Noble

Living With Scleroderma

This book by Anne Mawdsley, has been written to guide patients, their relatives and carers, towards a greater understanding of the problems experienced by scleroderma sufferers. The Foreword has been written by Lynn Faulds Wood who presented the BBC's Watchdog programme for eight years, giving it up to make medical programmes. She has won numerous awards for her work and is currently Medical Broadcaster of the year. After the success of the book 'Living with Raynaud's', Anne decided that there was a need to write a new book on scleroderma.

Thanks to Professor Carol Black for her help in ensuring that the text was medically correct, to Jennie Iliffe, Senior Social Worker at the Brompton Hospital for her contribution and to Jan Scott for the hours which she spent in preparing the book ready for the printer.

The following are a few quotes from the book:

"When diagnosed as having an illness it can be distressing but when it is a rare disease of which little is known, the situation is even more disturbing. Now more than ever before patients want to know more about their condition so that they can learn how best to cope and live with it".

"If you have mild Raynaud's which is little more than a nuisance, the chances are that you have Primary Raynaud's. This means that it is benign and taking measures to help with keeping warm or drugs such as vasodilators, which open up the blood vessels allowing blood to flow through more easily, may be sufficient. However, if you have Raynaud's severely or if the condition appears to get worse, it is worth going to your G.P. and asking for a blood test, in order to eliminate or confirm the presence of an associated condition such as scleroderma or systemic lupus erythematosus".

"Studies of lung fibrosis in systemic sclerosis have suggested that the earlier the disease is detected, the more likely there is to be a good response to treatment. Lung disease in scleroderma usually has a long slow progression and patients have to learn to adjust to what they can and can't do. It is advisable to do regular exercises and try to maintain a good basic level of physical fitness".

"Ulcers can develop, particularly on the fingertips and underneath the nails. They can also appear on the feet, elbows and legs. These ulcers are extremely painful and can take a long time to heal due to the poor circulation. They may be associated with pieces of calcium which work their way to the surface and break through the skin, becoming infected and causing pain".

"Our need for life to be logical, fair and under our control is challenged when living with discomfort, disability and awareness of losses incurred by illness. The questions what if, why me, why now, what next are all part of a search for meaning".

"It is important for patients and their families to recognise their strengths, their resources, and to try to remember previous survival tactics and strategies. Many people are surprised at the resources they find within themselves to adapt and accommodate change and transition. There is often a need for reassurance that strong and conflicting feelings are normal. Feelings like anger, guilt, regret, fear, lack of self-esteem, and that it is legitimate to acknowledge and express them".

Workshop in Cambridge

A three-day workshop was held in Cambridge in the spring of 1997 discussing preliminary scleroderma research and possible future directions for therapy. The workshop was attended by doctors from around the world.

The following is a summary by Dr. Daniel Furst, Director of Clinical Research at the Virginia Mason Research Centre in Seattle, taken from his report which appeared in the Scleroderma Spectrum newsletter from the USA.

Basically, the hypothesis suggests that, upon a genetic background, environmental effects could cause immune activation. In turn, this can cause blood vessel injury, fibroblast proliferation and collagen formation. Collagen formation can also cause immune activation. Feeding into this 'circle' are blood vessel effects such as Raynaud's Phenomenon, which can cause blood vessel injury and mast cell (a type of immune cell) activation. These, too, can cause further immune activation and fibroblast proliferation. On this basic background, potential and preliminary data on future therapy, which may take many years to come to fruition, was discussed. Oxygen radicals, collagen producing enzymes, antibody production, collagen therapy and Iloprost were examined. Oxygen radicals are a transient species of oxygen that occur during inflammation and can cause tremendous tissue damage during healing, thus promoting fibrosis. One substance the body produces to prevent such damage is called superoxide dismutase (SOD). Unfortunately, this substance is also very transient and its previous use in humans has been disappointing. There is, however, a lecithenized SOD that is extremely effective in test tubes and prevents blood vessel cell injury. Since it lives much longer than SOD itself, this may be a future therapy in treating systemic forms of scleroderma.

Other researchers described a search for the genes that promote fibrosis, the cell receptor that responds to the proteins by causing fibrosis and the possibility of blocking that receptor. In addition, enzymes that prevent the production of mature, stable collagen or that increase the programmed cell death of fibroblast cells were described at the workshop, along with enzymes that convert collagen precursors to mature collagen. Clearly, appropriate inhibitors (or activators) of some of these pathways or enzymes could result in a decreased collagen formation, or fibrosis, and could be a form of treatment for scleroderma. Cambridge Antibody Technologies, a British company, described the general principles for producing a human monoclonal antibody. Such an antibody could be formed to inhibit immune factors causing scleroderma, without causing the body to react against those antibodies. In the future, this might be a form of effective medication.

Other discussions included the attempt to 'tolerize' some scleroderma patients with type 1 collagen. The use of type 1 collagen to turn off the body's immune response was tested in 33 patients. From six months to one year, no serious side effects were seen and it is possible that some response occurred. It is far too early in the study to say much about this approach, but more investigation needs to be done.

There has been much discussion about Iloprost. The results from the European Iloprost study in Raynaud's Phenomenon were discussed. In the study, about one hundred patients were treated with either placebo or doses of Iloprost for six weeks and then observed for another six weeks. Tests indicated that the pain and discomfort from Raynaud's and the duration of attacks improved for six weeks, although the number of Raynaud's attacks did not decrease. Noted side effects included headache, flushing, nausea and painful tightness of the jaw muscles. The results of the larger, more stringent study on Iloprost in the USA will be completed within the next several months.

Development of anti-fibrotics

r. Xu Shi-wen

Good news for Scleroderma patients

At the beginning of this year, I was fortunate enough to be able to visit Fibrogen Inc., a major American centre of expertise in connective tissue biology. This visit enabled me to acquire a number of techniques that are proving invaluable in our work at the Royal Free. The studies that I carried out whilst at Fibrogen used many skin cell lines that were derived from biopsies taken from patients at the Royal Free. I was able for the first time to show that the cells from the skin of scleroderma patients produce a high level of a protein called CTGF which strongly suggests that this protein is very important in the development of scleroderma. We have equipped our laboratory with the appropriate apparatus in order that we can utilise these new techniques at the Royal Free.

We are currently working towards investigating the role of CTGF in dermal and pulmonary fibrosis. The Rheumatology Unit database provides us with the necessary background information that allows us to access and study suitable samples from our tissue and cell banks. The research results that have already been obtained, together with those arising from current research, place us in a very good position to fully examine the role of CTGF in scleroderma and to assess whether an effective therapy can be found.

The support of the Raynaud's & Scleroderma Association Trust has been vital in enabling this important and ground breaking work to proceed.

Dr. Xu Shi-wen, Royal Free Hospital

Vasospasm of the Nipple

Nipple pain is the most common symptom in breastfeeding women and it is the second most common reason given for abandoning breastfeeding, exceeded only by perceived low milk supply. A report was given in the British Medical Journal, Volume 314, 1 March 1997, Page 644, entitled 'Vasospasm of the nipple is a manifestation of Raynaud's phenomenon' which reported on five cases of patients who had signs and symptoms, suggesting a diagnosis of Raynaud's phenomenon affecting their nipples. The major presenting complaint of each of the five women was severe, debilitating nipple pain. The concept of Raynaud's phenomenon occurring at sites other than the digits is not new. Vasospasm affecting coronary, gastrointestinal, genitourinary and placental vasculature has been described in patients with Raynaud's phenomenon. Breastfeeding may increase the risk of nipple vasospasm because the nipples are exposed and subject to mechanical stimulation during the breastfeeding process. Raynaud's phenomenon in breastfeeding women poses the dual problem of distressing pain in the patient combined with an increased risk of failure of breastfeeding.

As a result of this BMJ report, the Association was contacted by a journalist to assist with an article for 'Parenting' magazine.

Hand in Hand with Saatchi & Saatchi

Cold Hands Need Warm Hearts

Due to a tremendous amount of recent publicity, we are aware that we have only just touched the tip of the iceberg and that there are still millions of people with Raynaud's who feel isolated but are unaware that there is an Association which could help. Saatchi & Saatchi, the prestigious advertising company, has come up trumps by working closely with us, to develop an advertising campaign, in order to create a greater awareness and understanding of Raynaud's.

Our sincere thanks to the Saatchi Healthcare Connection team. It was been a pleasure to be involved with such a professional and dedicated team who provided their skill and expertise (at no cost to the Association) in creating the artwork for the new poster, which we are sure all Raynaud's sufferers will closely identify. The wording 'If your hands feel like this, you may suffering from Raynaud's' describes how many Raynaud's sufferers feel during an attack. The posters are very striking and should certainly put Raynaud's on the map.

Tribute to a Princess

Fund is launched with a donation of £800

It was with profound sadness that we heard the tragic news of the death of Diana, Princess of Wales on 31st August 1997. The world mourns for someone who devoted the last few years of her short life to helping others through her enthusiastic charitable work. Many members contacted the Association asking if they could send donations to us in her memory. People wanted to do something positive, to show just how much they cared for and loved this very special lady, yet have been unsure how best to direct their grief. After discussing the matter with the Trustees it was decided to launch an appeal, the proceeds of which will be used specifically to purchase equipment, namely a Capillary Anemometry and CapiScope Capillaroscopy System. This will be for the

University of Birmingham where research is being carried out involving children who have significant poor, peripheral circulation.

It was felt that this would be appropriate as children were so close to Diana's heart and the Association has not previously funded research specifically aimed at children. The appeal began with a most generous donation from Alsager Golf Club, where Anne Mawdsley was presented with a cheque for £800 on Sunday, 31st August, the day on which Diana died. Barbara Campbell, Ladies' Captain, chose the Raynaud's & Scleroderma Association as one of her charities during her year of office. When Anne asked Barbara if she was happy for this donation to be used to launch our special fund, she said "I would be delighted and honoured for the money to be used in this way".

Raynaud's, Scleroderma and Vasculitis in Children

Poor peripheral circulation is a common symptom in children and in some cases (probably about 1,000 children U.K. wide) it is a severe enough problem to require medical assessment and advice. It appears as reddening or blanching of the skin of the fingers and toes, often in association with pain in these areas. Cold weather is a frequent trigger for these symptoms, but they sometimes occur without any clear reason. If the symptoms are particularly severe, the child may have Raynaud's or an underlying condition such as inflammation of the blood vessels (vasculitis), scarring of the skin and tissues in other organs (scleroderma), inflammation of the muscles (dermatomyositis), or other systemic inflammatory disease. Fortunately, the latter conditions are rare in childhood, but may be difficult to diagnose in the early stages.

In the Department of Rheumatology at the University of Birmingham, we have been undertaking two programmes of research into disorders of the peripheral circulation in children. The first is a survey to assess the frequency of these diseases in the West Midlands. The second involves using a specialised microscope to detect abnormalities of the small blood vessels (capillaries) around the fingernails in children with poor peripheral circulation. The microscopy technique is known as nailfold capillaroscopy. Our results have indicated that we can detect differences in appearance of the nailfold capillaries in children with poor peripheral circulation who have a significant underlying disease such as vasculitis or scleroderma. We have also shown that the capillaries of normal children have important differences to capillaries in normal adults. We are now seeking to build on these encouraging initial results using specialised research equipment which will allow us to detect abnormalities of blood flow within the capillaries (capillary anemometer). The question we wish to answer is whether we can detect a change in blood flow through the nailfold capillaries in those children with symptoms of poor peripheral circulation who will go on to develop serious diseases such as vasculitis or scleroderma. If these diseases are detected early, treatment may be more effective and eventual disease outcome improved.

The key piece of equipment which we require is a CAMI Capillary Anemometry and CapiScope Capillaroscopy System. We have already tested the system on a trial basis in several children, in whom it was well tolerated and non-invasive. Once the system is in place, we aim to screen the nailfold capillaries of 150 children with a variety of illnesses and also normal children. The results of this investigation will be published in peer-reviewed scientific journals and presented at national and international meetings. We hope that the use of early detection systems may improve the quality of life of children afflicted by this painful and potentially debilitating group of conditions.

Dr. T. R. Southwood,
Senior Lecturer and Consultant in
Paediatric Rheumatology, University of Birmingham

News from the Royal Free

1997 has been even busier than previous years and the department has seen a lot of exciting changes. For my part, I have been busy trying to develop my role as nurse specialist/educator. In January I successfully completed a one year postgraduate course in The Management of Rheumatological Conditions which has given me a lot of new ideas and an insight into what goes on in other hospitals. In turn, I have had lots of nurses from other rheumatology units spending the day with me to find out more about scleroderma and what we do here at the Royal Free. Other new developments for the future are that I plan to train in intravenous cannulation techniques (e.g. for iloprost infusions), and I am planning to do an intra-articular joint injection course. At the beginning of the year the department also acquired a new outpatient clinic Sister and she and I worked closely together to set up a nurse-led monitoring clinic, and design a shared-care card for the monitoring of second line drugs. Professor Black and I have been updating some of the drug information sheets and writing new ones for drugs such as CGRP. We also have a new doctor from Italy who is spending a year with us and together we have been busy recruiting patients for our winter Raynaud's trial. This year we are comparing a new drug, losartan, with the more familiar nifedipine. Whenever possible I attend the ward round and I work closely with the medical staff to facilitate the patients' ongoing education needs. I also still work in the connective tissue disease clinics assessing and monitoring existing patients and educating new patients about the disease and its treatment. The scleroderma helpline has proved very successful and I deal with up to 15 calls a day from patients, their relatives, G.P.'s and other health care professionals.

On Thursday morning I have my own clinic for patients with primary Raynaud's phenomenon. In 1998 we have plans to further improve the service we offer in this clinic. We hope these future improvements will make things even more efficient. The changes will include a fast-track system for local patients whereby we can arrange the routine tests necessary to differentiate primary from secondary Raynaud's phenomenon before their first appointment. This prior knowledge will help in the way we educate the patient and will help to determine their future management.

Helen Wilson, Royal Free Hospital

Fifteen years on 1982-1997
£3 million raised

The following articles and comments were sent in as a result of asking several consultants how they felt research had progressed during the past 15 years.

> "The last fifteen years have seen major changes in our understanding of systemic sclerosis and this has resulted in important changes in the way we approach and treat the condition."
>
> **Professor Carol Black**

> "I think that it is a useful exercise to stop and examine the progress that is being made in our understanding, diagnosis and management of such a complex set of diseases such as Raynaud's and scleroderma."
>
> **Dr. Douglas Veale**

> "We have a much clearer understanding of Raynaud's and scleroderma than we did fifteen years ago. We will continue to fight against this terrible disease of scleroderma with our best ammunition - scientific research."
>
> **Professor Jill Belch**

When will our research provide a cure for Scleroderma?

All of us dearly wish to know the answer to this question. Unfortunately there is no simple answer. This is a disease which is the end product of a number of factors which include the interaction between the genetic predisposition of individuals and environmental triggers to which they become exposed. There are likely to be many such factors which are relevant. It is because of the complexity of this relationship that we have no simple answer to the problem despite many years of research into the disease. The way we can make progress in battling the problem requires a multi-disciplinary approach.

Awareness

Through the efforts of the Raynaud's & Scleroderma Association, patients are becoming better informed about diseases such as Raynaud's Syndrome and scleroderma. The growth of the membership is a testimony to the tremendous work that it has done, and patient education has never been better. The Association, through its newsletter, disseminates information about new treatment approaches, new technologies, new research ideas which will all help to improve further the care of patients. It will also serve to achieve what is one of the primary goals of the new National Health Service - a patient demand service. Patients who are aware of the facilities that are available to treat their disease should ensure that they do receive the best available treatment, at centres which have a specialist interest. Patients can ensure that their local health care providers are aware of the Association and the specialist expertise that is available throughout the country.

Clinical progress

Over the last 15 years tremendous strides have been made in the identification of early disease in various organs involved by scleroderma and new treatments have resulted in protection of those organs. A good example of this is the way in which kidney disease has been more successfully treated since the introduction of ACE-inhibitors. The recognition of early scarring of the lungs has been achieved since computed tomography was introduced and prediction of fibrosis progression is now possible using a combination of techniques. Advances such as these will improve the way in which patients are treated, but cannot of course provide the all elusive 'cure".

Laboratory Research

Numerous new laboratory techniques have been developed over recent years which have allowed us to understand better what it is about our bodies that causes organs to scar. Importantly, we are also able to identify from studies of the genetic make-up of a patient what it is that might predispose them to develop disease in particular organs. These laboratory approaches will result in our being able to identify individuals who are most at risk, which of their organs are most at risk from the disease and to combat this with strategies which will target specific treatment to specific organs in specific patients. What we all want would be some major treatment discovery which would instantly transform the way in which this disease is treated, but unfortunately there will be no such 'magic bullet'. The path to better treatment involves better education and awareness, better technologies to identify disease and assessment of response to newer specific therapy through multi-centre clinical trials. This process is painfully slow to the frustration of patients, doctors and other health professionals alike but progress is indeed being made on all these fronts. It is only through the continuing combined efforts of all of us that we will have the opportunity to continue to make inroads into this crippling and distressing disorder.

Dr. Ron du Bois, The Brompton Hospital

Great strides forward

The last 15 years have seen major changes in our understanding of systemic sclerosis and this has resulted in important changes in the way we approach and treat the condition. The disease which used to be considered as a single untreatable connective tissue disease now has subsets and stages. This is a very important step forward as it permits a much more rational approach to helping a patient, determining their prognosis and managing their treatment. In the past there were no proper methods of assessing severity or activity of systemic sclerosis. It was very difficult to know whether treatments had been effective or not. A severity assessment score has now been developed by an international committee and is in use around the world and an activity score is being developed. There is now much greater appreciation of the importance of individual organ involvement. Fortunately, very few patients get all their organs involved and the disease often hits one particular part of the body, for example the lungs, either with pulmonary fibrosis or pulmonary hypertension or sometimes it affects just the kidneys or perhaps the heart. Understanding this has permitted us to investigate the individual organs intensely and to treat at an earlier stage of the disease and therefore to offer the patient a better quality of life. For example, if we take the lung and pulmonary fibrosis, over the past 12 years in work performed with the Brompton Hospital, we have with the help of very specialised high resolution CT scans, DTPA scans, broncho-alveolar lavage and lung biopsy, been able to detect the earliest possible disease, the amount of lung involved and how the patient is likely to respond to treatment. This is an enormous step forward. We have also been able to match to this the antibodies which indicate that a patient is susceptible to pulmonary fibrosis and with Dr. Welsh's help the genes which also make a person susceptible to lung involvement. There are also an increasing number of very well defined disease specific antibodies or proteins which circulate in the blood. These proteins enable the disease to be subsetted and stratified and tell us what type of organ might become involved. For example, a protein called RNA polymerase is associated with kidney disease and this of course is very useful to know in advance as we can watch the blood pressure very carefully, watch the kidney function very carefully and stop things going wrong very early on.

The basic work which has been done in the past is possibly more difficult for the patients to understand but still very important. I think possibly the best way of describing this is to say that the research endeavours have been in several areas: (1) to understand the genes which not only predispose to the disease but predispose to progression of the disease; (2) to look in more depth at the environmental factors; (3) to work out the role of the endothelial cells (cells which line the blood vessels), the lymphocyte cells which are part of the immune system and fibroblasts, which are the cells which produce the collagen. In each of these areas there have been major advances. For example, we now know what the 'endothelial cell membrane' looks like in a scleroderma patient or to put it slightly differently, the way it is activated and what type of molecules appear on its cell surface. These molecules interact with the lymphocytes which are almost certainly the cells causing much of the damage. We know more about free radicals and their effects on the endothelial cells.

Pulmonary hypertension is a dreadful problem in scleroderma which we all know and one in which we very much need to make major steps forward. Over the past two years we have been collecting and analysing information on all our patients with pulmonary hypertension. Bowel disease, particularly the mid and lower bowel, has always been a major problem in scleroderma and is little understood. We now have at the Royal Free a research fellow for two years dedicated solely to investigating this problem and I anticipate that we will, at the end of it, understand much about the early stages of this complication and whether it is driven by the neurological damage or by vascular damage leading to disruption to the normal nerve impulses to the gut. There is also now much better management of renal scleroderma. It used to be that at least 9% of the scleroderma population developed kidney disease. Our figures are now down to 5% which is very much better.

Finally, in the clinical area we have much more co-ordinated endeavours in the field of clinical trials. We are developing a national register and have lots of physicians around the country who are happy to sign up to this idea.

Carol M. Black, Professor of Rheumatology,
Royal Free Hospital

No dramatic breakthrough

Dr. David Scott

There have been a number of developments in the last 15 years in terms of drug treatment for Raynaud's, surgical treatment (a microvascular approach) and in communication and understanding. I think the dramatic change that I have seen in the last 15 years is an improved patient awareness and I think the Raynaud's & Scleroderma Association has been almost entirely responsible for this. Scleroderma research has also progressed. Studies with intensive immunosuppressive regimes and some of the local skin treatments have been helpful, but it has not been too dramatic. However, the use of intravenous iloprost has certainly made a difference to many patients. It is very difficult to target future research as the interplay between the microvasculature and the fibrosis that occur in scleroderma are probably integrated and I think the only way one can advise is to take a combined approach, i.e. to support pure biological research looking at intra-vascular changes. I do not think, unfortunately, you can expect dramatic breakthroughs. We have been living with arthritis for a long time and although our understanding continues to improve, breakthroughs are still few and far between.

Dr. David Scott,
Consultant Rheumatologist Norfolk & Norwich NHS

A useful exercise

Dr. Douglas Veale

I think that it is a useful exercise to stop and examine the progress that is being made in our understanding, diagnosis and management of such a complex set of diseases as Raynaud's and scleroderma. As you are aware one of the critical areas of progress over the last twenty years has been to identify different sub-sets of this disease allowing us to prognasticate. Much of this work has concentrated on the clinical manifestations of the disease, in particular kidney problems, lung disease and vascular problems including pulmonary hypertension. There has been significant research examining the character and the natural progress of such complications and their implications for disease outcome. In addition there has been much work examining the patterns of auto-immunity, in particular those antibodies such as anti-centromere and anti isotopomerase which may have clinical and prognostic complications. There have been a number of advances in the area of treatment of specific problems; the most obvious of these is the reduction in mortality from renal complications and hypertension due to the introduction of ACE inhibitors. Indeed from recent research the pro-active use of ACE inhibitors at an early stage before any renal complications are present may have beneficial effects. The other major groups of drugs include the calcium antagonists and the prostanoids including prostacyclin analogue such as iloprost. These drugs have undergone extensive clinical trials over the past fifteen years to the extent that we now know a great deal about their mechanisms of action, about their clinical uses and in addition their shortcomings and limitations.

With regard to scientific research it has always been my personal aim to link the scientific research as closely as possible to the clinical spectrum and I think that a number of advances have been made over the last two decades. I realise that on the face of it some of this research will provide a negative response. This is not necessarily always a bad thing and sometimes negative results may give us positive information.

In summary, therefore, I believe our understanding of the molecular, cellular and indeed specific tissue mechanisms important in Raynaud's and scleroderma are being much advanced by the research over the last two decades. I believe there has been some progress on the genetics in particular with relation to lung involvement in scleroderma and also with regard to regulation of collagen genes. Our understanding of the endothelial and its role and also the role of blood cells and molecules expressed on the surface of these cells such as cell adhesion molecules has also advanced significantly. I believe that our clinical classification and standardisation of methods of assessment and monitoring will lead to a greater standardisation and co-ordination of clinical trials which is essential for future progress. I also believe that there are a number of areas which future research should address including the interaction of the neurological and the immune systems and the immunogenetics with relation to the different forms of vascular diseases associated with these complex conditions.

Dr. Douglas Veale,
Leeds General Infirmary

Important achievements

Dr. Barbara Ansell

I am not in receipt of any grants and never have been from the Association. I was Head of the Medical Research Council Rheumatism Unit at the Clinical Research Centre, Northwick Park Hospital, Harrow, but I am now just in private practice as a rheumatologist with a particular interest in children, particularly those with scleroderma, that I have worked with.

I think the first and most important thing to say is that scleroderma is a rare disease and until about 20 years ago it was regarded as a single entity; the children having more localised disease being a 'little different'. To me one of the most important achievements has been the recognition that there are many subsets in scleroderma and many stages in the disease. That allows a rational approach to assessment and management of patients. As I have already indicated, my own work was related to paediatric scleroderma when just over 20 years ago we drew attention to the problems of morphea associated with nodule formation mimicking juvenile arthritis, the problem of growth in the a limb of a child with linear scleroderma and subsequently that this type of scleroderma could be associated with a severe inflammatory arthritis and different management had to be considered.

In the last few years with the thermography, we have been able to assess the activity of the localised lesion and therefore what type of management, i.e. anti-inflammatory or long term therapy with a potentially dangerous drug is called for. In the adult world I was involved with the standardised methods of systemic sclerosis severity and these have now been developed through an International Committee together with a skin score which allows comparison of patients in different centres and several countries. In basic research, the importance of different parts of the blood vessels in determining the different problems in the disease, has to be attacked, as do the properties of cells in systemic sclerosis. It is also very important that we try and understand better the differences between cells in different affected organs. Genetic studies should continue to proceed as newer techniques become available. I think one of the important things that this Association has done has made people more aware of both Raynaud's phenomenon and scleroderma, and it is important that we continue this because earlier diagnosis and better application of the knowledge that has been developed over the past 15 years will, I suspect, lead to a very much better outlook for patients in the next 15 years.

Dr. Barbara M. Ansell, CBE

Significant progress

Dr. Ariane Herrick

Significant progress has been made in several areas. Compared to 15 years ago we understand far more about the underlying disease mechanisms responsible for Raynaud's phenomenon and scleroderma. Although it would be quite wrong to claim that we know 'the cause', we do understand far more about the abnormalities of the blood vessels, about the excessive production of collagen, and about the abnormal immune responses which occur in systemic sclerosis. Because of our increased understanding of the disease processes underlying Raynaud's phenomenon and scleroderma, a number of treatments have been proposed. Some of these have been aimed at suppressing the underlying disease process (for example, alpha-interferon), others have effects on specific aspects of the disease (for example, prostacyclin and prostacyclin analogues in the treatment of finger circulatory problems). Disappointingly, none of the 'disease modifying' therapies tried so far has been shown to be very effective, but it was important to test these out.

Much more is known about how to measure disease progression compared to 15 years ago. Systemic sclerosis (scleroderma) and its different subgroups are now better defined. The natural history of the disease process is different between patients with limited cutaneous and diffuse disease. This is an important point. It would be inappropriate to try potentially toxic 'disease-modifying therapy' to a patient in the early stages of limited cutaneous disease. Although no satisfactory 'disease modifying' drug or 'cure' for Raynaud's phenomenon or scleroderma has been found or developed, a number of 'palliative' treatments (treatments which alleviate disease without curing) have been developed or their use refined. Examples include proton pump inhibitors (an example of which is omeprazole or 'Losec') for upper gastrointestinal symptoms, and prostacyclin and its analogues for the finger circulation. Doctors caring for patients with Raynaud's and scleroderma can predict which patients with Raynaud's phenomenon are likely to go on to develop scleroderma. One reason is the increased availability of nail-fold microscopy (which allows patients with early changes in their small blood vessels to be detected). Of course awareness of Raynaud's phenomenon and scleroderma is helped greatly in the U.K. by the Raynaud's & Scleroderma Association itself. Patient education packages produced by the Association have also had an important direct benefit to patients.

Much research is currently ongoing, and much more is needed. We need to continue to study the underlying disease processes responsible for Raynaud's phenomenon and scleroderma because only in this way will we be able to identify new lines of therapy.

Dr. Ariane Herrick,
Hope Hospital, Salford

Donation from HSA

Anne receives a cheque for £5,000 presented by Steve Redgrave and Matthew Pinsent on behalf of the Hospital Saving Association, at a dinner held at The Brewery in London. This money funded the Scleroderma Support Day.

Jennie's Story

I'm Jennie and I'm 11 years old. I'm writing to tell everybody what it feels like to have scleroderma. I'm especially writing to those people who are suffering from this condition. I suppose it all started when I was 9. I used to always play football with my brother so when it appeared I thought it was a bruise. Soon it got bigger, so I went to see my local doctor. He thought he knew what it was but to make sure he sent me to a specialist. They then diagnosed scleroderma. About a month or two after, I went on a golf course and half way round I could barely walk on my right leg which the scleroderma was on. I was in so much pain. For the next six months I had to go around on crutches. During the six months I had constant physiotherapy. I can remember my first ever appointment. I thought my physiotherapist would make me do things I couldn't do but he was really nice and by the end of the session I wanted to be a physiotherapist to help children like me. I've had four different physiotherapists and the one I have now said a few words which made me realise that you don't get something for nothing in this world. If I wanted to run and jump I had to work at it. I had to leave school early every Monday for about two months for physiotherapy. After the two

Jennie McMonagle

months the appointments weren't as often and now I'm 11 the appointments are about six months apart. When my condition was really bad and I used to go every Monday, I can remember thinking "I'll never be able to walk again". Every school has a sports day and everyone from the school runs and jumps but for the last two years I've been different. I haven't been joining in and I've been very disappointed when my friends came back with 1st, 2nd and 3rd stickers. This year I was determined to join in all possible sports and, because of my physiotherapist's words, I have been able to do so. Together, all the doctors helped me to overcome my problems and helped me to believe that if I did my exercises, I could achieve, and that is what I did. I even achieved our year sports cup at school, which was an achievement, but I think of it more as a bonus to show that I did what I wanted to do and because I tried.

I hope that what I have written has helped you to understand what I and others go through and I hope that you will support the Raynaud's & Scleroderma Association to help them find a cure for my condition. I also hope that anybody with the same condition as me will understand that if they put a determined effort in, it could make a lot of difference in what they are able to do.

Jennie McMonagle

Kym's Plea for Help

My name is Kym Astbury. I am a 16 year old girl with morphea. I started suffering from this disease at around the age of 7. At the time the doctors did not know what was wrong and just said that I had eczema and prescribed hydrocortisone cream. When I was 14 I was referred to the local hospital in Tooting where I had various blood tests, photos taken and a skin biopsy. I was later diagnosed as having morphea. I was put on a course of tablets called Penicillamine and had to go to the hospital every other week to check that my white blood cell count wasn't decreasing. Four months after treatment the doctors told me that the tablets had done all they could (which wasn't much!) and referred me to a skin camouflage specialist from the Red Cross, where I was given two types of creams. As the marking is on such large areas of my body the cream did not look very good. It also looked very unnatural even when done by the specialist. Due to the large amounts of hydrocortisone cream I was given when I was younger, my skin has very badly thinned. My skin is quite badly marked and my veins are very visible. As you can imagine for a girl of my age this affects my confidence and upsets me a great deal. Not only in the hot summer but also in the winter I have to wear certain types of clothes and really cover myself up. When I go out with my friends at night I have to wear thick makeup, which looks very unnatural and I am very conscious of being in the light. These are just a few of the things that affect me because of having morphea.

Kym Astbury

We're Getting There

New Book

New publication available from the Raynaud's & Scleroderma Association, Raynaud's - Your Questions Answered by Anne H Mawdsley MBE with the Foreword written by Matthew Corbett. This book attempts to answer some of the most commonly asked questions by people with Raynaud's and associated conditions.

- Is Raynaud's hereditary?
- Is there a cure?
- How can a chilblain be treated?
- Would it help if I moved to a warmer climate?
- Should I have a blood test?
- Is Raynaud's contagious?
- Is carpal tunnel syndrome rare?

Freezer donated to new Scleroderma Clinic in Belfast

We are starting a Scleroderma clinic in Northern Ireland. The clinic is going to take place weekly and will be based in the Belfast City Hospital. A specialist clinic will obviously give good quality care to our patients, furthermore it will allow standardised assessment of patients. The latter point is particularly relevant as Belfast is going to be another centre in the U.K. Scleroderma Multicentre Clinical Trials.

Dr. Anita Smyth

To date my research, which will form part of my MD thesis, has looked at patients with Raynaud s phenomenon including their disease categorisation and the question of genetic susceptibility through a candidate gene approach, examining the frequency distribution of polymorphisms of genes encoding endothelial-derived vasoactive molecules implicated in Raynaud's phenomenon. During the experimental part of my research I was given some temporary freezer space for storage of DNA.

To summarise, the reasons for requesting a minus seventy degree freezer, involve the storage of research samples already acquired and to enable the storage of samples collected from patients who will be seen at our new clinic. Through the establishment of a comprehensive database and the simultaneous storage of samples of blood and tissue, our centre will be equipped for future research to build on our initial work on patients with primary Raynaud's phenomenon.

My thanks to members of the Association for making it possible for our department here in Belfast to purchase this freezer.

Dr. Anita Smyth, Department of Rheumatology,
Musgrave Park Hospital, Belfast

Dr. Yusuf Patel

Research news from Bath

'Apoptosis' - Programmed to Die

The buzzword in biomedical research today is apoptosis. Like fashions which come and go, scientists and medical researchers also have favoured topics of research at any given time. Apoptosis has been the topic of research in almost every medical discipline over the last few years, but the idea is not a new one. For some time now it has been known that cells die in different ways. When cells are injured they swell and literally burst to release their contents which in turn stimulate 'scavenger' white blood cells including neutrophils and macrophages to clear things up. This form of cell death is known as necrosis, and is associated with a tremendous amount of collateral damage to normal surviving cellular tissue because of the associated inflammatory reaction caused by proteins and chemicals released by both the dead cells as well as the scavenger cells.

It is over twenty years now since Wyllie and Kerr identified an alternative form of cell death called apoptosis. Apoptosis is a process where the cells progressively shrink and in a highly organised fashion become a series of membrane bound blobs which are very rapidly engulfed and removed by scavenger macrophage cells. Research into this field is very active and progress has been made extremely rapidly in many areas of medical research related to apoptosis. The ability to measure the process in the laboratory has become easier as a result, but we are still some way from understanding everything about the process. It appears that all cells have a number of genes that regulate the ability to 'self-destruct' by apoptosis when the appropriate signals are received by that cell. Apoptosis is by no means unique to human cells, and in fact much of what we know today about the genes that regulate apoptosis has been learnt from the study of a worm called C.elegans and a fly called Drosophila.

Some examples of apoptosis in action include:

i) The disappearance of webs between our fingers and toes in embryonic stages of development (otherwise we may all have looked like frogs!)

ii) The removal of excess lymphocytes that make up the swollen lymph glands we get after infections.

iii) The disappearance of cancerous tissue following treatment with some anticancer therapy.

iv) The depletion of lymphocyte cells from the blood in 'AIDS' infections.

v) Apoptosis applies to plant biology as well and the falling of the leaves we see in Autumn is probably also due to the process of apoptosis.

So we can see that this highly regulated process of cell death may malfunction in certain diseases, such as cancer or autoimmune disease where apoptosis is decreased or conditions like AIDS and other autoimmune states (thyroid disease) where apoptosis is increased. What happens in scleroderma? Could the excess skin thickening and the fibrosis seen in other organs like the lung and kidney be due to a breakdown of apoptosis? If not, could we influence these processes by inducing selective apoptosis of overgrown tissues? Not enough research has been done into apoptosis in scleroderma, but this is changing now and whilst some researchers are looking into the possibility that apoptosis of endothelial cells (lining the blood vessels) may be abnormal, others are considering if the increased fibroblast cells seen in scleroderma may not be due to a failure of the control mechanisms of apoptosis. We have just embarked on research into the latter, but it is going to take some time and effort before we can learn if and how apoptosis may play a role in the causation or propagation of this disease. We have much to learn, but as long as these new avenues of research open up to us there will always be hope that we may yet be able to influence the disease outcome, with new therapeutic approaches in the future.

Dr. Yusuf Patel, Senior Clinical Research Fellow,
Royal National Hospital for Rheumatic Diseases, Bath

News of younger members

Ben Down Under

Ben aged 2

In December several articles appeared in the national newspapers and on television about one of our younger members, 6 year old Ben Whiting. Ben has had Raynaud s since he was very young. With the help of the Dream Team his family decided to emigrate to Australia where they feel that Ben will be able to live a more normal life, playing football outside rather than having to watch his friends from indoors.

Ben and his family left for Australia in February and we received the following letter from his Mum.

I am enclosing a photo of Ben taken by one of your posters on a bus shelter in Brentwood. We would like to say thank you for all your help and advice you gave us in helping to understand Ben's condition. I hope with all the publicity which Ben has generated that more people will understand about Raynaud's. We hope that people in this country can help and support the Association to find a cure and more research into the condition. We have been very lucky to have been accepted into Australia and are looking forward to a new life. We will certainly keep in touch and send photos of Ben in his new country and give you updates on his progress. All we can say is thank you.

Sharon Whiting

The following article appeared in an Australian newspaper.

"It was freezing in England and I couldn't go out" says Ben Whiting, 6, who has followed the sun to a new life in Brisbane. Ben packed his bags and moved out of his home in chilly Brentwood in England to enjoy the warmth of the sunshine State. Suffering from a condition, only made bearable by warm weather, Ben was brought to Queensland by an English charity. He has Raynaud's phenomenon and erythromelalgia,

which stems the blood flow to his hands and feet when the temperature drops below 20 degrees C. As the mercury rises again Ben suffers great pain. The cheerful six-year old has settled in at Aspley East State School and, like most children his age, he loves playing. Ben's greatest wish is to be a soccer goalie and he can now play outside for the first time. In his Year 2 classroom, Ben's seat is next to the open window, where leaves blow in and sunshine streams through. England is only a memory now".

Ben by our poster at a bus stop

Beginning to understand

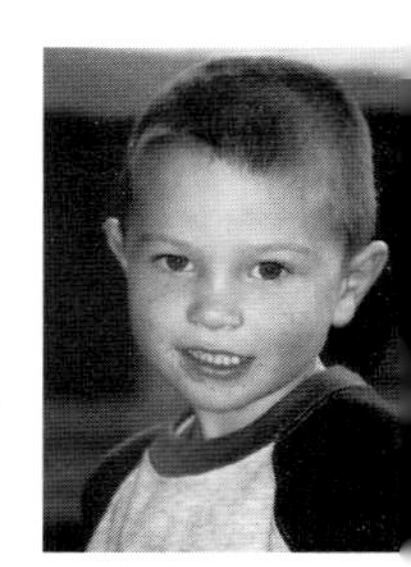

Lewis Currell

"Hello, my name is Julia and my husband is Stephen. We have two sons Travis who is 7 years old and Lewis aged 4. Lewis was diagnosed with Raynaud's two years ago after a long battle. After seeing a specialist they recommended us to dress Lewis in clothing made of a fabric called Polypropylene, so our first step was to find who stocked such clothing. We found our local ski shop stocked these items so we purchased vests, socks and long johns for undergarments, coats, gloves, hats and Salloupets for outer wear. To save money we bought larger sizes for longer use. These items have helped Lewis to keep a constant temperature. Shoes were a problem as the ski shop only stocked ski boots but they suggested 'Elafanten' at our local shoe shop. They recommended buying 'Gortex' boots, which keep out the cold and wet (they are also machine washable). His feet were measured and plenty of growing room was allowed for longer wear to save money! For the first time Lewis does not suffer any longer from chilblains. Bedtime was always a problem with sleepless nights, so he goes to bed with socks, vest and pyjamas on. His bed has a duvet, two blankets and a hot water bottle. We tuck the blankets in so the duvet does not slip off and consequently wake Lewis through temperature change. In order to keep the body core warm, we were also advised never to give Lewis cold drinks and ice cream. When Lewis has an attack and complains of the cold we rub his hands or feet until the circulation returns. Heat pads are excellent and a novelty for Lewis to play with.

Now good news - it has become easier as Lewis has got older - he now understands what causes his attacks and pain and we are able to react and help him by adding clothes or massaging. I would love to hear from other Mums with young children and have suggested to Anne that it would be a good idea for people to send warm clothing which their youngsters have grown out of to the Association so that they can be passed on to others. The children grow so quickly and having spent a lot of money on warm clothing one winter, they seldom fit the next".

Julia Currell

We have to keep our daughter warm

Cara seen here with her father, Les, who raised £282 in the Hoy Half Marathon

The following has been extracted from an article in The Sunday Post on April 26th.

It is a particularly cold day in Orkney and Debra Watson has to swaddle her gorgeous daughter. A typical scenario enacted every day in recent weeks by mums everywhere. But Debra has more reason than most to keep little Cara (13 months) warmly wrapped up - even on a cool summers day for the toddler is one of the youngest babies in the world to suffer from a form of Raynaud's phenomenon, a circulatory condition which makes its victims permanently cold. It's difficult for blood to travel to her hands and feet - her little toe nails fell off last week. Her nose frequently blisters with the cold. The onset of the illness was signalled when Cara's arm turned blue when she was only seven months old. Doctors on the island were so worried they flew her to a specialist at Aberdeen Royal Infirmary. They thought that the tot had an extra rib which was cutting off her circulation.

"But after a series of tests they concluded that she was suffering from Raynaud's', Debra explains. "It's normally something that affects adults, particularly women - and no one had seen it before in a baby". The vessels narrow and trying to get blood through is like forcing treacle through a straw. Cold weather slows down the circulation even more, and can make matters seriously worse. But the climate of Orkney and its exposed position off the north coast means temperatures can plummet. At present, treatment consists of simply keeping Cara warm. She's too young for the drug therapy normally given to adults with Raynaud's. Snow and hail are no strangers to the island, so Cara has to wear several layers of baby clothes when she's taken out. Debra and her husband Leslie have three older sons - Luke (7), Jake (5) and Todd (3). "We were upset when doctors told us about Cara's problem, but once you accept it then you can live with it. Many other parents have much bigger worries to cope with. Cara won't come to much harm if we are vigilant and keep her warm," Debra adds, "though we don't know the long term outcome because the doctors don't either. She didn't appear to be in any pain when her toe nails came off, I just needed to make sure her feet didn't become infected. Shopping for baby clothes provides a challenge. Fleecy lined soft cotton socks and gloves can help a lot. Cara rarely goes anywhere without two pairs of each. When the temperature really drops, the family simply don't go out, but stick in by their warm fireside".

Scleroderma Support Day 1998

On March 1st we held our first Scleroderma Support Day at the Manor House Hotel in Alsager. The aim was to offer a wide range of support through self help and practical knowledge from health professionals. Most people who came stayed at the hotel and enjoyed the warmth and friendliness of the hotel, with good food, company and the opportunity to use a heated swimming pool. Other members who lived nearer, joined us for the day on the Sunday.

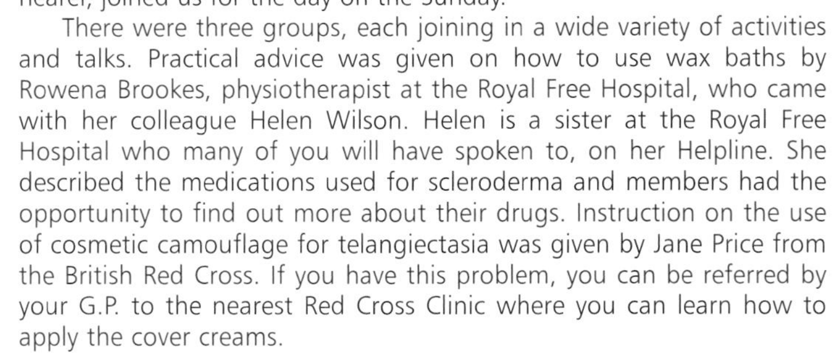

There were three groups, each joining in a wide variety of activities and talks. Practical advice was given on how to use wax baths by Rowena Brookes, physiotherapist at the Royal Free Hospital, who came with her colleague Helen Wilson. Helen is a sister at the Royal Free Hospital who many of you will have spoken to, on her Helpline. She described the medications used for scleroderma and members had the opportunity to find out more about their drugs. Instruction on the use of cosmetic camouflage for telangiectasia was given by Jane Price from the British Red Cross. If you have this problem, you can be referred by your G.P. to the nearest Red Cross Clinic where you can learn how to apply the cover creams.

These photographs show the difference in Eileen Stevens before (above) and after having cosmetic camouflage.

Frank Webb, the author of our chiropody booklet, gave an excellent talk on how scleroderma can affect the feet and gave advice on how to cope. Liz Haskell from the Brompton and Ros Robb from Ninewells in Dundee talked about the skin. Liz gave help with exercises for the face and Ros showed samples of the various dressings which can be used in treating ulcers. Jennie Iliffe, from the Brompton Hospital involved patients in discussions on how individuals cope with their emotions relating to their condition, with their doctors and whether they felt that enough was being done for patients locally. Gaynor Loghan from Hope Hospital gave an interesting talk on stress, anxiety and relaxation in relation to scleroderma. Finally, Ros Garside and her colleague introduced members to Sahaja Yoga Meditation which is a form of healing yoga. This was very soothing and caused a few of us to drift off especially after such a wonderful lunch!

Our thanks to all the participants who gave up their weekend to take part. The members were certainly appreciative and went away with a greater knowledge of how to cope with scleroderma. We are already making plans for next year's Support Day!

Congratulations

We were thrilled to hear the news that Roger Jefcoate, an ardent supporter of the work of the Association, was awarded a CBE in the New Year's Honours list. This was in recognition for his dedicated work with disabled people. Over the last 30 years he has worked on developing technology to give thousands of disabled people a better quality of life. He has been associated with the work of our charity since the early years and the Trustees have recently invited Roger to become a Patron. We are delighted that he has accepted.

Roger Jefcoate CBE

National and International News Summer 1998

National Activities

The U.K. Scleroderma Study Group, which is a group of doctors especially interested in scleroderma and Raynaud's, has been very busy with two major projects. The first of these is the organising and raising of funds for studies of new drugs in systemic sclerosis and Raynaud's. We have been particularly interested in targeting early diffuse disease, pulmonary hypertension, pulmonary fibrosis and limited disease. Each of these subsets. has a different set of problems and requires a different approach to treatment. We are particularly pleased that the Arthritis and Rheumatism Council have provided funding for a U.K. multi-centre study in pulmonary fibrosis which is now recruiting patients. It is very important that we undertake these studies so that the best available drugs can be found for each aspect of the disease.

The second project is the establishment of a central register of patients. This register is being devised in part to facilitate entry of patients into drug trials, although it will have many other benefits. Once it is established any doctor, not just those particularly interested in Raynaud's and scleroderma, could offer to register any patients they have with the disorders and the referring doctor would then be informed of available studies to suit their particular patient. If both the patient and his or her doctor are happy, the patient's name would then be sent onto the centre organising the study. The referral must of course, come through the patient's doctor, which can be a G.P. or hospital specialist. Such an undertaking obviously requires a lot of organisation and financial support and we are currently trying to arrange this.

In addition to the U.K. Scleroderma Study Group there are also units around the country who have agreed to act as collaborating centres in any of our protocols and to help collect patients and monitor their progress. We are particularly grateful to have found friends and colleagues to do this in the parts of the country where hitherto there had not been a particular focus on Raynaud's and systemic sclerosis.

Educating as many doctors as possible about Raynaud's and scleroderma is very important and the first postgraduate update on both the basic and clinical features of Raynaud's and scleroderma was held at the Royal Free Hospital in January. The course was attended by some 80 doctors. We hope we will be able to make this a bi-annual event.

The treatment of scleroderma, as you all know, is very difficult and there has been much interest in using a form of bone marrow transplantation to treat patients with disease which is progressing very rapidly. This is of course a very new idea and a very interesting one. In order to inform doctors and to permit more discussion about this highly specialised technique, a one day meeting was held at the Royal Society of Medicine in February, with experts from America, Switzerland and Holland joining us to discuss this treatment. At present, some 7 people have received the treatment in the United Kingdom.

International Activities

Dr. Scorso organised a meeting in Milan which I attended. Amongst other topics, the vascular aspects of scleroderma were discussed in detail and there was also a most interesting session with the Italian and French patients' groups which I was fortunate enough to chair. Despite our language difficulties, we had a lively and interesting exchange of views.

In December Dr. Abraham and I were fortunate enough to be invited to attend the one day scientific workshop on scleroderma at the National Institute of Health in Bethesda, USA. This organisation is the equivalent of our Medical Research Council and we were therefore delighted and privileged to go along. David has summarised below some of the research topics which were discussed and each will indicate to you what people are thinking is important on the basic research front at the present time. The workshop at the NIH was held as part of the emerging opportunities in scleroderma research, an initiative by the NIH to increase awareness and funding into scleroderma and allied disorders. The programme was limited to three main areas which were deemed to be current and important in scleroderma research and divided into three discussion sessions.

These were; Firstly, a session devoted to the role of microchimerism in scleroderma. The aim was to address the potential role that foetal cells play in the pathogenesis of scleroderma. Foetal cells are known to cross into the mother's blood stream during birth and foetal cells from an earlier pregnancy can be found in the blood and tissues of women with scleroderma. It seems incredible that these foetal cells can persist in the mother for many years, but it is believed by some investigators that these foetal cells might contribute to the disregard in some women.

Secondly, a session devoted to the endothelial cell (the cells lining the blood vessels) and free radicals. It has long been thought that damage to the endothelium is an early event in scleroderma and that free radicals (reactive oxygen chemicals) may have a prominent role in this injury. A number of factors have been recently isolated that are produced by endothelial cells and that influence both smooth muscle (vessel contraction) and fibroblast function (fibrosis). These results appear to place the endothelial cell at the centre of attention in early disease, and provide a biological link between vessel damage and later disease manifestations. In addition to the damage to cells by free radical reactions, recent data has also shown that these chemicals may cause changes to some of the cells normal proteins, leading to the production of auto-antibodies that are characteristic of the disease.

Finally a session covering opportunities in clinical trials. These discussions centred on the particular facets of the disease that needed to be addressed when embarking on any trials, such as the damaged endothelium, the activated blood system and inflammation and tissue fibrosis and the factors that might represent good targets for therapy. The lack of effectiveness of previous trials (interferon-a and D-Penicillamine) was described as well as initial observations on current trials underway (relaxin and immunosuppression). Issues raised by previous trials were also discussed such as specific organ-based therapy, the importance of measuring critical endpoints and the recent perhaps more radical approaches to therapy including bone marrow transplantation. There was agreement that in general, trials would be much better performed within a multi-centre environment.

In March we all went to Italy to an international meeting on scleroderma and Raynaud's. It covered every aspect of the diseases; clinical, education, research and patient affairs. Dr. Marco Matucci Cerenic and his committee did a wonderful job.

We have one more meeting to go this year and that is the Scleroderma Research Workshop, which is to take place in Boston, USA. This is a scientific workshop which this year will have an additional one day meeting on childhood scleroderma. This is an important and neglected aspect of the disease and I am delighted that this will happen. As you can see, a lot is happening in scleroderma - of course never enough, but I believe we can look forward with excitement and hope.

Professor Carol Black & Dr. David Abraham, Royal Free Hospital

International Conference

Anne Mawdsley, presenting Dr. Marco Matucci Cerinic with one of our hand badges at the Conference.

An International Conference on systemic sclerosis was held in Montecatini, Italy in March. Speakers from the U.K. included Professor Jill Belch and Professor Carol Black. During the conference there was a support group session. I represented our Association and the Irish Raynaud's & Scleroderma Society delegate was Ann Philp. Much knowledge was gained and it was good to meet so many doctors at an International level.

The Conference was organised by Dr. Marco Matucci Cerinic from Italy, who is working on a collaborative project with Dr. Pamela Milner and Professor Burnstock at the Royal Free Hospital funded by our Association. This was a medical conference but we, as representatives of patient organisations, were made to feel very welcome by the medical profession. Although many of the technical medical papers were understandably difficult for lay people to understand, it was wonderful to hear that so much is being done to find a cure for scleroderma. Virtually every aspect of scleroderma was covered during the conference, including an inspiring talk by Dr. Casale, from Montescana, on rehabilitation in scleroderma. Professor Black presented work on lung fibroblasts, much of which you will have read about in previous issues of Hot News. Professor Belch gave a talk on the contribution of platelets to the modification of the vascular wall. She explained that platelet activity is increased in scleroderma and this may be an important factor in disease causation, consequential to it, or even coincidental. Whatever the primary role is, however, the outcome of this abnormal activity is further disturbance of tissue nutrition and vascular damage. Treatment to attenuate this platelet 'hyperactivity' e.g. with iloprost, may therefore be beneficial.

Dr. Ariane Herrick gave an oral poster presentation of 'antioxidant therapy in limited cutaneous systemic sclerosis - a double-blind placebo controlled trial', and Dr. Francis Gilchrist 'Polymorphism of the serotonin transporter promoter region in 75 SSc patients'. The very significant financial support of the Raynaud's & Scleroderma Association was fully acknowledged by the British doctors. An interesting presentation, entitled 'Microchimerism and HLA-compatible relationships of pregnancy in scleroderma', was given by Dr. Lee Nelson, a researcher at the Fred Hutchinson Cancer Research Centre, in Seattle, who had published the results of a study that showed women with scleroderma had significantly higher levels of 'non-self' foetal cells circulating in their bodies than did a sampling of healthy women who had also given birth. The foetal cell theory can also explain how men and women who have never given birth might have contracted the disease. She stated that cells move both ways during a pregnancy and foetal cells may engraft and persist in the mother and the mother's cells can persist in the child. In the case of twins, cells may pass back and forth between fraternal twins in the womb, so that one or the other ends up with some 'non-self' cells.

Another very interesting talk was given by Dr. Daniel Furst from the Virginia Mason Research Centre in Seattle. This concerned a relatively new treatment for scleroderma - stem cell transplantation. The idea for using bone marrow transplant (using the patient's own blood or bone marrow cells) to treat scleroderma started when Dr. Lee and Dr. Furst were discussing the peculiar similarities between scleroderma patients and patients who suffer from graft-versus-host disease after getting bone marrow transplants with donor marrow. The two researchers were wondering what the common link between the two diseases might be when inspiration struck. Graft-versus-host disease occurs when the body recognises the donor marrow cells are not its own and turns on them, attacking itself in the process. In its chronic form, it looks a lot like scleroderma, causing thickening of the skin, and affecting the lungs and gastrointestinal system, but it rarely happens with autologous transplants, which use the patient's own blood or bone marrow cells for the transplant. Such transplants are usually used to treat cancer patients.

They knew that scleroderma looks very much like graft-versus-host disease and also knew the peak incidence of scleroderma was in women in the years that would follow child bearing. In addition, they knew researchers had recently discovered that foetal cells could persist in a woman's body up to 27 years after giving birth. That third fact helped the theory to fall into place. Dr. Nelson and Dr. Furst speculated that the body sees the foetal cells as 'non-self' in the same way it sees donor marrow cells as invaders. In both cases, the 'non-self' cells somehow trigger the wrong reaction in the immune system, making it attack itself and causing autoimmune disease. Their theory has since gained some scientific backing. The foetal cell theory also gave rise to the idea of doing autologous bone marrow transplants to treat scleroderma. The researchers speculated that if they could reprogram the immune system by replacing it with fresh cells (a bone marrow transplant), the immune system would no longer attack the 'non-self cells', stopping the disease from progressing further. The hope is that whatever combination of environmental and genetic events triggered scleroderma, would no longer be present, giving the new cells the chance to operate normally. It is still an open question, however, whether the cells might revert to the same process that caused the disease in the first place. The bone marrow treatment study is currently under way at several study sites, including Seattle, Los Angeles and London. Researchers hope to do transplants for 13 to 15 patients by the end of the year.

No one knows precisely what combination of events causes the disease but something happens to trigger the immune response. If that factor is no longer operating, and you take out the cells, in theory the disease could be eliminated. If it works, it will be a significant breakthrough for a disease that has baffled researchers for more than 25 years.

I feel that it was a very worthwhile experience and came away from the Conference with the knowledge that many eminent doctors and researchers worldwide are working together for the benefit of patients. This should give us all tremendous hope for the future, as it is only by everyone working together, sharing ideas and information that we will eventually conquer scleroderma.

Anne Mawdsley

Joy's New Lease Of Life

Joy McDermott

"I have been a Raynaud's and scleroderma sufferer for nearly 20 years. My first symptoms were Raynaud's and swelling of the feet. For I5 years I suffered with minor nuisances such as stiff joints, ulcerated fingers and digestive problems. I regard these as minor, compared to what happened five years ago. After feeling rather tired and putting it down to my job as a PA Secretary to a Managing Director, my age and having scleroderma, I went to my G.P. feeling very sick. Within 24 hours I was diagnosed as having acute kidney failure and was put on dialysis. I was on dialysis three times a week for four hours each session and was told I could not be considered for transplantation because of scleroderma. The reason for kidney failure was put down to the main artery into my kidney becoming thickened, therefore not allowing an adequate blood flow to the kidney. I was on dialysis for three and a half years when I started having stomach pains due to lack of oxygen getting to my stomach. This was later put down to a low blood count and I was referred to a specialist who prescribed the necessary drugs. During one of our meetings, the specialist asked me if I had ever been offered a transplant. I said 'no', I had been told I could not have one and explained why. It turned out that he was the Head Transplant Specialist at the Royal Liverpool University Hospital.

Six months later, on 22nd August 1997 after a lot of tests, I received a phone call telling me that there was a kidney available and would I make my way to hospital and have tests for tissue, blood match, etc., to see if I was a suitable recipient for the kidney. I waited with my two daughters, son and granddaughter for approximately four hours, before I got a tap on the shoulder from a nurse to say I was a good match and was taken to my room for preparation. The operation took place the following day. It took two weeks for my new kidney to start functioning and I was quite worried that it wasn't going to work. However it gradually started to work and two weeks later I was discharged. As with every major operation, it took time for me to feel the benefit and feel fit, but today, six months later I feel really well. Each day is a bonus and I intend to make the most of my new life. After being so restricted with dialysis I am planning going to Las Vegas next year to see my second daughter marry!".

Joy McDermott

Childhood Memories

"I am sending a brief history of my condition in the hope that it may help other Raynaud's and scleroderma sufferers. Childhood memories are of my twin sister and I both with bad chilblains. Our widowed mother gave us malt which we liked and had lots - it was like toffee. We always had chilblains on our hands and feet and tried soaking our feet in urine in the chamber pot. Mother became very ill when we were about 12-13yrs. We had to change schools and had over a mile to walk in the frosty mornings and our hands became agonisingly painful with the cold. During the war years I started my nursing training and always found it painful to put my hands in cold water or touch cold things. Patients referred to me as the nurse with the cold hands and a warm heart. During this time my hands were often painful and I was very conscious of the changing colour, white, blue and sometimes hot, very red and moist. I felt ashamed to shake hands with anyone. After the war Raynaud's syndrome was diagnosed and I was allowed to have a long sleeved navy cardigan when on night duty. I attended a few appointments at Guy's Hospital where a sympathectomy was suggested, but as my sister had previously had the 'bilateral thoracic' operations with no relief, I decided against it and have overcome the spells of pain by keeping warm and in an even temperature whenever possible. I have always found soluble aspirin gives some relief from pain. Constipation and abdominal pain have been very troublesome for years. Since my retirement I am able to study my diet and increase fibre intake and fruit.

Now diagnosed as having scleroderma I have calcium patches on my fingers, the most painful being on the thumb and first finger of my right hand. In my case I think the main causes are being very sensitive to climate changes and temperatures, stress and lack of understanding by others, causing worry and distress to my nearest and dearest. The information given in the publications 'Living with Raynaud's' and 'Living with Scleroderma' has been very helpful".

Marjorie Parker, Cranlelgh

Star for a day

Jean Jeffery

"The 'fateful day' was March 20th when I switched on my TV at the end of the 'Weathershow' and I heard "please write to tell us why you prefer certain types of weather". On the spur of the moment I wrote to say I can only enjoy cool, cloudy weather because of having erythromelalgia, which means I have problems when exposed to heat of any kind, - and I then forgot all about it.

Ten days later my phone rang - "Hello this is John Muir from the 'Weathershow'. We'd like to come and interview you - will next week suit you?". I was so taken aback I said "Yes - next week's fine". I also suggested they contact Anne Mawdsley because knowing she has Raynaud's, she would have an opposite story to tell. I put down the phone and panic and disbelief swept over me. What had I done? I've never given an interview before but then I saw what a God-given opportunity this was to help other sufferers nationwide. I rang Anne and we talked about it and she assured me that I would be fine! Three days later the BBC confirmed they would drive up from London on April 6th and Anne would come from Alsager to Nottingham. The next 4 days were just like preparing for a difficult exam and I couldn't concentrate - or sleep properly!

On the day, Anne and her mother arrived on my doorstep with lovely flowers, followed later by John and Zoe, the TV crew, who quickly put us at our ease. I spoke first, feeling so nervous that I repeated everything 3 times over. In contrast Anne was very calm and composed - in spite of a sudden stream of interruptions from my phone, doorbell, cat and next door's dogs and rabbits, in addition to the battery running out on the camera and the bulb going on the lighting! The filming went on for almost 4 hours - all for a programme of a few minutes. After everyone had gone I collapsed in my chair with exhaustion!

We had expected to be 'on air' 3 days later, but instead it was transmitted on 15th April, for the good reason that we were given the whole 5 minute programme. I hardly dared to watch but when I did, I was so intrigued with the presentation of the programme that I almost enjoyed it - except for the close ups of my horrid burning feet! Even now I cannot believe that person on TV was really ME".

Jean Jeffery

Nitric Oxide

Potential Role in Fibrotic Lung Disease

Little attention has been paid previously to the possible role of nitric oxide in lung fibrosis and the results of this project may offer a different perspective on the pathological process providing new avenues for treatment.

A major complication in systemic sclerosis is lung disease, most frequently manifesting as fibrosing alveolitis where the terminal air sacs (alveoli) become inflamed and the cells lining them die. The underlying tissue is thus exposed and undergoes a process known as fibrosis (scar tissue formation) whereby the walls become thickened and stiff. The air sacs are the site where oxygen is taken up by the bloodstream and waste carbon dioxide is excreted. When the air sacs are scarred, this gas exchange cannot occur and the affected lung ceases to function properly. At present, treatment for the condition is non-specific (steroids, immunosuppressants etc.).

Nitric oxide was first thought to be a toxic component of polluted air but we now know that it is produced by various cells in our bodies. Under normal conditions, nitric oxide can perform physiological functions, e.g. blood flow and memory. However, in excess it can be harmful and can damage or even kill cells. One way in which it harms cells is by reacting with another substance, superoxide, to produce highly reactive molecules known as oxidants which can enter cells and damage proteins or nuclear materials.

Our interest in fibrosing alveolitis stems from our observation that, when new lining cells grow over the fibrotic tissue, they contain an abundance of nitric oxide. The same observation was made for the cells that form scar tissue in rats. This is in contrast with normal air sac lining cells that contain little of the enzyme. Furthermore, we can stimulate human fibroblasts maintained in culture to show expression of nitric oxide synthase. Our findings thus indicate that the epithelium and the scar tissue cells themselves may be rich sources of nitric oxide in fibrosing alveolitis. We hypothesize that this excessive local production of nitric oxide promotes formation of scar tissue and that by blocking the actions of nitric oxide it may be possible to slow down or even stop the fibrosis.

We propose to use living human cells maintained in a tissue culture system to test our hypothesis. We will stimulate lining (epithelial) cells and fibroblasts using known stimulatory substances (cytokines) to produce nitric oxide and consequently, produce nitric oxide and test the effects on each cell type separately. We will then grow the two cells types together without any stimulation, to see if they have any effect on each other under normal resting conditions. This experiment will be followed by stimulation of epithelial cells to produce nitric oxide prior to combining them with fibroblasts and monitoring the effect and then the process will be reversed and fibroblasts will be stimulated and added to epithelial cells.

Once the effects of the nitric oxide production have been assessed, specific blockers will be added to the system to test the specificity of the effect and also to explore the possibility of their use as therapeutic agents for preventing fibrosis. Once the effects are blocked, nitric oxide will be restored to the system by application of donors of the molecule, in order to confirm the specificity. Little attention has been paid previously to the possible role of nitric oxide in lung fibrosis and the results of this project may offer a different perspective on the pathological process, providing new avenues for treatment.

Professor Julia Polak
Hammersmith Hospital

Assessing the circulation in children with Raynaud's

It is now well recognised that Raynaud's phenomenon can affect children as well as adults. Even very young children can be affected. Doctors looking after children with Raynaud's always need to ask themselves whether this is primary Raynaud's phenomenon, or whether there might be another associated condition. When assessing adults with Raynaud's, two of the tests which can be used to obtain further information are nailfold capillaroscopy (when the small blood vessels beneath the finger-nails are examined under a microscope) and thermography. Thermography involves imaging the hand with an infra-red camera. This gives a measurement of temperature, which is an indirect way of measuring blood flow. Usually what is examined is the temperature response of the hand after a cold challenge (placing the hand in cold water).

At Hope Hospital we have undertaken a small study to see whether the techniques of nailfold microscopy and thermography are feasible in children. Problems which we anticipated included that children might have difficulty keeping their hands still in an unfamiliar environment. However, we found that children over the age of 6 years were able to co-operate very well with the testing. We also found that children with Raynaud's did not rewarm after a cold challenge (measuring temperature by thermography) as well as children without Raynaud's. Therefore these techniques may be useful in children, at least over the age of 6 years, and now form part of our routine assessment of children with Raynaud's. The study has recently been reported in the Journal of Rheumatology.

Dr. Ariane Herrick,
Hope Hospital, Salford

How can treatment of scleroderma be improved?

In a recent article in the British Medical Journal, Professor Carol Black stressed the importance of a national database of all cases and entering patients into trials. Systemic sclerosis is a rare disease (about 10 cases per million per year) and for which at present no cure exists. However, much can be done to alleviate the organ based complications of the condition, and many different agents are used in an attempt to modify disease progression.

Professor Black states:

Unfortunately, few drugs have been properly evaluated in clinical trials and even the standard treatments are not of proved efficacy. More aggressive therapies are now being tried in some centres - for example, immunoablation with autologous peripheral stem cell rescue - and there is an urgent need to compare these novel regimens with standard treatments. How can we improve the management of this condition and ensure that management is based on the best possible evidence?

Research over the past 20 years has led to a clearer understanding of the cellular and molecular pathology of systemic sclerosis and implicated new causal agents. Substantial advances have also been made in disease assessment and in the detection and monitoring of visceral complications, especially interstitial lung fibrosis, pulmonary hypertension, and vascular disease. Risk stratification based on autoantibody profiles and HLA typing together with the results of specialised tests such as DTPA lung scanning, high resolution computed tomography (CT scanning), and broncho alveolar lavage have permitted more accurate identification of patient subgroups at increased risk of particular complications. For example, autoantibodies directed against RNA polymerase 1 or 111 have been associated with increased risk of renal crisis and anti-topoisomerase antibodies with pulmonary fibrosis.

Anticentromere antibodies are associated with limited cutaneous scleroderma, the subset in which isolated pulmonary hypertension most often occurs. Doppler echo cardiography has been shown to be an effective non-invasive technique for detecting scleroderma associated pulmonary hypertension, provides a useful means of screening patients at risk, and allows earlier diagnosis of symptomatic cases. Standardised methods of severity assessment have now been developed by an international committee, which should allow the comparison of cases in different centres. The main treatment used worldwide for diffuse skin disease has for many years been D-penicillamine, though alpha and gamma interferon, methotrexate, and relaxin have been trialed more recently. Options now exist for treating the main complications, such as prostacyclin (iloprost and flolan) infusions for vascular complications such as severe Raynaud's phenomenon, skin ulceration, and pulmonary hypertension. Active fibrosing alveolitis is currently treated in most centres by either oral cyclophosphamide and corticosteroids or intravenous cyclophosphamide, with encouraging results. Less serious complications such as reflux oesophagitis can be dramatically relieved using proton pump inhibitors. However, the use of these organ based treatments is largely based on small studies or experience with other diseases, and their use may well be improved if specific trials in scleroderma were performed. Some of these issues have been addressed in multicentre trials of interferon in Britain and D-penicillamine in America, and the data from these studies are currently being analysed.

We can now define the natural history of systemic sclerosis much better, and this allows the effectiveness of established treatments as well as potential new ones to be examined. Moreover, the growing understanding of pathogenetic mechanisms at cellular, molecular, and genetic levels may eventually lead to specific targeted therapy.

Although many trials have been performed in scleroderma, there has been a lack of statistical power and other methodological problems have often prevented reliable interpretation.

How can this situation be improved?

One way would be to establish a central database for new cases of systemic sclerosis and to maintain a minimum data set on all cases. This would also provide the infrastructure for multicentre clinical trials. Good examples of coordinated approaches to management and research exist in several disciplines, often using a 'hub and spoke arrangement of cooperating central and regional centres with an emphasis on local supervision of patients but centralised assessment. In oncology and haematology these approaches have undoubtedly improved management as well as helping to educate those involved in the various aspects of patient care. We suggest, firstly, that a national registry should be established so that protocols for national and international trials can be enabled. Secondly, standardised treatment protocols should be established by consensus, based on the evidence that does exist, probably through the national and international societies for systemic sclerosis. Thirdly, both clinicians and patients must be better educated about advances in disease assessment so that individuals at risk from certain complications may be investigated appropriately. This will provide more reliable prognoses and better quality information for patients. A centralised database will provide enough numbers of motivated patients and clinicians to permit high quality clinical trials to be undertaken, which the disease and its sufferers deserve.

Professor Carol Black
on behalf of the U.K. Scleroderma Study Group

Over 70% benefit from trial of Seredrin

We have been delighted to hear from members who took part in this non-clinical study of Seredrin. It is only by doing studies of this nature amongst people who have Raynaud's that we can be convinced of the value of taking studies further into clinical trials. Results have indicated that over 70% of those who took part found some benefit for their Raynaud's.

75% of the respondents took the whole four months course. Out of the 251 who returned their questionnaires within the time scale given, 79% were female and 14% male, 57% live in the South, whilst 43% live in the North. 72% of the respondents felt that Seredrin had helped their Raynaud's condition over the six month period. If the sample is restricted to those who completed the full course of Seredrin, 81% of the respondents felt that Seredrin had helped their Raynaud's.

Of the actual benefits perceived, 24% said that they felt warmer, 21% felt that their mind was more alert and 11% also felt that there was less pain or joint aches in their arms and legs.

Those not completing the course (61) were asked for reasons. Many of the reasons do not reflect on the Seredrin itself. 11% responded that 'other treatments took priority', 23% had forgotten doses or were still taking the course and a further 20% had had to interrupt the course through holiday or illness. One respondent stopped taking Seredrin because she became pregnant and another stopped on doctor's orders. 4% stopped the course because of the warmer weather and 18% did not complete the course because of the side effects they experienced and a further 9% found no benefit from the Seredrin and therefore stopped taking the course. Side effects included headaches and hot flushes. Some mentioned/realised that the side effects may have been due to other factors and not to Seredrin.

The following are a few quotations taken from the questionnaires of those who found benefit:

> *"I felt generally in better health, helped by the gradual increase in confidence that my extremities were less likely to seize up".*
>
> *"I had no chilblains this year for the first time in years".*
>
> *"I am feeling more alert with more energy".*
>
> *"I am feeling better in myself and my circulation has improved".*
>
> *"Significant help to Raynaud's in my hands".*
>
> *"I felt more mentally alert".*
>
> *"I seemed brighter and happier".*
>
> *"Helped me sleep better".*
>
> *"My whole body feels warm".*
>
> *"Had better brain activity".*

The following letters are from members who found significant help from taking Seredrin:

"I took part in the recent trial of Seredrin High Strength Ginkgo Biloba for my primary Raynaud's and was delighted at the improvement in my condition. I live in Shetland where we have a lot of harsh winds. I have previously suffered from permanent cold feet and chilblains in the winter. Also my fingers would go white and numb almost as soon as I left the house, especially when driving the car. Since taking the Seredrin, I noticed an improvement in my condition almost immediately and within a month my symptoms had virtually disappeared. If it is very cold, one finger on my right hand still goes white but only from the top joint. I would also say that my circulation feels better all round, my cheeks and ears do not go burning hot after being cold and I felt more alert and energetic. I am therefore now an ardent enthusiast of Seredrin High Strength Ginkgo Biloba with Phytosome and will continue to use it. I would like to thank the Association for allowing me to take part in the trial, without which I probably would never have discovered this product".

Barbara Henry

"During the whole four months of trial I only had two attacks on my fingers, but my toes had none. I cannot express how much the quality of life has improved for me since then. With regular training throughout the whole winter, this has enabled me to race better and faster in the new spring season, competing more confidently in the knowledge that good winter training was my base to success. I had probably been suffering from Raynaud's for quite a few years before it finally got diagnosed only three or four years ago. I am normally an extremely fit and healthy athlete, competing in both running and duathlons or triathlons. The summer time was my 'season' when I would excel in what I enjoy most, winning the odd trophy here and there. Come winter though, the picture was a completely different one - chilblains on both big toes would stop me from running altogether because of the immense pain, cycling was out of the question because my fingers were too cold to safely steer the bicycle or change gears, and swimming triggered off attacks most of the time during the winter. Various medication was tried after the diagnosis which tended to make me feel sick or interfered with my normally very good vision. Then I had my 'misery' published in the Raynaud's & Scleroderma Association publication, Hot News, in search for some fellow sufferers. Along came Virginia Lumbden, another sufferer from Raynaud's who pointed me into the direction of ginkgo biloba. She advised me where to get it from and I started the tablets immediately. The result was pretty good: I was able to train through most of the winter days, my hands were very much better and did not suffer as many attacks as usual, but unfortunately I was still developing the odd chilblain on my big toes which took some time to go away. Anyway, things were a lot brighter than they used to be, and I was most grateful to the Raynaud's & Scleroderma Association for publishing my letter, thus enabling Virginia to get in contact with me.

Little did I know how much more things would improve, when the Raynaud's & Scleroderma Association asked their members if they would like to take part in new Ginkgo biloba trials with a product called Seredrin. As you can imagine, I was only too keen to oblige. I eagerly awaited the four months supply that came through the post and when it came I could hardly wait to open the packet. Well, I could hardly believe it, after only one week my chilblains healed up and none have come back since then! My body core temperature definitely went up which also made my fingers warm. I certainly will not miss out on Seredrin again, especially during the autumn and winter months".

To all fellow sufferers out there, Seredrin is well worth a try!

Petra Otto

"Since my early 20's (I am now 43) I have suffered from Raynaud's. Winters became a nightmare of daily attacks in my hands and feet and I had chilblains everywhere. I run a little santuary for small animals and coming and going to my garden sheds to see to them all was a very painful business. I wanted to write and tell you that since I went on the Seredrin trial it has done wonders for me. Obviously I still suffer from the cold and have to be careful but I can honestly say that the only attacks which have happened are when I have forgotten to take the tablets. The chilblains have completely gone. I would certainly recommend Seredrin to anyone with circulation problems".

Sandra Arnold

Profile of artist Paul Klee

Paul Klee

Paul Klee was born in December 1879 near Berne, Switzerland, the son of a Swiss mother and a German father. During his life, through his works, Klee attempted to open up an inner world for himself in which fantasy, dreams and the poetry of nature interlock.

In 1935 Klee was diagnosed as having measles but this turned out to be wrong and he fell seriously ill with progressive scleroderma. At that time very few treatments were available and Klee felt his situation was utterly hopeless. His work stagnated and only 25 items of his work were listed for 1936.

Klee went away twice during that year for treatment to a health resort. To begin with he was paralysed with fear by the thought of having to die soon. However in his final years he considerably increased his productivity again. In 1937 he created 264 works, in 1938 the total was 489 and the list for 1939 runs to 1,254 pictures - more than ever before in one year. His style changed once more and the pictures gradually became larger. The subjects covered by the pictures continued to express his twofold view of life, examining his personal fate and the political situation in Germany but still full of wit and his joy in depicting life. An example is Musiker (Musician) painted in 1937 with its 'matchstick man' effect and thick black lines, it seems to depict Klee's inner conflicts.

He could take only liquid food, specially prepared and he had to watch carefully for the desire and opportunity to eat. But that was a subject he would not discuss. He accepted his illness, he never complained and never devoted any particular attention to it. The best way of overcoming it was to integrate it through discipline into his work and daily life. His subconscious told him that he had to hurry, that time was pressing and death - as can be seen from many of his pictures - was a constant and inexorable threat. What struggles both physical and mental, lay behind this labour no one I would ever know for Klee was a man of great silences.

Paul Klee did not die in Berne but in Ticino where he had gone for further treatment in May. He was admitted to hospital in Locarno where he died on 29th June 1940. His painting big Stilleben (Still Life) was still standing unsigned on his easel in his flat. This upright picture differs greatly in style from his previous works. Klee had a photograph of himself taken in front of the picture on his 60th Birthday. This was certainly not a coincidence. It is not known why he did not sign it nor why he placed it on his easel before leaving for Locarno. It has been said that he regarded this picture which is now generally called Stilleben (Still Life) but which he did not give a title, as his artistic legacy.

A great example

"My name is Laura O'Connor and I was featured in the Summer newsletter in 1995 when I was 10 years old. I am now 13. On the 28th August 1996, I went into Great Ormond Street Hospital to have a below the knee amputation. The cause of my amputation was Linear Morphea scleroderma which I had since I was about 3. It started off not too badly then gradually got worse over the years leading up to my amputation. I was in a lot of pain with my leg and I had to walk with the aid of crutches, because of my limp and the pain was so bad. My foot was rigid and twisted outwards.

I decided that to have my leg amputated would give me a better life than a life in a wheelchair. After the operation I stayed in hospital for 8 days. My first dressing was taken off one or two days before I left. This is usually done under anaesthetic. Most of the time

Laura O Connor

when I first got home from hospital I slept. But after the first couple of weeks all I had to do was wait for the wound to heal. I went back up to Great Ormond Street every other day, which from West Mersea near Colchester is quite a long car drive. I had a few complications with my healing so the fitting of my leg was delayed. I also had a home tutor who came every school day for about an hour. After my leg had healed completely I had my artificial leg fitted at Christmas 1996. When I first stood up on my false leg it felt really good to be standing up straight which I hadn't really felt before in my life. I had physiotherapy to help me to walk. but quite a lot of it was practice at home.

After two weeks I could walk confidently without a walking stick and I also attended school. My friends were very supportive, both before the operation and now, and they treat me normally. The best thing is now I can do everything with them. Having my leg amputated has given me a lot of confidence, especially in my clothes. A lot of people stare at my outrageous clothes, not the way I walk like they used to. I do everything - I go to town shopping for hours, go to the cinema and go bowling. I also have singing lessons which I go to every Saturday morning. Most of the time I listen to music; my favourite singer is Whitney Houston, and one day I hope to sing like her. I went to see her sing live in Manchester in July. She was brilliant. When I attended a football match at Wembley I was jumping around like everyone else (especially when Colchester won 1-0 to Torquay) and nobody could tell I had a false leg!'

Laura O Connor

A battle with pride

"I was diagnosed as having scleroderma in 1991 and referred to the Royal Free in 1992. I will never forget the relief and joy of meeting and talking with other people who had scleroderma. The first evening I spent in the day room talking about problems with a few others - often very mundane things - for example I still remember discussing how irritating it was not being able to open jars and packaging when in the house alone. The absolute frustration of wanting a marmite sandwich and having to settle for a marmalade one instead because I was unable to get the lid off!

For me scleroderma has meant a continual battle with my pride. Now I will ask anyone who is passing if they will open a jar, a packet of biscuits or individual little pots, but at one time I would rather go without than ask for help. My feet have been a problem from the beginning. It was like walking on Brighton beach without shoes. The only comfortable ones were men's trainers but these are not appropriate for special occasions. A friend's wedding or an evening out were a real problem. Whether to wear a smart pair of shoes or swallow my pride and have comfortable feet.

I had difficulty in doing the housework and eventually got a lady in to help. Once again, my pride had to be overcome. To begin with I used to go to the bottom of the garden because I didn't like watching her do jobs which I felt I should do. I was very ungrateful! I developed osteoporosis and was given a wheelchair but I took weeks to actually go out in it. Pride again - what would people say? What would people think? It has taken me years to realise that people want to help. It brings out the best in young and old alike if only I would let them help. My mother taught me that it is better to give than to receive". I am trying to teach my children that to give and receive gracefully is even better".

Anne Jones

1998 Raynaud's Swimalong raises over £13,600

From left to right, Bridget Ferguson, Anne Mawdsley, Dr. Chris Steele (ITV's This Morning's resident doctor), David Wilkie and Jo Kaddish, preparing for the start of the Swimalong.

Before Chris Steele started the event the photographers present seemed to go crazy, with their flash bulbs. I have never seen so many cameras and it was somewhat daunting. We were photographed from every angle one could imagine and it all seemed very unreal. That is until we were poised to dive in and start the swim. Then reality hit and 50 lengths seemed a very long way. After all the buildup, the final rush of adrenalin caused me to have difficulty breathing which was something I hadn't bargained for, nor experienced in training. David and I were spurred on during the swim by friends and members who were attending the Conference and I apologise to those of you who thought I wasn't going to make it. I have to admit that it was probably the longest twenty minutes of my life and yes, it was a struggle but had it been easy it wouldn't have been a challenge! David on the other hand gave much pleasure to the spectators while doing a leisurely 114 lengths.

The swim was followed by a dinner sponsored by Health Perception (who also funded the Champagne Reception) and attended by our guests Dr. Chris Steele and his wife Monica, and of course David Wilkie together with his partner Helen. After a superb dinner David gave a most interesting and humourous account of his swimming career and explained how he became interested in health food supplements. Those present had the opportunity to hold a real Olympic gold medal which David won in 1976 and had brought with him. Chris Steele has promised to help bring about a greater awareness of Raynaud's and Scleroderma through his media work.

Anne Mawdsley

National and International News Winter 1998

National Activities

Since the last newsletter, the U.K. Scleroderma Study Group has had a very useful meeting. One of the major points of discussion at the meeting was clinical trials. We now have trials that are either up and running, or trials that are in preparation. The one we are trying most hard to recruit to at the moment is a trial for patients with pulmonary fibrosis. This trial will probably run for the next 2-3 years. It is for patients with early disease, and it is really trying to find out how effective drugs such as cyclophosphamide and azathioprine are in stopping the spread of the fibrosis. We need over a hundred patients for this study and therefore we are all busily recruiting as fast as we can.

The second study is for patients with early pulmonary hypertension. As you know, this is one of the most difficult problems in scleroderma and we are now looking for patients with early disease who would be willing to try iloprost in its oral form, rather than via injection. This trial is what we call a 'placebo controlled trial'. It means that half the patients on the trial will not receive the medication. Sometimes patients find this difficult to understand, but in very early pulmonary hypertension it is not a dangerous thing to do and it is the quickest way of us trying to find out how effective Iloprost, given in an oral form, will be. There are several other trials which are being planned, some of which we hope will start in the middle of next year or sooner.

In order to help recruitment to trials we are now starting a central register. We hope that this register will encourage doctors to offer their patients for multi centre studies. We believe that this will enable us to do the trials more quickly and efficiently and permit patients to try new medication as quickly as possible. We also recently enlarged the membership of the group; Dr. R Moots a Rheumatologist, from Liverpool, and Dr. Christopher Lovell a Dermatologist, from Bath, will add their expertise and enthusiasm to the group. We very much hope at our next meeting that a Paediatric Rheumatologist will join us, as children with scleroderma, although not many in number, have numerous problems which we need to address. I mentioned in the previous newsletter that bone marrow transplantation is now being performed around the world for patients with autoimmune connective tissue diseases, including patients with systemic sclerosis.

This is still very experimental, but as you see below when I talk about international affairs, there have been two meetings discussing this form of therapy in the last few months. A new skin preparation is being developed by a company in Israel. The drug, called Halofluginone, has been incorporated into a cream. This preparation is about to go into pilot studies and there will be an opportunity in the first pilot study to treat a few patients in the United Kingdom. It is hoped that this cream will permit the softening of the skin, which would be a tremendous help to all of our patients.

International Activities

Since I last wrote there have been at least four meetings at which scleroderma has been an important point of discussion. The first was the Bi-annual Scleroderma Research Workshop. This took place in Boston and was organised by Dr. Korn and myself. It is a meeting that looks at the scientific advances that have occurred in the field of scleroderma and tries very hard to look to the future and see which might be the most important areas to pursue. It was an extremely well attended and exciting meeting. The feedback we have received has been excellent and we look forward to having the next one in the United Kingdom in Oxford in the year 2000. In addition at the Boston meeting, we had a symposium on childhood scleroderma. This meeting tried to bring together the doctors in both Canada, North America and Europe who were interested in childhood scleroderma. As a result of this meeting we have agreed to try and design an international protocol for a drug trial in childhood scleroderma.

I went to Toronto in September to take this project further forward, and I hope very much by the early spring that we will have not only a protocol which we can all use, but also a much closer international collaboration. In addition in September, there was an important meeting on fibrosis in Boston. Fibrosis is a major problem in scleroderma and Dr. Abraham represented us at that meeting. Of course the meeting discussed fibrosis which occurs in many conditions other than scleroderma, for example atherosclerosis, kidney sclerosis, liver sclerosis and the scarring which occurs after surgery. It was however, very important for David to meet research workers who are trying to understand fibrosis in other diseases, in case there was anything which might be very important to our understanding of systemic sclerosis. David found the meeting very stimulating and came back with some new ideas and additional collaborators.

In the last three months there have been two meetings on bone marrow transplantation. A one day meeting was held in America at which we were represented and a European meeting was organised in Basle by Professor Tyndall and colleagues. The one day meeting in America was to look at the protocols which were already available and to look to the future to plan controlled trials. It was obvious from this meeting that one of the diseases which features most frequently in discussion was scleroderma. Once more preliminary data has been collected and now a controlled trial will be planned. The Basle meeting was extremely well attended and very well organised. Many diseases were discussed and scleroderma again featured prominently in the discussion. To date, twenty five patients throughout Europe and America have received a bone marrow transplant for scleroderma. It is really too early days to state whether this procedure completely stops the disease, but there was enthusiasm to continue to collect more information and then to see which of the regimes we are using are the most effective. At the moment there are several different ways of performing a bone marrow transplant and it is useful that different groups are using different methods so that we can eventually compare the results.

I also attended two European meetings about blood vessels. It is very encouraging to see so many groups are now interested in the damage which occurs to blood vessels in scleroderma. I very much enjoyed meeting people from specialities other than my own, learning from them and setting up new collaborations. In November I will be going to the American College of Rheumatology meeting in San Diego, together with lots of U.K. rheumatologists. There will not only be a meeting of the Scleroderma Trials Consortium, but also a bone marrow meeting and a special symposium on scleroderma. This is all good news because it gives the disease a high profile and emphasises the need for both more clinical and basic research.

Professor Carol Black

Elene Susol

Studies of the Genetics of Raynaud's Phenomenon and Systemic Sclerosis

Within the Epidemiology Research Unit at the University of Manchester, we have been investigating the cause of Raynaud's phenomenon (RP) and systemic sclerosis (SSc). One of the questions being addressed is why some individuals develop RP and/or SSc whereas others do not. The line of investigation being followed is that genetic (inherited) factors play an important role. Increasingly, it is realised that the best opportunities for the development of novel therapies lies with understanding of disease process at the level of gene sequence. Many patients have kindly donated a blood sample for use in these studies. These samples provide the DNA, which contains all the genetic information. The DNA can be directly investigated to determine whether there are differences in the genetic information from patients with RP and/or SSc compared with disease free individuals. The ultimate aim is to identify specific sequences within genes that predispose individuals to developing RP and/or SSc. These studies have already produced some interesting findings.

Families with multiple members with RP have been collected by Professor Carol Black at the Royal Free Hospital in London as part of a collaboration. Using a panel of approximately 300 genetic markers, which map along the length of each chromosome, we have studied patterns of inheritance within these families with the aim of identifying chromosomal regions which are linked to disease. We have identified markers in five regions which appear to be linked to RP, indicating that a gene/genes in these regions are important in determining susceptibility to the disease. The next step is to study these regions in more detail in order to identify the genes and understand how minor changes in their sequences, which are found more frequently in individuals with RP, contribute to the pathology of the condition. Similar techniques have been used to study the genetics of SSc. One of the features of SSc is that it is a very heterogeneous condition. There are differences, for example, in the degree of fibrosis from one patient to another. Fibrosis involves the interplay between many proteins, some which promote and others that inhibit fibrosis. In collaboration with Dr. Ariane Herrick at Hope Hospital in Salford and Dr. Neil McHugh at The Royal National Hospital for Rheumatic Diseases in Bath, we have been studying the genes of some of these proteins and preliminary results indicate that there are genetic differences between patients with SSc and individuals without SSc.

We have preliminary evidence that polymorphisms (minor variations in DNA sequence) near two fibrosis-promoting genes; transforming growth factor beta 2 (TGFB2) and tissue inhibitor of metalloproteinase I (TIMP I), may occur more frequently in patients with SSc. Interestingly the association with TIMPi is seen most strongly in patients with the limited form of SSc and TGFB2 with susceptibility to the diffuse form, suggesting that these genes may have a role in determining the degree of skin fibrosis the patient develops. We are currently carrying out further studies to confirm our findings.

I would like to take this opportunity to thank all the patients and family members who have kindly provided a blood sample for these studies and also to encourage anyone approached in the future to respond positively. Thorough understanding of the genetic basis of disease will require investigation of large numbers of affected individuals but the knowledge gained will be central to development of new treatment strategies.

Elene Susol, Postgraduate Student,
ARC Department, Manchester University

Helped by Minocycline

You may recall me writing to you singing the praises of Minocycline recently. I feel now that I must add further to my previous correspondence because so much has happened that I feel an obligation to yourself and other scleroderma sufferers to let my experiences be known. I visited my G.P. in September/October 1996, with strange feelings and discolouration in my fingers. This I now know to be Raynaud's, but at the time it was suspected as being a reactionary arthritis following a period of prolonged use of a chainsaw in my garden. At this point I was prescribed Salazopyrin but in February/March 1997 this drug completely knocked out my immune system and I was admitted into solitary isolation with a white blood cell count of '0'. This was a very frightening time. On recovery my consultant asked me if I would be prepared to try Penicillamine but because of my reaction to the previous drug it would involve weekly blood and urine tests. It was also at this stage that I was diagnosed as having the severest form of scleroderma - diffuse systemic sclerosis.

Over the next few months the disease spread quite rapidly to my forearms, legs, chest, shoulders and slightly into my face. I had difficulty in holding cutlery, pencils (I am a draughtsman), walking became a chore rather than a pleasure, and I could not even bite into an apple properly. I remained on Penicillamine until mid June this year when it was stopped because of a sudden drop in my platelet count. It was having no beneficial effect on me anyway. It was shortly after this that I saw the Hot News article on Minocycline. It was also around this time that my G.P. informed me of a sudden decline in my renal function and I was referred to a renal specialist. So that is a brief history up to and slightly beyond the point of my starting on Minocycline. Over the past three weeks or so I have been seen by my G.P., my scleroderma consultant and just a couple of days ago by my renal consultant. It appears, but in no way confirms, that the scleroderma has not only slowed down but we believe may have gone into reverse. It has all but disappeared from my chest and face, my hands are quite soft and flexible again, (my wife says that it is no longer like holding hands with an Edam cheese), and above all my renal function has returned to normal (albeit the high side of normal). I am in no way believing that Minocycline has cured or is curing my scleroderma completely, but the relief has been quite incredible, and it is thanks to the Hot News reference to the drug that all this has happened.

I understand that Minocycline is a harmless anti-biotic used for acne etc. and that taking it can cause no harm, indeed I have had no side effects, yet!

Peter Williams

A word of caution on Minocyline

Since this therapy was first reported in Hot News there have been a number of reports in America on Minocyline. We have been in touch with the Scleroderma Foundation in New York who in turn contacted the researcher responsible for the study, as well as members of their Medical Advisory Board and the American College of Rheumatology. It would appear that the press have exaggerated this as a possible but not proven, approach to treatment.

"It is regrettable that this study was announced in a press release rather than in a medical journal so that other researchers could evaluate the results in detail. This action suggests that the study results would not stand up to scientific scrutiny and concludes that the announcement was premature and the results were exaggerated".

New Recipe Book

Our thanks to Moira Ellice who put together an ideal book comprising 100 recipes sent in to her by members of the Association. It was launched at the Annual Conference and many people were delighted to see their recipes in print. Moira had worked extremely hard to get the book published and her husband Neill raised £1,500 which was matched by Barclays Bank (of which he is an employee) to fund the publication. The Foreword to the book was written by David Brooks, well known by people in the Anglia Television region where he was the weatherman for many years.

Member's News

My Experience

Felicity House

"In the autumn of 1955, quite by chance, I read an article in a magazine about Raynaud's Phenomenon and how Anne Mawdsley had founded the Raynaud's Association. I had suffered from very cold feet and general symptoms of Raynaud's for many years but what interested me most was the inclusion in the article of the associated condition, erythromelalgia. For the previous three years I had been experiencing a burning sensation, first in the feet, then slowly a progression up my legs until the lower limbs felt as if they were on fire. Hot weather made the situation far worse, and it was almost impossible to sleep at night with such constant burning despite the use of a bed cradle to lift the weight of the bed clothes from my legs.

I was already receiving treatment for Sjögren's Syndrome and cervical spondylosis and it was generally agreed by the rheumatological and neurological consultants that the burning sensations had nothing to do with the Sjögren's but was related to the severe spondylosis in my neck or the effects on my lumbar spine from operations I underwent forty years previously. Despite my repeated protests that this newer condition was quite dissimilar to existing neurological problems, I had no further help until I read that very useful article about erythromelalgia. I contacted the Raynaud's Helpline for further information and was given advice as to which Raynaud's clinic may help me. My G.P. then referred me to the Royal Free where I eventually received two iloprost infusions to ease the continuous burning. These were temporarily successful but did not prevent recurrence and I felt there must be an alternative way of treating the condition.

In June 1997 I commenced homeopathic treatment from a doctor trained in orthodox medicine but who had gradually moved across to homeopathy. To combat my very diverse symptoms from Sjögren's, Raynaud's and erythromelalgia, I was put on a special diet and remedies to overcome the auto-immune difficulties which caused not only the burning in the lower limbs but severe muscle weakness, digestive tract disorders, rigors, fatigue and other symptoms. The diet excludes foods to which I am intolerant but includes the supplements of OMEGA 3 fatty acids and the food supplement B-ALIVE. The diet causes difficulties when eating away from home and the remedies often make me feel ill for the duration of the course, but the result has been so worthwhile, giving relief from many of my symptoms.

The burning in my legs and feet almost completely ceased within a few months (my toes still burn when I am very warm or have been walking) and, after 15 months of treatment I am now able to walk, on a good day, for about a mile. For the past seven years I have been restricted to within my garden or at the very best to a quarter of a mile, as my muscles have been so very weak. A wheelchair had been very much a part of our lives during that time. It can be imagined what joy I feel being able to walk a little way along the coastal paths in the very scenic area of Dorset where we live and to be free from the constant burning pain in my legs and feet.

Throughout the years since I first contacted the Raynaud's & Scleroderma Association I have received so much help, advice and support from Anne and her staff and I would like to take this opportunity to thank them for all their hard work and kindness".

Felicity House

Iris's Story

Iris Ennis

"I was diagnosed with scleroderma in November 1989. Previous to that I had been suffering with Raynaud's, although I didn't know it at the time. In 1987 I had an operation for carpal tunnel syndrome which I understand can be connected. When I first noticed my right hand was swollen and my skin was very hard to the touch which also affected my arm, I went along to see my G.P.; I also had discolouration of the skin on various parts of my body. My G.P. suggested I had arthritis and gave me some kind of cream for the 'rash'. Somehow I knew it wasn't arthritis as I didn't have any stiffness or pain so I requested a second opinion and was sent for an x-ray which proved negative. I was then referred to a skin specialist who performed a biopsy and I was then diagnosed with scleroderma. I had never heard of scleroderma and the doctor at my local hospital was very vague about the condition. Suffice to say, it could spread over my whole body and my internal organs may also be affected. With those words ringing in my ears and questions flashing through my mind, he shook hands with me and wished me Good Luck. He ended by saying that there was no cure and no treatment. I was devastated and felt I was going to die. How could I explain to my family? Six months passed and I was summoned to the hospital again, by which time the disease had spread to my legs, stomach and midriff and I had severe reflux problems.

I was seen by another doctor who suggested I attend London's Royal Free Hospital to see Professor Black. Since then I have never looked back. I was reassured that treatment was available (but no cure). I made frequent visits to the Royal Free in the next few months for a series of tests and scans and to the Brompton for lung function tests. Although I have gone on to develop pulmonary hypertension and attend my local hospital every four months for iloprost infusion, I have learned a great deal about the condition and feel confident about the future. The help given to me by Professor Black and her team and the information in Hot News has given me reassurance. I do tend to feel rather isolated at home as I know of no-one else locally with the same complaint but I know there are helplines I can contact if need be".

Iris Ennis

Icy Fingers Poster Campaign

We were delighted that Schering Health Care Ltd sponsored our Awareness Campaign on 2000 bus stops nationwide. Saatchi & Saatchi Healthcare once again came to our aid by creating a new poster with the icy hands but with different wording. The design of the Icy Hands remains the same but the wording has been changed to read:

'People with Raynaud's have to keep their hands in their pockets. What's Your Excuse?'

These posters were put up on adshels nationwide and the bulk of them have been sponsored by Schering Health Care Ltd., together with a smaller batch by Astra Pharmaceuticals. We are most appreciative for this support. Merck Pharmaceuticals have been generous in their support following on from the Waiting Room Information Service, which placed 95,000 of our leaflets in doctors' surgeries nationwide and to which we had an excellent response. They have recently sponsored new display panels for our notice boards and folders depicting the icy hands logo, which will be used for sending medical packs to health professionals.

It is interesting that in addition to the hundreds of calls stating what a brilliant poster it is, we had a couple of calls from people saying that they felt the icy hands were rather shocking. However, after talking with them and explaining that the idea was to get across the message that for someone with Raynaud's, the most common description is "my hands feels like blocks of ice', they appreciated the meaning behind the illustration. For many years we have tried to describe the condition but without having a graphic to actually capture the feeling of excruciating pain during an attack, it has been difficult to get the message across. Saatchi & Saatchi have created what most people would describe as a brilliant illustration which causes non sufferers to think and sufferers to say at last "That is exactly what it feels like".

The campaign last winter was the most successful we have ever had and we are confident that this winter will bring an equally good response. We are now seeking sponsorship to cover posters on the mainline railway stations.

Some of the comments we have received include the following:

"Wow, what a spectacular poster presentation. I am working over here in the week and live in Belgium. My wife has scleroderma and her hands are always just as you have described so spectacularly on the poster - they are like ice. I didn't realise that the cold hands and the scleroderma were connected".

"Just been diagnosed, seen poster and delighted to know there was an Association. The picture of the hands show exactly how it feels".

"I was travelling to Brixham from Paignton recently and saw one of your posters on a bus shelter in Dartmouth Road just on leaving Paignton. Very impressive!".

"I was only diagnosed last week and today came from the underground onto Euston Station and saw your poster. Brilliant timing! I didn't know there was an Association".

Research News

A Gift Warmly Received

Staff in the Department of Rheumatology, which is a referral centre for Raynaud's and scleroderma patients throughout the North West, are very grateful for the gift of a thermographic camera. The camera was presented by the Raynaud's & Scleroderma Association, which has previously donated equipment to the Department. The camera is used primarily for imaging the hands of patients with Raynaud's who are extremely sensitive to cold. It records surface temperature which is an indirect indication of blood temperature. Consultant Rheumatologist Dr. Ariane Herrick said "We are extremely grateful to the Association for their gift. It replaces a previous camera which was broken beyond repair. Thermographic equipment provides very valuable information when investigating Raynaud's and with our major interest in the management of blood flow it will be very well used".

Dr. Ariane Herrick & Tonia Moore

The above was published in The Gen., a newsletter for Salford Royal Hospital

David Wilkie MBE

New Patron

We are delighted to announce that Olympic Swimmer David Wilkie MBE has accepted our invitation to become a patron of the Association. At our Annual Conference last year David had the opportunity to meet with and talk to so many people with Raynaud's and scleroderma. He was greatly moved by the courage with which people coped with their problems and is pleased to be able to support the Association in whatever way he can.

How growth factors control the thickening of tissues in scleroderma

Professor Carol Black, Royal Free Hospital has been awarded two grants.

The first is a combined application with Dr. David Abraham to look at how growth factors control the thickening of tissues in scleroderma.

Summary

One of the major problems of scleroderma is thickening of the skin and internal organs. This thickening, which is due to the production of more connective tissue than is needed, causes the organs to function poorly and may eventually result in organ failure and premature death. One of the major components of the connective tissue is the protein called collagen. Collagen gives the tissues in the body their structure, strength and resilience. The cells which make collagen and which control the amount of connective tissue in the body are called fibroblasts. In scleroderma there is an 'over activity' of these fibroblasts which results in them producing too much collagen and too much of specialised growth factors which in turn enhance even more collagen production by these fibroblasts, thus exacerbating the disease process. These growth factors which are soluble and can be found circulating in the blood stream, are like keys which fit into specific locks or receptors that are found on the surface of cells. Only cells that have the unique lock will respond to a given key. In the case of growth factor keys the fibroblast responds by growing faster and producing more collagen.

One of the most important growth factors or keys that scleroderma fibroblasts produce in excess is called connective tissue growth factor (CTGF). We think the reason why scleroderma fibroblasts produce more CTGF is that the fibroblasts express more of the specific lock or receptor that CTGF can fit. Cells that do not have the specific lock cannot recognise CTGF or rather only cells expressing CTGF receptor are able to respond to the growth factor. The aim of this project is to find out more about these cell surface locks which we believe are driving the production of collagen and ultimately the disease. We would then like to be able to stop the production of the receptors or block their function by specialised therapy and thereby stop the fibrosis.

Our overall goal is therefore to increase our understanding of the role of the receptor for connective tissue growth factor in scleroderma. This information will allow us to develop a useful therapy in the form of drugs or receptor antagonists (blocking agents) that are able to regulate the amount of CTGF receptors on the fibroblasts. In the long-term it may also be possible to design other therapeutic approaches even perhaps to target affected tissues, once we know more about the nature of the CTGF receptors.

The second application from Professor Black was with Dr. Abraham and Professor Bruckdorfer entitled 'Abnormal blood development in Systemic Sclerosis'.

Summary

Patients with scleroderma, in addition to the many problems they endure from abnormal collagen metabolism in the skin and other organs, have further difficulties associated with the abnormal nature and functioning of their blood vessels. These include Raynaud's phenomenon and also hyperactivity of blood platelets, both of which may arise from abnormalities in the cells that line the blood vessels and other cell types. These vascular abnormalities may underly the abnormalities with collagen metabolism. Remodelling of blood vessels is a normal process, but in some diseases this may give rise to arrangements of the vessel which are abnormal. The formation of blood vessels is a closely regulated process which begins during foetal development and continues during adulthood. There is increasing recognition that a protein tissue factor is intimately involved in this process. Historically it was always considered to be involved in the coagulation mechanism, but now this new role has been linked with it. Very recently, some Japanese workers showed that tissue factor protein was abnormally expressed in some cells obtained from the lungs of patients with scleroderma.

The main aim of the work is to establish whether this abnormal expression of tissue factor occurs in other cells in these patients, particularly those which are readily available i.e. the skin and the blood. Preliminary tests suggest that it is there, but further work is required to make this conclusive. We would seek to determine whether an agent in the serum of the patients is responsible for any such changes by incubating the patient serum with cells from healthy individuals. We should be able to establish these facts in just over a year. This would spawn new investigations of the mechanisms by which these changes could occur. In our previous work on tissue factor, we have discovered that certain small fragments of naturally occurring proteins are excellent inhibitors of the activity of tissue factor. We will then determine whether these substances would be effective against any abnormal expression of tissue factor in scleroderma cells with a view to using them in future therapies.

Professor Carol Black,
Royal Free Hospital, London

Dr. Anne Crilly

TGFß gene polymorphisms in scleroderma

Dr. Rajan Madhok

A grant was awarded to Drs. Rajan Madhok and Anne Crilly at Glasgow Royal Infirmary

Summary

Scleroderma (SSc) or Progressive Systemic Sclerosis (PSS) is a generalised connective tissue disorder which predominantly occurs in females. The cause of the disease is unknown although environmental factors along with the individual's genetic make up may influence the development of the condition. It is already well established that expression of a number of proteins such as growth factors and cytokines is influenced by an individual's genetic makeup. Many of the genes which code various protein mediators have been found to be highly polymorphic i.e. differences exist between individuals. In turn, these polymorphisms can result in changes in the level of expression of a particular protein. A feature of SSc is an over expression of a number of proteins in areas affected by the disease. One of these proteins is transforming growth factor ß (TGFß). The aim of this study is to look at TGFß polymorphisms in patients with SSc or CREST and compare them to a group of controls. We believe that in undertaking this study we will be able to establish whether there is a genetic predisposition to developing this condition and also whether patients can be divided into subsets of disease depending on the polymorphism they carry.

Dr. Rajan Madhok

Candidate Gene Investigation in Systemic Sclerosis

Grant awarded to Dr. Jane Worthington at the ARC Epidemiology Research Unit at Manchester University.

Summary

Systemic sclerosis (SSc) is a complex disease with excessive fibrosis as a hallmark. A number of observations indicate that there is an inherited (genetic) element to SSc and this may not only determine susceptibility to SSc but also the amount of fibrosis. Fibrosis is a normal process involving a large number of proteins. Our hypothesis is that affected individuals have minor differences in a number of these proteins causing a dysregulation in fibrosis. We believe that such differences will be encoded in the genes for these proteins. Thus, if an individual inherits a critical number or combination of abnormal genes they may be susceptible to developing systemic sclerosis.

We have begun studying a number of the genes that encode proteins involved in fibrosis, using genetic markers to look for evidence of differences between patients with SSc and healthy controls. We have preliminary data that two such proteins, Transforming Growth Factor Beta 2 (TGF152) and Tissue Inhibitor of Metalloproteinases-1 (TIMP 1) may be different in affected individuals and may also have a role in determining the extent of fibrosis the patient develops.

In this project we plan to further validate these preliminary findings by examining a larger group of patients and looking in a separate group of Black American patients with SSc, known to suffer a particularly severe form of disease with widespread fibrosis. It will be our aim to study the genes for TGF132 and TIMP 1 in detail, looking for differences in the gene sequences in affected and unaffected individuals. These differences may be as little as one base pair and may affect regulation of the synthesis of protein or may lead to alteration in structure or function. These differences may not only be involved in the genetic susceptibility to SSc, but also determine the extent of fibrosis.

These studies will allow us to better understand the genetic susceptibility to SSc and to fibrosis. Clearly, understanding a disease process at the molecular level will lead to the identification.

Dr. Jane Worthington

Dynamic Responses in Nailfold Capillary Permeability in Patients with Systemic Sclerosis

Grant awarded to Dr. Ariane Herrick at Hope Hospital.

Summary

Doctors caring for patients with scleroderma (systemic sclerosis) do not fully understand the underlying disease process. However, we know that there are abnormalities of the very small blood vessels, called capillaries. These are too small to see directly, but it is possible to study them if we look at the edge of the fingernail (the nailbed) through a microscope. This led to the technique of nailfold microscopy, which is available in centres with a special interest in scleroderma and related conditions. Patients with scleroderma usually have abnormal capillaries - they are enlarged and fewer in number than in healthy individuals. We also know that in patients with scleroderma the capillaries are abnormally 'leaky'. This can be demonstrated using a technique called intravital nailfold capillaroscopy (also known as dynamic fluorescence video microscopy). This is an extension of nailfold microscopy and involves injecting a dye (sodium fluorescein) intravenously. This dye is also used by ophthalmologists studying eye disease. The dye injection involves a small risk of an allergic reaction, but this is very unlikely if suitable precautions are taken.

In the Rheumatology Department at Hope Hospital, we have a special interest in nailfold microscopy and we are currently undertaking a study to improve ways of measuring the capillary abnormalities which occur in patients with scleroderma. The aim of the proposed study is to develop the technique of intravital nailfold microscopy, because we believe that this technique has considerable potential in helping us to find out more about why patients with scleroderma have leaky capillaries. It is very important to gain as much information as possible from the pictures which are obtained, and we believe that we can improve considerably upon the method of image analysis which has been used in previous studies using this technique. The project will be collaborative between the University of Manchester Departments of Rheumatology and Medical Biophysics. Therefore the first step is to improve upon existing methods of analysing the images obtained from intravital nailfold microscopy. Once developed, we shall use our improved image analysis technique to measure nailfold capillary leakage in patients with scleroderma before and after one month's treatment with Larginine, and in other patients with scleroderma before and after one month's treatment with vitamin C (ascorbic acid). L-arginine is a precursor of nitric oxide, which is believed to be important in scleroderma, although we are not exactly sure of its role. Vitamin C (ascorbic acid) is an antioxidant therapy, and we believe that supplementation with vitamin C may reduce capillary leakage.

We hope that the proposed project will help us understand more about why capillaries are leaky in scleroderma. Damage to small blood vessels is crucial, and so understanding more about the damage/leakiness is an important part of scleroderma research, especially if it points us in the direction of new forms of treatment. In the longer term, the technique will be used to measure nailfold capillary leakiness to help us to evaluate other forms of therapy for scleroderma.

Dr. Ariane Herrick, Senior Lecturer in Rheumatology,
Hope Hospital Manchester

Members' Section

The tale of a recovering pessimist

"I really hate it when people, usually men on building sites, tell me to "cheer up luv it might never happen". Well it has happened, I want to shout, "I have Raynaud's and scleroderma and polymyositis and Sjögren's and osteoarthritis and glaucoma and lichen planus". My face in repose is lugubrious and builders are no different from anyone else, they feel better for being smiled on. As a natural born pessimist my body language reflects my lifelong addiction - long face and bowed shoulders. All that has changed since I converted to optimism. I still have my cocktail of conditions but there's no more shouting from the scaffolding. As a recovering pessimist life is hard work but a lot more amusing. I walk taller and anticipate things with pleasure instead of foreboding - well almost. The hard work lies in keeping it going after the euphoria has worn off

Heather Redmond

Conversion happened quite suddenly last year when a fridge freezer I had bought was delivered while I was out with my daughter, despite asking to be notified beforehand. Pessimists always need to be prepared for the worst and this was the worst. I went into overdrive. The shop hadn't phoned me, I wasn't prepared, my neighbour might not have been around to let them in and who was going to shift the thing and so on. I suddenly heard myself and was shocked. Even Nikki, who is used to my negative mantras, was shocked and told me off - like I was really lucky that my shiny new fridge had just arrived - no problems and no effort on my part - and what did I think daughters were for if not to heave fridges around!

Sustaining a positive attitude entails unlearning a lot of bad habits. Cups become half full instead of half empty and I don't get into the 'yes but' game. "Have you thought about....?" "Yes I have but "This can be kept going indefinitely until family and friends are thoroughly wound up. In spite of a negative outlook where my health is concerned, I have always been a fighter. A priority in that fight to maintain myself, has been information about what is happening and what could happen to my body. As a pessimist it was important to know about all possible outcomes so that I could prepare for the worst. As an optimist information is still important but the difference now is that I know the worst doesn't always happen and if it does - I will probably cope".

Heather Redmond

Kim has scleroderma under control

Kim Fligelstone

"I thought I would write and update you on my new dialysis machine which was delivered and fitted last October, although I didn't start using it until November. The first night was a disaster mainly because I was frightened of making a mistake and I didn't read the manual properly. Anyway it was an evening and morning of phoning the 24 hour help line and learning much more on the job, so to speak, than when practising at the hospital. Now that I have had some time to adjust to my new machine, I can write and thank the Association for all the work you did in securing the funding to purchase it. This machine wouldn't be suitable for all dialysis patients but it is perfect for me in that it has one huge advantage over the old one because it heats the fluid solution to body temperature throughout the night. For the first time in 7 years I am not woken up by fluid that isn't quite warm enough when it enters my peritoneum (a membrane surrounding the kidneys and stomach) during the night. I need to be a little more organised and programme the machine to start heating the fluid 2 hours before I intend to start dialysing. When it's ready I wash my hands thoroughly and load the tubing and weigh bag, wash my hands again, this time for a full 3 minutes, then attach myself to the machine, go to bed and sleep. By the time I wake up the next morning it's time to take myself off the machine and dispose of the tubing.

Thankfully the scleroderma seems to be well under control, by dialysing twice a week, taking tablets for my blood pressure and Losec for reflux. I can now worry about more trivial things such as telangiectasia on my face for which I'm having Laser treatment and so far it appears to be working. The next thing that I have to get to grips with is exercise. I think I am one of the laziest people I know and need to find some inspiration from somewhere. I've thought about joining a Gym, swimming, fitness videos, exercise bike but thought is as far as I've got. If anyone has any ideas on how to fire me with enthusiasm please don't be shy in coming forward! Thank you once again for everything you continue to do for me and the rest of our members".

Kim Fligelstone

Golden Pound Appeal

In the photograph David Wilkie MBE is seen with Anne Mawdsley and Colin Whittle (centre), Chief Executive of the Cheshire Building Society. This was taken at the official launch of the Golden Pound Appeal sponsored by the Cheshire Building Society. At the request of members a new pin badge was designed - a golden hand holding a £1 coin.

National and International News 1999

Always of great interest to our patients are new developments in treatment. There are one or two of these. The first thing to report is that relaxin, which is a hormone and which has been shown to be of help in the small, early studies in scleroderma, has now moved into the next phase of the study. This trial will test two doses of relaxin against placebo in 200 patients with diffuse disease. The study will serve as the major trial in order to permit the company producing the drug to ask the regulatory authorities in the USA for a license. This is. as you all probably know, a very complex and difficult business and it does require very carefully performed studies before a license is granted.

Relaxin is a naturally occurring protein hormone which is associated with pregnancy in that it helps prepare a woman by relaxing the ligaments in the pelvic area. Relaxin works by decreasing the amount of collagen produced and increasing the amount of collagenase, the enzyme that breaks down collagen. The anti-fibrotic characteristics of relaxin have been known for a long time, and were first recognised in 1958 when a study of purified pig relaxin was published in the journal of the American Medical Association. This article concluded that relaxin had a good effect on scleroderma. However, the relaxin which was produced from the pig proved too difficult to purify reliably and it was removed from the market. The trial. which is now ongoing, will last for six months and the primary end point for the trial, is an improvement in the modified Rodnan skin score. This is a measure of skin thickness at 17 areas in the body.

Another major problem is the type of scleroderma which occurs in childhood, particularly the type of scleroderma which produces linear scars and shortening of the limb. It is hoped that a pilot study will soon be started in this country, using methylprednisolone and methotrexate and comparing these 2 drugs with vitamin D, which is thought to be of possible use in this condition. It is also hoped that colleagues in Canada and the USA will undertake similar studies and that perhaps we will be able eventually to join in an international study once some pilot data has been collected.

Pulmonary hypertension is of course a major problem in scleroderma and it is therefore always good news when there are new drugs which may be tried for this condition. Currently there is an international trial taking place in several European countries and the USA using a prostacyclin, which is given through the skin via a very small pump. This trial is for patients who have quite severe pulmonary hypertension and is obviously an exciting development. It is also hoped that an inhaled form of prostacyclin will go into trial for this condition in the early part of next year. Unlike last year there are no major scleroderma conferences in 1999. There will, however, be the first meeting of the Scleroderma Interest Group at the European League Against Rheumatism meeting in Glasgow in early June. This meeting will be devoted to talking about the new trials that are about to start in systemic sclerosis in this country and to discuss the ones that have just begun. It will include trials such as those for pulmonary fibrosis, pulmonary hypertension, juvenile scleroderma, early diffuse disease, macrovascular disease and limited cutaneous scleroderma. There are a lot of exciting things happening at the moment which is excellent news. To help recruitment for all these trials, and we do need to find as many people as possible, there is now a central register. This has been mentioned before, but just to remind you, it is a register which any doctor can use to register their patients and make them potentially eligible for a new trial. On the basic science front a number of interesting areas of research are currently being pursued both in Europe and the USA. Microchimerism, where foetal cells cross into the mother is still a hot topic, and the precise role these cell have in scleroderma is being studied. The examination of differentially expressed genes that may have a role in the progression of scleroderma is also an area of excitement, with researchers both in the U.K. and USA, identifying potential candidate genes.

The other research area includes the investigation of the processes that may be responsible for the generation of the auto-antibodies which are commonly found in scleroderma patients. In the next few years many advances will be made in these and other areas which will increase our understanding of scleroderma.

In the year 2000 there are at least two scleroderma meetings. The first is in January at the Royal Free, which will be a teaching course for doctors interested in learning more about the disease, how to measure it and how to manage it. It will not be a research meeting; this is being reserved for the summer when the International Research Symposium will be held at Keble College, Oxford. Both of these meetings promise to be exciting and interesting events.

Professor Carol Black, Dr. David Abraham
Royal Free and University College Medical School

1999 Support Day

Our Scleroderma Support Day held on 28th February was well attended and enjoyed by all the participants. The day began with member Jed Malins giving a positive talk using cartoons to describe his experiences of living with scleroderma. Jed inspired the audience with his humorous but moving account of the various problems which he had encountered from diagnosis. Jed stressed that he now lives a very different but much richer life than before he developed scleroderma.

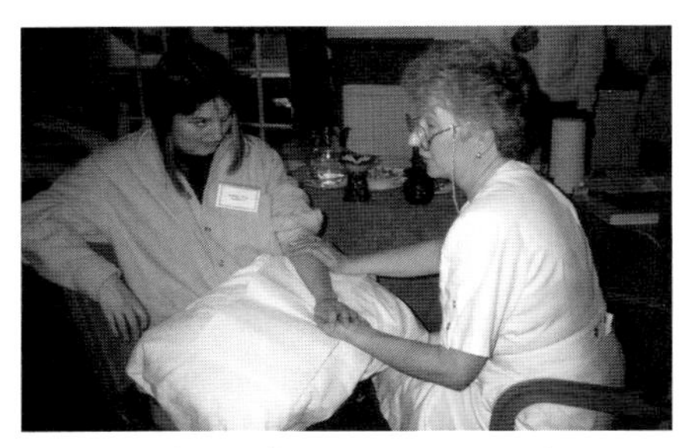

Margaret Nimmo demonstrates aromatherapy on Kathryn Price's arms.

Aromatherapy sessions were given by Margaret Nimmo who discussed the various oils used and those which were recommended for Raynaud's and scleroderma. She concentrated her session on hand massage and demonstrated on member Kathryn Price who has very tight skin on her arms.

Jane Price representing the British Red Cross, once again gave an excellent demonstration of cosmetic camouflage. Members found this very helpful, particularly in helping to gain confidence by disguising the telangiectasia on the face and chest. Tonia Moore, Vascular Technician from Hope Hospital in Salford, gave a most interesting and informative talk using overheads, slides and photographs, together with a video to explain the tests used for diagnosing Raynaud's and scleroderma. Of particular interest were nailfold capillaroscopy and thermography which is used in many hospitals. Tonia's presentation helped many people who have had the various tests, to understand how they worked. Nurse specialists Ros Robb from Dundee and Naomi Allen based at Leeds, held a joint group session. Ros talked about wound care and the various dressings which are available to treat ulcers. Naomi, who is a qualified chiropodist, pointed out the pitfalls for scleroderma patients if their feet are not cared for by an expert.

The social side of the weekend was of equal value - swimming in a heated pool, relaxing in the jacuzzi or just sitting and talking to each other about common problems.

Reflexology was very popular with many questions being asked. Debra Walker is seen demonstrating the technique with member Barbara Knox. For those who had not experienced reflexology before, this session proved to be of great interest to the participants and the audience.

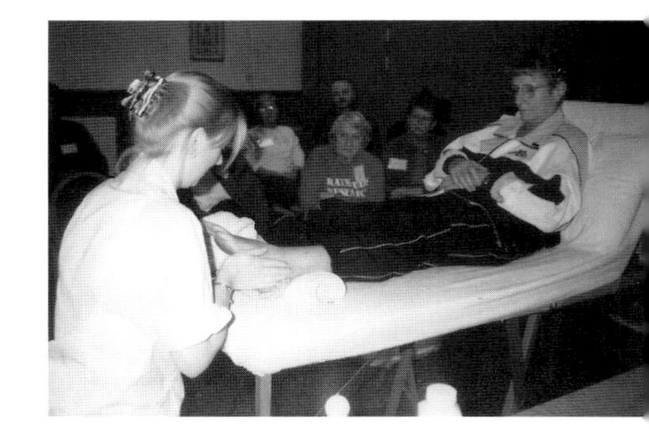

Debra Walker is seen demonstrating reflexology techniques with Barbara Knox.

When the immune system turns traitor

Blame Your Mother

When the immune system turns traitor, it may have an unlikely accomplice. Although we have mentioned this subject briefly in previous newsletters we have received many letters asking for more information.

Autoimmune diseases, in which the body attacks its own tissues, may in some cases be triggered by cells from your mother that have been lurking within you since you were in the womb. Researchers also have evidence that women may contract autoimmune diseases because of cells from their foetuses that persisted for decades after crossing the placenta. Many autoimmune conditions appear similar to graft versus host disease, in which cells from a transplanted organ mount an immune response against the host. That has led some researchers to speculate that microchimerism - a condition in which small numbers of another person's cells persist in the body - could be involved in some cases of autoimmunity. The idea is bolstered by the fact that autoimmune diseases are more common in women, who may be repeatedly exposed to their foetuses' cells while pregnant.

Two years ago, researchers in Boston made the surprising discovery that foetal cells can survive in a woman for as long as 27 years after her last pregnancy. Since then, other studies have shown that women with autoimmune diseases such as scleroderma, which causes the skin to become thick and leathery and can damage internal organs, seem to have an unusually high incidence of microchimerism. In one study male cells were detected in 32 out of 69 women with scleroderma, but just one out of 25 women who did not have the disease. Women with scleroderma and microchimerism also seem to have ten or more times as many foreign cells in their bodies as women with microchimerism who are not suffering from any autoimmune disease.

The problem with the theory has been that men get autoimmune diseases too. But at the Experimental Biology 1999 meeting in Washington DC, researchers announced that maternal cells can also cross over to male foetuses and survive for decades. J. Lee Nelson and her colleagues at the University of Washington in Seattle hunted for maternal cells in a 47-year-old man with scleroderma, using the polymerase chain reaction (PCR) to search for the gene for a molecule found on the surface of his mother's cells but not his own. Sure enough, they found maternal cells. The researchers also looked at blood from a 15 year old boy with lupus, another autoimmune disease that attacks the skin and internal organs, using a technique that stains X chromosomes one colour and Y chromosomes another. They were able to find a female cell which has two X chromosomes, and using PCR they confirmed that it came from the boy's mother. Nelson admits that she is still some way from proving that maternal cells can trigger autoimmunity. "But I think they're likely to be a significant piece of the puzzle," she says. Antony Rosen, an expert on autoimmunity at John Hopkins University in Baltimore, says: "It's at that stage where the hypothesis is reasonable and the preliminary data are supportive. But you can't get unequivocal data in a minute". Carol Artlett of Thomas Jefferson University in Philadelphia, who has found maternal cells in five out of eight men suffering from scleroderma, says a that microchimerism cannot be the whole story, as it can occur in people without autoimmune disease. Artlett suggests that autoimmunity can arise when a trigger such as a viral infection spurs the foreign cells to begin attacking their host. She believes this reaction disrupts the host's immune system so that it joins the attack against the body's own tissues.

The above article appeared in New Scientist on 24th April 1999

Fast Study

(Fibrosing Alveolitis in Scleroderma Trial)

A brief update

Four centres participating in the FAST Study have now been authorised to recruit patients. They are Royal Brompton & Harefield NHS Trust, Leeds General Infirmary, Hope Hospital in Salford and Royal National Hospital for Rheumatic Diseases and the Royal United Hospital in Bath. Two of these centres (Royal Brompton & Harefield NHS Trust and Leeds General Infirmary) have already recruited seven patients onto the trial.

Scleroderma patients either newly diagnosed with early lung fibrosis, or with some degree of lung fibrosis that as yet has not required treatment, are potentially suitable participants in the study. The principal investigators of the FAST Study are Professor Ron du Bois and Professor Carol Black. The trial is being funded by the Arthritis and Rheumatism Council, and is supported by the Raynaud's & Scleroderma Association.

Patients entered into the Clinical Trial will be treated for three years. At least 60 patients need to be recruited in order to get meaningful results. The aim of the study is to provide for the first time, unequivocal information about the benefit of what is currently held to be the optimum treatment for improving lung function or preventing further deterioration in scleroderma. The study treatment involves either being allocated to receive three active drugs, cyclophosphamide, prednisolone and azathioprine or placebo (dummy treatment). Patients are then carefully screened and monitored initially monthly, then three monthly for one year and subsequently yearly over the three years study period.

The major value of this trial will be to demonstrate for the first time that a course of treatment does or does not have a significant impact on the progression of a chronic lung disease, occurring as part of a rheumatological disease. Perhaps more importantly the design of the FAST Study will provide a template for future studies of chronic diseases not only in the lung but also in other organs affected by rheumatological disease.

New Feature in Hot News

Professor Jill Belch answers your questions

American Conference

Anne Mawdsley, Marie Coyle & Ann Philp taken at the Conference.

In August 1999, I travelled to San Diego to attend the American Scleroderma Foundation Conference entitled 'Wave of the Future'. This was held at a Conference Centre at the Town & Country Resort in San Diego. The conference was for scleroderma patients, their family and friends and was held over three days, during which time delegates had the opportunity to exchange information with each other and with members of the medical profession in order to gain valuable insight on coping with effects of scleroderma. Delegates attended from all over the United States and from Canada. Ann Philp, Chairperson of the Irish Raynaud's & Scleroderma Society and I were the only representatives from Europe. The conference offered the opportunity to enlighten those who attended with the latest advances in treatments, medical research and coping techniques and we found it of great interest to talk to scleroderma sufferers from another country.

A wide range of topics were included in seminars and workshops. These ranged from various strategies to cope with Raynaud's and scleroderma to nutrition, oral problems and stress management. It was not possible to attend all the seminars or workshops as these ran concurrently but the ones which I did attend proved to be most interesting. An all day general session featured leading researchers and clinical practitioners working in the field of scleroderma. Topics included current research investigation, treatments and overviews of many aspects of living with scleroderma.

I was particularly interested in the talks given by Dr. Richard Silver on pulmonary hypertension and fibrosis in which he described the problems of both aspects of lung disease and discussed the management and treatment for patients. He stressed the importance of not smoking, as smoking can not only worsen the lung process but also make Raynaud's worse. Patients should take measures to prevent reflux at night by elevating the head of the bed in addition to taking their medication, as acid from the stomach can filter into the lungs. If pulmonary fibrosis is present, medication using immunosuppressants with or without prednisone should be used. He explained the tests available to investigate lung disease and the necessity for regular lung function tests. If fibrosis is severe, oxygen therapy may be required at home. Oxygen treatment could also be used for pulmonary hypertension and if severe, prostacyclin given intravenously may be required to bring down the artery pressure.

Dr. Daniel Furst talked about the causes of scleroderma. With such a complex subject there is not just one cause but many factors which relate to genetic susceptibility. In scleroderma there is injury to the lining of the blood cells, which when damaged release a large number of inflammatory substances some of which activate fibroblasts. This can occur in scleroderma even when there is no injury and this causes the fibroblasts to make excess collagen. It is not yet known what causes the blood vessel damage, what factors activate the fibroblasts or what will prevent this activation. What they do know is that the injury to the lining of the blood vessels activates the immune system. He referred to external stimulation as a cause for scleroderma, such as silica, vinyl chloride and other chemicals. One of the more recent theories relates to the foetal cells, where during pregnancy the cells of a male child have entered the mother through the placenta and may be a contributory cause. It is also possible that the reverse could occur in cases of a male child carrying female cells from the mother in the same way. Dr. Furst is a pioneer of the stem cell transplants for scleroderma patients and his second presentation featured this aspect of his work. During question time, one of his patients who had been successfully treated by this method, answered questions from the audience on how she had coped with a stem cell transplant and how her life had changed for the better.

Dr. Philip Clements, who teamed with Dr. Furst in 1996 to edit the first medical textbook devoted solely to scleroderma, gave a most interesting talk on the work of the Scleroderma Research Consortium. This consists of 17 United States medical centres who are participating in a study to determine whether a double blind comparison of high versus low dose D-penicillamine in patients with early generalised scleroderma can improve skin sclerosis, decrease internal organ involvement and improve survival. Dr. Clements has also been involved in the multi-centered clinical trials of human recombinant Relaxin in the management of generalised scleroderma to determine if the drug can improve skin sclerosis and decrease heart, lung and kidney involvement in scleroderma.

Dr. Humphrey Gardner gave a fascinating overview of collagen sensors in the skin. His research focuses on how collagen production and breakdown are regulated through collagen receptors, as well as the role of collagen receptors in blood vessels and the immune system. Dr. Gardner is the recipient of the 1996/97 Dr. Mark Flapan Memorial Grant Award given by the Scleroderma Foundation. Dr. John Reveille spoke about genetic and ethnic considerations in scleroderma during which he described a project in which he was studying the impact of genetic, sociodemographic and behavioural factors on outcome in systemic sclerosis in three ethnic groups. His research concentrated on why one particular group of Native American population has a particularly high frequency of scleroderma.

Dr. Maureen Mayes, the Keynote Speaker at the Awards Luncheon, held a workshop on the management of Raynaud's. She was moderator for the general session during which she gave a report on her experiences with the relaxin study. Relaxin is a naturally occurring hormone which promotes small blood vessel formation. The study which is in its second phase, is to determine the safety and effectiveness of relaxin in the treatment of diffuse systemic sclerosis. Fifteen Centres across the United States have started, or will soon start, screening patients to participate in this six month treatment protocol. The study is double blinded and therefore neither the patient nor the doctor will know if a patient is taking one of the two doses of relaxin or the placebo. Dr. Mayes has patients on this study and although she is not able to determine which of the patients she is treating are taking the relaxin, early indications are that this treatment may well prove to be very exciting for the future. Unfortunately it is not able to be given orally and patients receive the relaxin by continuous infusion. I talked to people who were on the study and they were hopeful that the improvement which they had, was due to the relaxin. Only time will tell and the results should be available by August 2000. I understand that a similar study may be taking place in the U.K. shortly.

Finally I met some very interesting people during the course of the conference and I found the whole experience to be most interesting and informative. Talking to the conference organisers and members of the Scleroderma Foundation Board of Directors, gave me an invaluable insight into their organisation and we were able to exchange ideas. There is still a long way to go before a breakthrough is found but as always it is good to know that a great deal of research is being carried out by devoted doctors and researchers worldwide.

Anne Mawdsley

Introducing Percy

During our February Awareness Month, Percy the Penguin, our new mascot, was officially launched by TV doctor, Dr. Hilary Jones, at the London Canal Museum on Valentine's Day, 14th February 2000. Dr. Hilary Jones has Raynaud's himself and was happy to support the Association's Awareness Campaign.

For some time we have been giving thought to having a mascot which would compliment our Icy Hands logo with a warm, rather than cold identity. Having spoken to Saatchi & Saatchi and investigated several avenues, we decided on Percy Penguin, a little fellow who comes from a cold climate but has lovely warm, red hands and feet and a red nose! Percy is a beanie, which as you will know are very popular with all age groups. He was given his name by delegates at our Annual Conference.

On the left of the picture, also supporting Percy the Penguin is David Wilkie MBE, a Patron of the Association, who sportingly wore a penguin outfit for the event. In the middle is Anne Mawdsley who together with Dr. Hilary Jones gave an interview for Central Television which appeared on the Six o'clock News.

Research News from the Royal Free

Professor Carol Black sent the following report on the core support given to her department at the Royal Free Hospital by the Association. The total amount of the core support for this grant is £200,000 between 1997 and 2001.

Professor Black writes:

This has been an exciting time for scleroderma research, both clinical and laboratory based and has also coincided with a very successful programme of expansion in the department. Thus the main laboratory is now better equipped, and there are two new satellite laboratories - for tissue culture and gene analysis. The success of our efforts has been recognised by an increasing level of project support, by our ability to attract high calibre research personnel to the laboratory and visiting clinical staff from other parts of Europe. It is also exemplified by our continued scientific output of presentations at international meetings and publications in major journals. The grant supports in full or in part: Dr. Xu Shiwen (Tissue Culture Laboratory Manager), Mr Chris Knight (Database and IT Manager) and Helen Wilson (Nurse Clinician/Patient Educator).

There has been substantial progress in all of the areas supported by this core grant and these are detailed below:

A. Nurse Clinician/Patient Educator

There has been a continued expansion of this role and the Scleroderma Unit has benefited extensively from having Helen Wilson in post as a Rheumatology Nurse Specialist/Patient Educator. A major focus of the position has been devoted to the development of clinical practice and the education of allied health professionals and patients. Helen has given lectures and talks to both groups and coordinates teaching sessions for the junior nursing staff and health care assistants working in the out patients department and on the ward. The education of new house officers and other junior medical staff about some of the particular difficulties experienced by Raynaud's and scleroderma patients, has also become a regular (and much appreciated) feature of this post. In addition to direct education of individual patients, this role has involved preparation of new information leaflets, as well as gathering and collating collective input from the U.K. SSc Study Group for preparation of a Scleroderma Handbook for patients and carers.

The scleroderma help-line continues to be a much-used resource. Many calls are received each day and having an experienced nurse specialist with broad expertise in dealing with the problems of Raynaud's and scleroderma sufferers, has been essential for this service to flourish. In her capacity as co-ordinator of clinical trials for Raynaud's and scleroderma, Helen has played an important part in clinical studies. Having an experienced nurse in place for these studies has proven invaluable. It has also facilitated recruitment by improving patient awareness of studies. It has helped trials to run smoothly and has helped patients make informed decisions about participation and made sure that claims for expenses etc. are made promptly.

There has been an expansion in Nurse-led clinics especially for patients with primary Raynaud's Phenomenon, where patients and their relatives are educated about their disease, treatment options available, skin care, exercises and other issues. The establishment of the scleroderma help-line also affords patients a quick and direct access to nursing staff and advice and information. Overall, these activities have undoubtedly 'added value' to the service that we can offer to patients and their families and facilitated both pilot studies of novel therapies and formal phase III controlled trials of promising agents. Such studies are the key to improved treatments for Raynaud's and scleroderma and we believe that the partial-funding of this post represents an excellent use of the Raynaud's & Scleroderma Association's resources.

B. Raynaud's and Scleroderma Database

Funding has significantly assisted growth and expansion, enabling the development of a computerised scleroderma patient data base. This data base is linked with the laboratory tissue, cell and sample database allowing direct retrieval of material for research. A number of collaborative projects have been initiated, which use the database to select patient study groups. Scleroderma is a heterogeneous connective tissue disease which follows a variable course. It is uncommon, and causes gradual multiple organ disability resulting in a reduced life expectancy, depending on the age of onset and the progression of organ involvement. Gathering clinical and research data on an uncommon complex connective tissue disease such as scleroderma, is therefore extremely important. One of the aims of the Royal Free Hospital Database is to provide information with which to address these problems.

A relational database of serial clinical observations and investigation was initiated in 1996. This database incorporates all clinical data and our laboratory results and genetic analyses. This is the largest single-centre scleroderma database in the U.K. Data is continually being added and in the last 12 months around 200 new cases have been included. The database provides a unique resource for ourselves and our collaborators; for example in studies on genetic predisposition and markers of early disease and progression, and to identify appropriate patient group for clinical trials and further investigation. It is currently being used in many collaborative projects including: Professor Mark Winslet (scleroderma bowel disease); Dr. Gerry Coghlan (pulmonary hypertension); Dr. Alex Macgregor (epidemiology); Professor Tim Cawston (metalloproteinase inhibitors); Dr. Ken Welsh (genetics); Dr. Ron du Bois (lung disease/aetiopathogenesis); Professor Patrick Vallance (genetic polymorphisms of nitric oxide synthetase) and Professor John Martin (oxidant stress).

The database plays an important role in the organisation and administration of research projects. Weekly audit meetings ensure that the quality of data is maintained at the highest possible standard, and there are regular progress meetings with collaborators.

IT infrastructure

The advantages of having IT expertise in-house have been especially apparent over the past 3 years. It has allowed timely and cost-effective upgrading of equipment, ensured that resources are used efficiently and produced tangible savings by allowing printers, hard-drives and software to be locally networked. Interfacing between hospital and medical school networks is important and our department would otherwise have been caught between two different systems. Mr Knight has also been able to educate departmental members concerning hardware and software issues.

C. Pilot Studies in Raynaud's and Scleroderma

The generous support from the Raynaud's & Scleroderma Association has been invaluable in allowing several trials to be performed which would have been very difficult otherwise. In particular it has helped us to maintain standardised records, to measure laboratory variables (by enabling the purchase of assay kits and reagents). Some projects were in the application/planning stage at the start of the current funding period and these have now been completed (e.g. probucol, bolus iloprost for Pulmonary Hypertension follow-up from digital sympathectomy) or taken to the next stage of evaluation. This is in itself a vindication of the usefulness of relatively small amounts of funding to help run pilot studies. One vital contribution has been to allow patient expenses to be reimbursed. For studies of a rare heterogeneous disease like scleroderma to be possible, patients living a long way from study centres should be able to enter studies and we are very grateful to the Raynaud's & Scleroderma Association that we have been in a position to support travel costs for trials where this would not otherwise have been possible.

D. Scleroderma Laboratory

Overview

Tissue culture and development of new techniques has formed the cornerstone of this part of the support. Culture of biopsy material has facilitated many of the projects ongoing in the department. The success of experiments depends upon consistent high quality cell cultures and the precious nature of biopsy specimens necessitates that careful utilisation. Xu Shiwen performs a vital function in co-ordinating cells for many of the on-going projects within the department.

1) Impact on other funded research projects

Of course many of the projects have definitive funding - including project or programme grant support from the Raynaud's & Scleroderma Association in several cases. However, to get to the stage of being competitive for funding pilot, data are needed and once these projects are on-going it is essential that they are co-ordinated, since this brings economical, practical and scientific 'added value'. It is the scientific gain that is most rewarding and we feel provides the strongest justification for this support. It has allowed the laboratory to pursue new areas which form the basis of future project grant applications. Some of these areas are as follows: Dr. Chris Denton, who was previously a Clinical Research Fellow in the unit, has now received comprehensive training in molecular biology in a first class laboratory in the USA and has very recently returned to the Royal Free. Without funding from the Raynaud's & Scleroderma Association it would have been very difficult for his previously funded project to be continued, leading to an additional publication and some important new avenues of research.

2) Support for research studies of Dr. Xu Shiwen

During the last 2 years Xu has successfully completed and defended his PhD thesis and has extended his research into new areas. He has been very productive and his preliminary data have formed the basis of new projects including the cloning of the CTGF receptor and an examination of tissue factor, and endothelial cell product, in scleroderma. Both areas now have project grant support which would not have been obtained without pilot data supported by this core grant.

3) Provision of special reagents to the Royal Free Hospital Reference Serological Laboratory

The number and range of samples in the core reference laboratory has increased considerably over the past 30 months and now stands at approximately 300 fibroblast lines (50 paired skin and lung samples) and more than 1000 DNA samples. The latter will be invaluable as the genes involved in the development of these diseases become elucidated though our own work and that of other laboratories.

The maintenance of this unique resource has been facilitated by development of integrated databases for samples and we plan to interface these with the clinical database over the next 2 years. This should facilitate seamless review of sample availability for laboratory studies and will both speed up projects and ensure that these precious materials are optimally and efficiently used. The funds have contributed to tissue culture reagents, liquid nitrogen etc., vital to the on going research effort.

Future goals for these projects

We are confident that all of the areas benefiting from core support will continue to develop. Undoubtedly the patient database will expand, although on-going refinement of the database software should make this very manageable. One important clinical goal for the next two years is to achieve closer integration between outpatient and inpatient management of scleroderma, and this will closely involve the clinical nurse specialist. Other new areas will be interventional studies of the effect of prostacyclin (iloprost) infusions on markers of fibrosis and a pilot study of methotrexate in childhood linear scleroderma which should soon receive ethics committee approval.

Professor Carol Black

Nursing News from Dundee

Ros Robb

I have been very busy over the last two years developing my role as a nurse specialist at Ninewells Hospital, Dundee. This has been possible through the generous support of the Raynaud's & Scleroderma Association. Prior to this most of the patients I saw who suffered from Raynaud's had been participating in the many clinical trials undertaken here. Since receiving support from the Association I have been able to extend and improve the service both to patients attending Ninewells and to patients living further away from the hospital. I thought I would give you a brief outline of my role over these two years and explain to you what we now have available for members and sufferers. My first task after taking up the post was to establish a telephone helpline. This had been identified as a particular need especially for those of you who don't have access to specialist nurses or doctors. The helpline is linked to a voice mailbox and is not manned but records messages from callers. It is available 24hrs and is checked on a daily basis. I try to return calls as soon as possible which is usually within a week but may take longer when I am not able to catch people at home. Please be patient if this is the case, and feel free to try the helpline again leaving me details of times during the day that I may be able to contact you. Of course if you have any urgent medical problems you should get in touch with your GP.

Helpline enquiries have come from a wide range of people looking for many different things. I receive calls from sufferers and their relatives as well as other health care workers such as G.P.s and Practice Nurses. It is encouraging to see that awareness of Raynaud's in the community is increasing. I also spend time with clinic and ward nurses to establish and provide the help and information they require. Those of you who attend the Clinical Investigation Unit at Ninewells for treatment or investigations will be familiar with seeing me there. I try to visit patients here at least once during their stay. There are also posters on the walls throughout the hospital displaying my number for both patients and staff. The research we are undertaking this winter is going to be keeping me extremely busy. In addition to ongoing projects being carried out in collaboration with Professor Carol Black at the Royal Free Hospital, we have started a double blind, randomised, placebo-controlled trial of Seredrin (ginkgo biloba with phytosome). This follows on from the study which many members of the Association participated in last winter. For those of you who have not taken part in research or are wondering what exactly is meant by the titles, I thought I might just explain a little in relation to the above study. We are recruiting 20 patients who will be given either ginkgo or placebo (dummy) medication. During the study neither the patients, nor ourselves will know who is taking the real treatment and who is taking the placebo treatment as the tablets look exactly the same. Participants will be randomly given either real or dummy tablets. This is what is meant by double blind i.e. the patients and the researchers are both blinded. The patients will be asked to keep diary cards recording their Raynaud's attacks on a daily basis for the duration of the study.

All the participants will be seen on a regular basis to check these diaries and to record any side-effects they might be experiencing. The study duration is 12 weeks. For the first 2 weeks patients will stop taking their normal medication for Raynaud's and keep diary cards recording each Raynaud's attack. At the next main visit we carry out blood flow measurements and obtain blood samples for research analysis. This is when we commence the ginkgo tablets. During the 10 weeks of treatment we see all the participants at 2 different time points to check their diaries and see how they are progressing. After the treatment is complete we perform the same blood flow tests again to see if there are any changes and we collect the diaries cards. All patients are seen again 2 weeks later to see how they are getting on and to discuss any other treatment they may require.

Another study that we will be carrying out this winter is with a new vasodilator drug. This study is being carried out in several U.K. and European hospitals as well as hospitals in Australia. Again, this is a double-blind, randomised, placebo-controlled study and involves participants completing diaries and attending my research clinics at Ninewells, on a regular basis. This study involves 7 weeks of treatment with either the placebo or the real medication.

Over the past two years I have been giving talks to health care professionals who have expressed an interest in Raynaud's and want to know what is available for their patients. I hope to give more of these talks to local G.P.s and Practice Nurses in future months. This would enable me to distribute more information to those not attending hospitals.

I have been invited to attend the Raynaud's Conferences and Support Days in Alsager during my time in this role. It has always been a great pleasure to meet many of the members and also to get the opportunity to catch up with my colleagues who run the other helplines. I hope this gives a small outline of what I'm up to here in Dundee and I look forward to hearing from any of you through the helpline or locally at clinics here.

Ros Robb, Ninewells Hospital, Dundee

Annual Conference 1999

Once again our Annual Conference held during the weekend of October in Alsager, was a great success with 150 delegates attending. This year we had an international flavour, with guests travelling from Denmark, Holland, Northern and Southern Ireland and Italy to join us. The weekend began with a dinner on Friday evening, kindly sponsored by Health Perception at which Patron David Wilkie MBE said a few words and introduced our guest speaker, Niels Sorensen. Niels is chairman of the Danish Association and has Raynaud's and scleroderma himself. He gave a very moving account of his experience of living with these conditions in Denmark and the difficulty of feeling very much alone with a rare condition. His wife, Ilona, accompanied Niels to Alsager and they both honoured us by making the Annual Draw. Saturday's programme was both interesting and informative. Patron Roger Jefcoate CBE opened the conference and handed over to our excellent chairman, Dr. John Bewley. There were slight changes to the programme, mainly due to Professor Julia Polak being taken ill at the last minute. We were very sorry that Professor Polak was unable to present her work but wish her well in her recovery. However, this did not deter from the quality of the presentations and we were grateful to Dr. Athol Wells, Consultant at the Brompton Hospital, who works closely with Professor du Bois, for stepping in and giving an excellent talk on lung involvement.

The first speaker of the morning was Professor Carol Black who gave an informative talk on treatments for Raynaud's and scleroderma. She described the many treatments and trials available, stressing that there is no 'magic bullet' which will cure these conditions but that researchers were trying hard to understand the mechanisms involved, particularly with scleroderma, as a greater understanding will help towards finding better treatments in the future. In the afternoon session, Professor Black gave a talk on bowel problems in scleroderma, a subject which is not often discussed but which is of great concern for many people with scleroderma. Both of Professor Black's presentations sparked interest and a great many questions were asked by the delegates.

Professor Marco Matucci Cerinic from Florence also gave two talks - the first during the morning session in which he spoke about research being carried out in conjunction with Dr. Pamela Milner at the Royal Free Hospital, on the involvement of the nervous system in scleroderma. This was a most interesting topic and we were most appreciative that Professor Matucci Cerinic had travelled so far to present his work. During the afternoon he gave the results of a study on the rehabilitation of patients with systemic sclerosis and this was also of great interest to all present.

Elaine Susol from Manchester University gave a talk on the genetic basis to Primary Raynaud's. This is proving to be a very exciting project and we will keep you updated through future issues of Hot News. Our member speaker this year was Louise Charles who has both Raynaud's and scleroderma. Louise gave a humorous and descriptive account of her personal experiences, her positive attitude being an inspiration to all who attended.

During Anne's talk two cheque presentations were made. The first was by Terry and Shirley Lawrence for £950, being the proceeds of a sponsored cycle ride. This was presented to Mr Alan Golding, Chairman of the Trustees. Secondly Derek Rustidge had travelled from Holland to present a cheque for £750 in memory of his wife Maureen, a member of the Association, who died earlier this year from cancer. Anne concluded the conference by reading a few humorous poems sent in by members, which were illustrated by Jed's cartoons. She then thanked everyone for their support both at the conference and throughout the year.

Delegates and speakers enjoying the atmosphere over lunch.

Arthritis patients on the move

In October I was invited to attend and speak at the Second Worldwide Conference of Arthritis and Rheumatism Patient Societies. This meeting was organised by the Social Leagues of EULAR (European League Against Rheumatism) in collaboration with Merck Sharp Dohme.

Over 100 delegates attended from 26 Countries and I had the opportunity to meet with and exchange ideas with representatives of other patient organisations. The main purpose of the conference was to discuss general problems shared by organisations such as ours worldwide. Speakers presented positive information on successful campaigns to create awareness of rheumatic conditions and others related their personal experiences.

My talk, entitled 'From Isolation to Communication' explained about our Icy Hands Campaign in the U.K. and the impact which the posters had in creating awareness of Raynaud's and scleroderma. I explained the trials and tribulations of getting our message across and how one cannot please everyone. The main objective of our on-going campaign is to help patients to get an early diagnosis and to offer support. As a result of the Icy Hands Campaign the Association received literally thousands of positive comments compared to a handful of letters and phone calls stating that the posters were 'beyond belief' or 'frightening'. The presentation was well received with good feedback on the posters.

Discussions played an important part in the two day programme, with topics including, how to improve funding, how to ensure patients are given good quality leaflets and information and how organisations can improve their relationship with doctors and health professionals in their respective countries. Also on the agenda were discussions on working with the media and influencing politicians and policy making. The two most important aspects raised were the need for a greater understanding amongst the medical profession, particularly in the medical school curriculum and more general awareness of the problems encountered by people with arthritis and rheumatic conditions.

I learned a great deal about other similar patient organisations from around the world and came away with much food for thought. The organisation of the conference was excellent and although it was quite an exhausting trip, with seminars for two whole days, I found it to be an invaluable experience. I met many interesting people, all of whom have a contribution to make to the well being of people with arthritis and rheumatism. We may be small fish in a large pond but problems and their solutions are universal.

Anne Mawdsley

Over £16,000 Raised on Annual Draw 1999

The winning tickets in our Annual Draw were drawn out by Niels Sorensen, Chairman of the Danish Scleroderma and Raynaud's Association and his wife Ilona. Niels and Ilona attended our Annual Conference, where Niels was our guest speaker on the Friday evening.

New Physio Booklet

Our range of health professional booklets has recently been increased to include a booklet for physiotherapists. We are grateful to Jill Lloyd for her help in the preparation of this booklet, which was launched at a health professionals conference in Bristol at which Anne gave a talk on the work of the Association.

Members News

Marjorie's erythromelalgia tips

"It has taken me years to actually find some comfort at night as opposed to constantly remaking my bed throughout the night, between doing foolish things like paddling in cold water in the bath, to taking a cold wash spray to bed to use between snatching some sleep. I have tried the frames to lift the bedding off my feet which were available in this country but it wasn't until Easter last year when my daughter brought some light ones home from the south of France for me to try, that I found any peace at night from my burning feet and legs. They are excellent.

Once in bed I give my feet the usual treatment and spread them with Neutrogena Dermatological Cream, the only neutrogena product available on prescription, and then a covering of Boots cooling mint foot gel. With the aid of two drugs Ketansarin and Clonazapam I'm soon asleep usually for 6-7 hours with just one rise to visit the loo and perhaps one or two foot adjustments, as sometimes they can be freezing cold. It's certainly the best in years for me. The snag of course is purchasing the item from France and I also realise that all of us EM sufferers are different in response to various drugs. I still take praxilene during the day.

The soles of my feet are particularly bad being permanently damaged and very painful to walk on. Having exhausted one local carpet supplier who patiently spent months trying to find suitable new floor covering for me, he had to give up having tried obtaining endless samples from all of the manufacturers that he could find. For years I've been struggling with the floors covered dangerously with bed sheeting and an absolute eye sore as they became kicked especially by Chloe my cat who during her twice daily mad half hours had great fun.

I suddenly came up with the idea of floor pads which are quite simple really. The local family upholsterer made these for me in 3 different thicknesses. They are cool, soft and heavenly relief for my poor feet. The kitchen ones are the thinnest and smallest, cut into washing machine sizes. (He assures me that they will wash). Anyone with a machine could easily make them but this firm is reasonable on working it out and I was surprised at how little they charged for making them".

Marjorie Goodliffe

Laura's dream comes true!

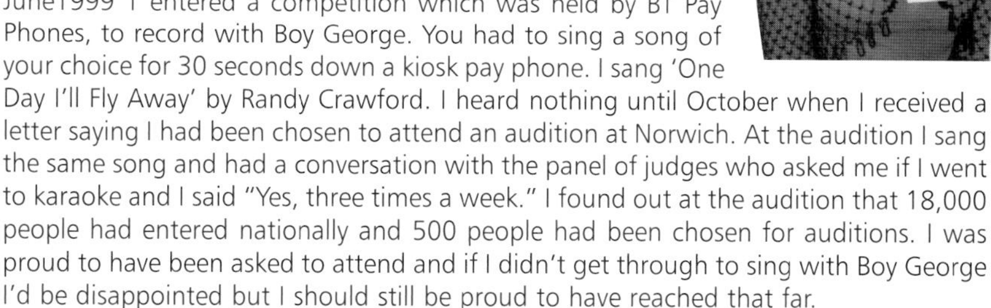

"Hi, it's Laura again. You may remember the article which I wrote in Hot News in 1996. Well I am now sending you an update to tell you of some really exciting news.

After having my right leg amputated below the knee three years ago, I had to return to Great Ormond Street to have a further amputation, as my bone had grown and was pushing at the base of my stump. During a further six months of convalescing and further six months of being bored after this operation, I threw myself into my hobby which is singing. In June1999 1 entered a competition which was held by BT Pay Phones, to record with Boy George. You had to sing a song of your choice for 30 seconds down a kiosk pay phone. I sang 'One Day I'll Fly Away' by Randy Crawford. I heard nothing until October when I received a letter saying I had been chosen to attend an audition at Norwich. At the audition I sang the same song and had a conversation with the panel of judges who asked me if I went to karaoke and I said "Yes, three times a week." I found out at the audition that 18,000 people had entered nationally and 500 people had been chosen for auditions. I was proud to have been asked to attend and if I didn't get through to sing with Boy George I'd be disappointed but I should still be proud to have reached that far.

A few weeks later I came home from school and my mum said there was a letter for me. I was so amazed when I opened the letter and it said that on November 1st and 2nd I would be at the famous Abbey Road Studios to re-record 'Karma Chameleon' with another 99 winners in aid of the charity, Message Home. It was the very same studio the Beatles did their recordings. I was excited for the weeks up to the Ist and 2nd November because it is my dream to see and record in a recording studio. The first day we practised and on the second day we sang with Boy George and Culture Club. I stood right next to him. What an experience! He was very nice and overwhelmed by the response he got from everyone. I have a video of the occasion to treasure always".

Laura O'Connor

Kay Tasker

The doctor said I had growing pains!

"Raynaud's is a condition I have suffered with ever since I can remember - I am now 23. The condition really took hold when I was about 12-14 years old. The doctors kept saying that I had growing pains and friends were starting to comment on the blackness of my feet whilst on the side of the swimming pool. As the symptoms became more severe I started to get more and more attacks of cramp and pain which eventually put a stop to my competitive swimming - now I don't swim at all as it starts off the attacks. The pain continued to intensify to such an extent that I had to give up university and I spent 6 months in a wheelchair - even getting around the house was a problem.

The doctors sent me to a rheumatologist. I was also sent to a pain clinic in the same hospital where I had a number of guanethidine nerve blocks directly into my feet. By this time my feet were continually black - so I had a lumbar sympathectomy which only helped for a couple of weeks. I have also taken action of my own - going to see a biochemist/doctor in London who advised me to take certain supplements which I still take and find beneficial. I have tried acupuncture, osteopathy, reflexology and Chinese medicine - some treatments are more effective than others. However, I still take slow release vasodilators daily. Dressing sensibly also helps as prevention is always better than cure - so thermal socks, thick soled boots, trousers and gloves are daily fashion items!"

Kay Tasker

Kay gave an interview to The Times and as a result we had a large feature on Raynaud's. Following this Kay and Anne took part in a television programme with Dr. Chris Steele on Granada Breeze where we were given 10 minutes air time!

Champion Fundraiser Chris

Chris & Steve Buckledee

"In the Autumn Newsletter my wife, Chris Buckledee was reported as 'Champion Fundraiser'. She has now raised over £30,000 to date. We love sending all this money but it is very hard work and keeps us busy all the year round. At Christmas Chris made fairies for Christmas trees. I know she made them on the kitchen table because I had ham rolls and tinsel for my tea! It is getting harder to know what to do next as most people in Bildeston have already bought what has been made. At the start of the year we go to the markets to try to get material and other bits and pieces as cheaply as we can but we do have odd bits and pieces, material and wool given to us. Children come and ask if they can do sponsored bike rides, and they raise a few pounds, other people make cakes and sponges for our big sale on the market square in June. We are very lucky with helpers, as without them we couldn't possibly do what we do. My sister-in-law visits the market in Ipswich and haggles to get fruit to make jams, marmalade, pickles, tomato chutney and red cabbage. The more senior ladies knit toys, jumpers and other things. Our Post Office collects stamps from their customers and we trim them up with one eye on the TV and the other on the stamps. It was my job to maintain the tables and so on whilst holding down a job but it is better now that I have retired.

Chris gets sweets and chocolate from a friend at the cash and carry and bags them up to sell to children and some 'big children'! Sometimes we have a house full of children who want small gifts for their school teachers at the end of term which all helps to raise funds. Sale tables are taken at various halls, old peoples homes and our local school and if our regulars don't come they give us a donation. When I was working and gave my customers an invoice one or two would say give this to your wife for her charity, which was very nice of them. We are very grateful to be one of the four charities supported by the Ipswich and Norwich Co-op who send us a regular cheque for £100, which we pass on to the Association.

Steve Buckledee, Bildeston

Chris and Steve have worked extremely hard for years and we are most appreciative for their efforts.

Fashion Show in Northern Ireland

In the photograph from left to right are models Pauline Wilkerson, Lindsey Armstrong, Liddia Greson, Beth Maginnes, Michael Baily, Patience Bradley (Chairman of the Raynaud's & Scleroderma Association, Northern Ireland Group), Charles Maginnes, Natasha Black and Helen Toner. The photograph was taken at a fashion show at Rockmount Golf Club where the event raised the superb sum of £1,100.

Percy goes on air!

Percy is pictured here with radio presenter Michael Van Straten during a recent interview with Anne Mawdsley on LBC's Bodytalk.

Percy goes on holiday!

Percy goes to Madrid *Percy in Italy* *Relaxing in Lanzarote*

To date we have received photographs of Percy in Italy, Lanzarote, Madrid and Dublin. Plans are underway for him to visit China, Mount Kilimanjaro, Mount Kenya, Antarctica and numerous other destinations. Sales of Percy continue to grow. Please help to make him known nationwide as our mascot.

New - The Scleroderma Patient's Booklet

Written by the U.K. Systemic Sclerosis Study Group, this booklet tells you and your family about scleroderma and the way it is treated. It may also be useful to your friends and carers. In order to make it easy to understand very few medical terms have been used and when they have been used, their meaning has been explained in a glossary at the end of the booklet. The booklet aims to give you simple, up to date ideas about scleroderma.

Our thanks to Schering Health Care Ltd for a donation towards the cost of this publication. Once the printing costs have been covered all proceeds will go towards funding scleroderma research.

Investigation of transforming growth factor ß1

(TGF ß1) gene differences in patients with CREST and Progressive Systemic Sclerosis

The protein, transforming growth factor ß1 (TGF ß1), is produced by a variety of cells in the body. As well as acting on cells of the immune system, TGF ß1 is known to be a potent mediator of tissue fibrosis, which is the formation of fibrous or scar tissue. Since fibrosis is a characteristic feature of CREST (limited scleroderma) and PSS (diffuse scleroderma), TGF ß1 is thought to influence some of the clinical features of these conditions.

The amount of TGF ß1 that an individual makes is dependent on their genes. In February 1999 we were awarded funding from the Raynaud's & Scleroderma Association to look at differences in the TGF ß1 gene in normal healthy individuals and in patients with CREST or PSS. The aim of this study was to see if patients with CREST and PSS were more likely to carry the TGF ß1 gene that predisposed to high TGF ß1 production compared to the normal population. The work was undertaken in the Department of Medicine at Glasgow Royal Infirmary and during the course of the study blood was donated by 90 individuals with CREST, 52 individuals with PSS and 150 normal controls.

The study showed that a higher percentage of patients with CREST (79%) or PSS (88%) carried the genes for high TGF ß1 production compared with the normal population (67%). Despite the small difference in higher producers between the CREST and PSS populations, it did not differentiate between the limited and diffuse states. The initial observations from this investigation would suggest that patients with CREST and PSS may be more likely to be high TGF ß1 producers. The study has generated some interesting preliminary data and further work to confirm these results should be undertaken. We are currently adding to our patient data base to increase the study numbers. We would like to take this opportunity to thank the Raynaud's & Scleroderma Association for funding this study and also to say a very big thank you to all the patients who so very kindly agreed to donate blood.

Anne Crilly, Jennifer Hamilton, Rajan Madhok,
Centre for Rheumatic Disease, Glasgow Royal Infirmary.

Reports from the Royal Free

Investigation of the abnormalities in blood vessel and vascular function in patients with scleroderma

Dr. David Abraham

Raynaud's Phenomenon (RP) and systemic sclerosis/scleroderma (SSc) are conditions that involve blood vessel malfunctions, characterised by poor circulation and a decrease in the number of small blood vessels. Tissue factor (TF) is a protein involved both in triggering the blood clotting cascade and the formation of new blood vessels (angiogenesis). We wondered whether a lack of tissue factor or an inability in certain cells to respond to tissue factor could be involved in the reduction in small blood vessels seen in both conditions. We have investigated the levels of tissue factor activity in white blood cells from patients with RP and also limited and diffuse SSc. Interestingly we found that tissue factor activity is significantly raised in both RP and limited SSc whereas in diffuse disease, tissue factor activity is normal. At present we don't know the significance of this increase in tissue factor activity but we believe that it may play a role in microvessel deterioration.

We are also looking at the location of TF protein in thin slices of skin taken from healthy controls and patients with diffuse SSc. In both controls and diffuse SSc skin, tissue factor is found towards the surface of the skin, in the epidermis. Importantly, in skin taken from diffuse SSc patients' tissue factor is also found associated with fibrotic regions found in deeper layers of the skin (the dermis). We are continuing to investigate which cell types contain tissue factor protein and what its role may be in fibrosis. The studies to date suggest that there is a factor(s), possibly circulating in the blood, that prevents the formation of normal vessels. It appears that the cells are unable to respond properly to the normal signals to form healthy vessels. We have some indirect evidence that, in scleroderma and possibly RP, there is an overproduction of free radicals, reactive chemicals that are produced as a by product of metabolism. These may influence the development of these vessels and the activities of the proteins involved. We are now studying this possibility in order that we may connect these two apparently different aspects of the disease.

Professor Carol Black, Professor Richard Bruckdorfer,
Dr. David Abraham, Researcher: Dr. Jilly Harrison

Identification and cloning of CTGF receptors expressed by scleroderma fibroblasts

Scleroderma (systemic sclerosis) is near universally characterised by thickening of the skin or internal organs, a process called connective tissue fibrosis or scarring. The reason why this process takes place is poorly understood, but it is believed that the cell type resident in connective tissues, the fibroblast, is responsible for the majority of the scarring in the affected tissue or organ. In addition to the production of excessive amounts of connective tissue proteins, scleroderma fibroblasts also exhibit abnormal growth properties. Connective tissue growth factor (CTGF) is a member of a family of growth factor-like proteins called 'immediate-early genes' because their expression is rapidly induced by stress or by other growth factors. In particular, CTGF, which is able to stimulate fibroblasts to grow faster, is induced by transforming growth factor beta, a protein known to be present in the skin of scleroderma patients. We have also shown that CTGF is elevated in both the skin and lungs of scleroderma patients, and in fibroblasts obtained from these tissues. This led us to believe that CTGF may be a major factor in controlling the abnormal fibroblast properties in scleroderma. Although the physiological function of CTGF is still unclear, a major advance in understanding the role of CTGF would be the identification of CTGF receptors. The localisation and structure of these recectors would help greatly to clarify how CTGF signalling results in extra cellular matrix production and fibrosis.

We have investigated whether there are specific CTGF receptors that are present on the surface of scleroderma fibroblasts. Using cross-linking experiments followed by a detection process we have been able to identify one fibroblast protein, which appears to bind to CTGF. This protein is very large, and may represent a complex of CTGF and CTGF receptors. Using a very sensitive method where we are able to label CTGF with a readily detectable tag, we have performed blocking experiments using unlabelled CTGF and an antibody which binds CTGF with high affinity. These experiments appear to confirm that this protein is a specific CTGF receptor. The identification of a CTGF receptor protein is extremely useful providing information on the structure of the receptor, which will ultimately allow us to develop a strategy which may be effective in inhibiting CTGF binding to its receptor, thereby blocking CTGF activity and fibrosis.

Professor Carol Black, Dr. David Abraham

Brompton Report

The molecular genetics group in the interstitial lung disease unit at Imperial College, London is continuing to evaluate the relationship between genetic polymorphisms and lung fibrosis in systemic sclerosis. We have taken two main approaches. Firstly, to determine whether there is a genetic basis to the autoantibody pattern that patients with systemic sclerosis carry. We have shown that one of the class 11 MHC (tissue type) molecules HLA-DPB1*1301 is significantly associated with the Scl 70 autoantibody and this in turn is strongly associated with lung fibrosis. By contrast the anti-centromere antibody appears to be 'protective' of the development of pulmonary fibrosis. These are the strongest associations yet described between genetics and lung fibrosis and may have implications for the identification of patients at risk of developing more severe disease.

We are now in the process of expanding these studies to try to identify if the T-cells (cells involved in the earliest stages of the immune response) from patients who are Scl 70 positive, react in an abnormal fashion to the DNA topoisomerase enzyme against which the antibody is raised. This will allow us to attempt to identify one of the earliest possible mechanisms in the initiation of the disease process. We have established the area of the enzyme protein that is the most likely candidate and are beginning preliminary experiments to determine whether these proteins promote the activation of the T-cells from affected individuals.

Our second approach has been to explore the relationship between molecules that are growth factors for fibroblasts that result in fibrosis in the lungs. We have shown that fibronectin a sort of 'glue' that is important in interactions between cells and also between cells and the surface on which they move. This 'glue' is important in the development of scar tissue in the lungs and is associated with pulmonary fibrosis in systemic sclerosis. We are now attempting to refine the methodology that is used to detect these polymorphisms which could speed up the screening process. Additionally, we are developing methods to determine whether the differences in polymorphisms are reflected in different levels of fibronectin production identified in bronchoalveolar lavage fluid, from individuals with systemic sclerosis and fibrosis.

The goals of these studies are two-fold. Firstly, we wish to develop screening methods to determine rapidly which patients are at most risk of lung fibrosis in systemic sclerosis. Secondly, we are trying to relate these factors to the functional consequences of these genetic differences to identify mechanistically what triggers lung fibrosis.

An understanding of the genetic basis of lung fibrosis in association with the mechanism of producing disease could therefore be important in developing new approaches to the treatment of this life-threatening condition.

Professor Ron du Bois

Hope Hospital

Computer analysis of blood vessel images

Dr. Danny Allen

The Imaging Science and Biomedical Engineering group at Manchester University have been working in collaboration with the Rheumatic Diseases Centre at Hope Hospital in Salford, on a project to bring computer image analysis techniques to the study of capillaries at the base of the fingernail (nailfold). These capillaries are tiny blood vessels which are often abnormal in patients with scleroderma. The project, funded by the Raynaud's & Scleroderma Association, was initially focused on studying their structure, but has recently been investigating their function using fluorescent tracer dyes.

When viewed by an optical microscope the capillaries in the nailfold appear as rows of long thin loops, and the appearance of these is used in the assessment of patients with Raynaud's Phenomenon and scleroderma. Typical abnormalities of the capillaries seen in scleroderma patients are enlargement of the capillary loops and/or significant regions without capillary loops at all, but there is also information in the way in which substances pass through the capillary wall (permeability). This permeability of the capillary walls can be investigated using Sodium Fluorescein dye which glows bright yellow/green when illuminated by blue light. The dye is injected into the patient's arm and between twenty to fifty seconds later it has travelled round the whole body and is visible in the nailfold.

For this study we have worked with a company called KKtechnology to develop a new system to acquire images of the nailfold capillaries, consisting of a specially designed microscope in which the images are recorded on a CCD video camera and fed directly into a computer for storage and analysis. First the person doing the test, scans across the finger with the microscope using normal illumination, whilst the computer takes the images from the microscope and automatically combines them to form a panoramic mosaic, giving a complete view of the area under study.

Next, when a suitable area for study has been chosen, the microscope is switched to blue illumination, the dye injected, and the images from the microscope are recorded by the computer system over a thirty minute time period. During this time the dye is seen to appear in the capillaries and then move out into the surrounding tissue. In patients without scleroderma the dye tends to stay within a well-defined halo region around the capillary, but patients with scleroderma tend to exhibit a more irregular pattern of dye around the capillary with no clearly defined halo region visible. So far data from around twenty patients has been successfully collected and we are currently working on a computer-based environment to enable medical staff to analyse the data themselves without the need to develop computer-programming skills.

Learning more about these capillaries will help us improve our understanding of Raynaud's and scleroderma, and to investigate the effect and usefulness of potential therapies. We are very grateful to all the patients who have helped with these studies.

Dr. D. Allen, Imaging Science and Biomedical Engineering, University of Manchester

Thermography

One year ago the Raynaud's & Scleroderma Association kindly funded us to purchase the thermal imaging camera for use in our Vascular Laboratory. The previous camera, which we had had for many years, stopped working and so it was very important to us to be able to replace this. We thought it was about time we let you know how our new camera was being put to good use. The camera is used to assess the responsiveness of the hands to a cold stimulus. If you have an appointment for thermography, then you are asked not to have any caffeine containing drinks and not to smoke for a period of four hours before the test. The reason for this is that caffeine and nicotine are vasoactive substances meaning they will influence the circulation.

All investigations are performed in a temperature controlled room, so the patient will acclimatise for a period of 20 minutes before the first image is recorded. A thermal image of the back of each hand is recorded and this allows the measurement of the temperature of the tips of the fingers. The hands are then immersed into water at 15 degrees for a period of 1 minute wearing latex gloves (this will cool the fingers without bringing on a Raynaud's attack). The temperature of the fingers is then recorded using the thermal camera for a period of 15 minutes. If the fingers were cold initially then the temperature-controlled room is heated up and, after a period of acclimatisation, another image is recorded.

Computer software available with the thermal imaging camera allows us to measure the temperatures of the tips of the fingers as compared to the back of the hand and to play back a sequence of images to see how patients describing symptoms of Raynaud's recover following the cold challenge. The temperatures of the hands before and after heating the room and the rate of rewarming, taken together with other important factors such as a description of the individual's symptoms and results of blood tests, can give a good indication of the type and severity of the Raynaud's phenomenon.

Tonia Moore, Vascular Technician, Hope Hospital.

University College London

The endothelial neuropeptidergic system in Raynaud's phenomenon in systemic sclerosis

Inappropriate constriction of blood vessels to the digits on exposure to the cold, known as Raynaud's phenomenon, is often an early event in the development of systemic sclerosis (or scleroderma), in which there is widespread damage to the skin and main internal organs. Blood vessel diameter is controlled by an interplay of several different vasoactive substances released by nerves surrounding blood vessels and by endothelial cells which line the inside of blood vessels and are in contact with the circulating blood. Many of the neuropeptides and purines released from endothelial cells, as well as regulating vascular tone, also affect the growth and division of cells of the vessel wall and interact with inflammatory cells and fibroblasts responsible for the fibrosis seen in scleroderma. Endothelial dysfunction in small blood vessels in skin have been implicated in the early stages of scleroderma. In Raynaud's phenomenon and scleroderma there is a selective reduction of sensory nerves which release two vasodilatory neuropeptides, substance P and calcitonin gene-related peptide and we know, from experiments on larger vessels, that this can result in changes in the release of substances from the endothelium.

In a pilot study, funded by the Raynaud's & Scleroderma Association, we have found that many of the vasoactive substances which we have previously localised in endothelial cells from larger blood vessels, are also present in endothelial cells isolated from microvessels of the skin. In addition there are notable differences in neuropeptide content between endothelial cells isolated from skin from healthy patients (controls) and from patients with scleroderma. Cells isolated from uninvolved areas of skin from scleroderma patients also showed selective changes: two neuropeptides not localised in control microvascular endothelial cells, were localised in the uninvolved skin endothelium. This is an indication that changes in neuropeptide endothelial expression may precede the inflammatory and fibrotic responses of this disorder. We are currently examining cells from a larger number of patients to confirm these findings. Biopsy skin samples are also being examined using immunohistochemical electron microscopy techniques, to ensure that the neuropeptide content of isolated cells is representative of the cells before isolation. It will be important to examine the release profile of these substances from control and scleroderma skin endothelial cells and investigate the influence of circulatory factors present in serum from patients with limited and diffuse forms of scleroderma, to understand the interplay of events in the course of the disease.

This research is being carried out in collaboration with Professor Matucci Cerinic (University of Florence, Italy) and my colleagues Dr. P Bodin and Dr. A Loesch at the Autonomic Neuroscience Institute, Royal Free and University College Medical School, University College London.

Dr. Pamela Milner

National and International News 2000

At the end of July we hosted the International Scleroderma Research Symposium at Keble College Oxford. The Symposium was attended by over 150 delegates and the programme covered basic and clinical topics. This was a tremendous opportunity for the Scleroderma community to get together, discuss ideas and establish new collaborative ventures. Delegates came from all over the world and it was good to to see many old friends. Combined with the symposium, we held a meeting of the United Kingdom Scleroderma Study Group and the European Club. The focus of this meeting being the clinical trials which are now in progress or about to start. There are some very exciting possibilities around.

In the autumn we hope to start a trial of relaxin, which is an antifibrotic drug in patients with diffuse scleroderma and also two pilot studies of very interesting compounds. The first is an antibody against transforming growth factor 13 which is a very important growth factor in initiating the fibrosis and also the possibility of using b interferon as a modulator of the immune system, and possibly a drug which affects the production of fibrous tissue. Also in the autumn there will be a new trial started for Pulmonary Hypertension. This will be using a drug which is an antagonist to endothelin-1, a most powerful vasoconstrictor substance and with a possible role in fibrosis. One of the exciting things about this drug is that it can be taken by mouth.

At the present time several centres in the United Kingdom are involved in trials of inhaled Iloprost, subcutaneous prostacyclin, or oral Iloprost in pulmonary hypertension. It is really exciting that this hitherto very dangerous complication of scleroderma is now receiving a great deal of attention. Two other important trials, which are supported by the United Kingdom Scleroderma Study Group, will be getting underway in the near future. The first is a trial of Quinapril in limited scleroderma. This is a trial supported by the British Society of Rheumatology and the Arthritis Research Campaign and secondly, a trial of oral Iloprost in scleroderma, funded by the Raynaud's & Scleroderma Association.

We will need to recruit as many patients as possible to these trials and this is where our Central Register will be helpful. Our Central Register is a venture supported by the United Kingdom Scleroderma Study Group, which aims to register as many U.K. patients as possible at a central source so that they might be offered a place on any of the available trials, provided they meet the inclusion criteria. The Central Register is growing rapidly and has already been a good source of patients for the Interstitial Lung Disease trial, which is currently ongoing.

With our European colleagues, the lead being taken by Italian Rheumatologists, we have been working on an Activity Index for scleroderma. We will discuss the results of this joint activity in Oxford. There are many doctors in Europe who are interested in scleroderma and we are very keen to work with them as closely as possible. As well as being interested in research in scleroderma, we are also very keen to educate our young doctors so there is a new generation of specialists interested in scleroderma and Raynaud's. We will endeavour to do this at a Post-graduate course at the Royal Free in January 2001. This is essentially a teaching course which will last for two days and which we hope as many trainees as possible will attend.

On the basic science front there have been a number of advances in scleroderma research recently. Research carried out in France has shown increased levels of a protein called endostatin in patients with SSc. This protein, derived from Type XVIII collagen is a known inhibitor of blood vessel formation. Elevated circulating levels of endostatin may therefore be an important link between tissue fibrosis and the development of the ischaemic manifestations in SSc. Another study from Japan identified an association between a genetic polymorphism (microsatellite) or change in the DNA around the collagen type I gene and increased levels of collagen transcription. These investigators also noted a significant risk for SSc with individuals with a certain genetic combination of polymorphisms. Researchers in Houston, Texas have also identified an association between polymorphisms in the extra cellular matrix protein fibrillin and the Choctaw Indians and SSc in general. These studies are very exciting in view of the recent evidence that auto-antibodies to fibrillin are also found in patients with SSc, suggesting abnormalities in this protein.

Other research has further highlighted the role of growth factors notably connective tissue growth factor (CTGF) in the fibrotic component of SSc. This growth factor appears to be a key fibroblast mediator in the disease process and further studies are underway to fully understand the role of CTGF in SSc, and examine whether it may represent a good target for future therapeutic approaches.

Professor Carol Black, Dr. David Abraham
Royal Free Hospital, London

University of Manchester

Genetic Study

Even though systemic sclerosis (SSc) is a clinically heterogeneous disease, one of the major hallmarks is fibrosis. We are testing the hypothesis that a genetic predisposition to fibrosis may make individuals susceptible to SSc and may determine the degree of fibrosis and thus disease subtype (limited or diffuse) that develops. We have investigated the genes for six proteins that are involved in fibrosis, namely transforming growth factor beta 1, 2 3 (TGFb1, 2, 3), tissue inhibitor of metalloproteinase 1 (TIMP1), platelet derived growth factor b and the alpha 2 subunit of collagen type five using DNA markers that are located very close to the genes.

We have evidence that polymorphisms (minor variations in DNA sequence) in the markers for TGFb2, TGFb3 and TIMP1 occur more frequently in patients with SSc. These results indicate that TGFb2, TGFb3 and TIMP1 may be involved in the genetic susceptibility to SSc. Interestingly, polymorphisms within the marker for TGFb3 have been found to differ between patients with limited and diffuse subtype, indicating that TGFb3 may be involved in determining the subtype of disease that the patient develops. To further investigate the role of TGFb2, TGFb3 and TIMP1 we have looked at markers that occur within these genes directly. Markers located within genes may be functionally important. They may, for example, determine the amount of protein that is produced. We again found association of the TGFb3 gene with SSc and differences between patients with limited and diffuse disease. These results are very exciting as they mirror the results found with the marker located outside of this gene and therefore strengthen the evidence that TGFb3 may be involved in the genetic susceptibility to SSc and may determine the disease subtype that develops. Currently, we are also analysing two markers that occur within the TIMP1 gene and identifying markers within the TGFb2 gene to be analysed.

We would like to take this opportunity to thank all the patients who attend Hope Hospital in Salford and The Royal National Hospital for Rheumatic Diseases in Bath for kindly donating blood for these studies. A thorough understanding of the genetic basis to SSc will increase our knowledge of the aetiology of SSc that will be central to the development of new treatment strategies.

Jane Worthington & Elene Susol, Manchester University

Hammersmith Hospital

A study of the potential role of nitric oxide in fibrotic lung disease

Hanna Romanska

Lung fibrosis, a feature and a major cause of morbidity and mortality of systemic sclerosis (SSc), is also the final outcome of a range of lung diseases that result from acute lung injury. It is characterised by a deposition of scar-like material which causes an increased rigidity of the lung and leads to and manifests as progressive breathlessness and exhaustion. At the cellular level, the main mediators of the disease are cells called fibroblasts, whose uncontrolled proliferation and increased synthetic activity are believed to be responsible for the development of this fatal condition. The mechanisms underlying activation of fibroblasts are not fully understood, but it has been suggested that chronic inflammation and oxidative stress might trigger their increased and unbalanced activity. The molecule-oxidant implicated in the process is nitric oxide (NO) and it is believed that its deleterious action is due to the overproduction of the enzyme, inducible nitric oxide synthase (iNOS). The aim of our study was to test the hypothesis that NO produced by fibroblasts themselves promotes the onset and progression of lung fibrosis both associated with SSc and of unknown cause.

We have previously reported to the Raynaud's & Scleroderma Association that using a technique of immunocytochemistry, we were not able to detect any differences in a pattern of iNOS expression between lung samples from patients affected and not affect by SSc. The characteristic feature of iNOS distribution was high expression in fibroblasts of early foci of extensive inflammation but not in late fibrotic lesions. These results led us to the conclusion that in human lung an excessive production of iNOS/NO, most likely caused by the initial inflammation, is a powerful stimulus contributing to the induction of a fibrotic process. This was further confirmed by our in vitro study, where using living human lung fibroblasts, we demonstrated that an 'inflammatory environment' created artificially in the laboratory, instigated acute response of the cells. Using molecular biology techniques, we showed induction of iNOS gene as early as 3 hours after the onset of inflammatory stimulation and this effect was associated with a significant increase in fibroblasts numbers. Our investigation of the potential role of NO in lung fibrosis continued and concentrated on in vitro study.

The aims of the most recent work was to assess 'efficiency' of iNOS gene activation in terms of synthesis and activity of iNOS protein and, consequently, the amount of generated NO. Using a routine technique of protein detection (Western blotting), we were able to demonstrate increased amount of iNOS in extracts from fibroblasts exposed to inflammatory stimuli. Since NO is a very short-lived molecule, evaluation of its quantity can be accomplished only indirectly by measurement of concentration of stable end-products (nitrites/nitrates) of its reaction with other substances.

In order to do that we employed a well established technique in our Department (chemiluminescence analysis) and showed an increase of NO production parallel to that of iNOS protein. Extrapolating these results to an in vivo situation, it seems justifiable to propose the scenario whereby the initial insult to the lung by a defined or unknown agent induces a massive inflammation which, apart from having an effect on various types of cells, stimulates residing fibroblasts to switch on iNOS gene. Up-regulation of iNOS gene is 'translated' by the molecular machinery of the cells into production of NO which in turn stimulates the neighbouring cells and that from which it originates to proliferate. This immediate response is followed by a sequence of events orchestrated by other powerful mediators but the precise mechanism of NO action as well as its relationship and influence on ensuing events are still unknown.

In summary, the results accumulated so far strongly support the hypothesis that NO is a mediator of an early phase of the development of lung fibrosis and provides a new perspective on this insidious and irreversible process. Blocking iNOS at the level of gene or protein expression may be a useful test to assess lung biopsies for the onset of lung fibrosis in high risk individuals including patients with systemic sclerosis.

Hanna Romanska,
Hammersmith Hospital

Nursing News

The Role of the Nurse Specialist

Helen Wilson

Confusion for both patients and medical staff surrounds the various titles and roles of nurse specialists (also known as nurse practitioners, specialist nurses and by many other titles!). There does not appear to be a universally recognised title and the role varies considerably depending on the individual nurse, her consultant and the type of disease that she specialises in. One definition of a clinical nurse specialist is "an academically prepared nurse with significant clinical experience in a specialised area of nursing practice', but I feel the job involves much more than that. By creating the position of rheumatology nurse specialist in our department we felt we could offer a more holistic approach to the care of individual patients. It is a developing and exciting role, which has developed out of patient need.

There are five main aspects to my role: clinical, education, patient advocacy/ support, liaison and research.

Firstly, as the name suggests, I am a clinical specialist. I tend to work closely alongside the doctors when they are in clinic helping to assess and monitor patients and also to evaluate their care. I also run my own clinic for patients with Primary Raynaud's Phenomenon. Many patients have commented that one of the benefits of a nurse-led clinic is seeing a familiar face each time they come to the hospital, as unfortunately our junior doctors have to move on a regular basis to gain experience. We have also set up a Raynaud's database and I enter all the relevant data from my clinic, which then provides us with information for medical records, G.P.s, clinical audit and for Raynaud's research. We also now have a fully functioning clinical service for scleroderma patients with pulmonary hypertension (PHT). We have a Pulmonary Hypertension Nurse Specialist and she is the liaison nurse for all scleroderma patients with PHT.

Another major part of my role is as an educator. There is an increasing tendency for all patients to want to know more about their diseases and treatment. At the Royal Free, the Scleroderma Unit attempts not only to treat scleroderma medically and investigate it scientifically but also to teach you, the sufferers, about your disease and how to live with it. Education is particularly important in chronic diseases such as scleroderma. These rare conditions are very complicated, most people haven't even heard of scleroderma until they are diagnosed with it, so however long a medical consultation may be, there are usually many more issues which patients may wish to discuss. This is where we come in. I work alongside the doctors both in the Out Patients Department and on the ward and together with my small team, we are available to sit down with you and discuss anything you wish to ask about your disease.

This need for information may not be fully satisfied by a single educational visit but extends throughout your follow up here. We hope it helps patients to know that we are always available to answer their questions. I am also kept busy writing specialised information leaflets and giving lectures and talks to nurses and other health care professionals to help raise scleroderma awareness. Nurse specialists like me are in an ideal position to act as patient advocates. Doctors and nurses can sometimes be in danger of assuming only they know what is best for patients, but by providing clear information and support we can help patients, particularly those who are vulnerable and without the support of family and friends, to feel confident to make their own decisions. Because of the chronic and deforming nature of many rheumatological conditions, many patients need a lot of emotional support and reassurance. I often find that whilst patients like to be given their diagnosis and discuss their medication with a doctor, they often find it easier to discuss other aspects of their condition with a nurse.

We also feel that patients need a point of contact when they feel ill, anxious or depressed so I run a help-line. The helpline provides direct access to the department for patients, carers, primary health care team, other professionals and anyone who wants information regarding their disease and its treatment. Many of our patients live a long way away and the helpline means there is an easy way to talk to someone without having to come to the hospital in person. If I can't help you, hopefully I can point you in the direction of someone who can. As a nurse specialist, I am often in the best position to co-ordinate care and support patients both in the hospital and the community. I act as a liaison with the doctors, the multi-disciplinary team, ward staff, G.P.s and Practice Nurses and, of course, the Raynaud's & Scleroderma Association, who have offered us such invaluable support and advice over the years.

Research is an equally important aspect of the role. Because scleroderma is currently still incurable we are continually working within our own laboratory and with outside pharmaceutical companies to find new drugs and to improve established therapies to treat this condition. Specialist nursing expertise is invaluable in helping to set up clinical trials and our role is to ensure that the patient is fully informed, written information is comprehensible and ethical issues are addressed. Funding from such studies enables us to do more research and provides patients with facilities and services, which would not normally be available. Sam, our clinical trials/research nurse, helps me with the day to day running of all of our current trials, both in-house research and pharmaceutical trials. However, she also plays an invaluable role in helping with patient education.

Future developments for nurse specialists depend not only on the individual consultant and nurse and how they choose to take the role forward, but also on you, the patients, and what you want or need. An experienced nurse specialist will have more specialised knowledge than a junior house officer and there are many ways the role could develop. One fact is certain - that the role will extend and expand further and nurse specialists will become commonplace in the next few years.

Helen Wilson, Royal Free

A nursing update from Leeds

As I come to the end of my second year in post as part time clinical nurse specialist based in the Department of Rheumatology at Leeds General Infirmary, I felt this would be a good time to update members of the Association on the work that I have been involved in with the Raynaud's and scleroderma patients in the Yorkshire region. When I started this new post in 1998, I began by finding out what the expectations of the service were, and putting these into a set of objectives which outlined four areas of my role; those being patient support, running of a telephone help-line, education and research. I will update you in each of these areas.

Naomi Reay

In September last year, I arranged a series of evening support groups for patients with scleroderma held at Chapel Allerton Hospital. We had a good response to invitations, with twenty patients and their partners attending. We based the group around a trial of exercise therapy and the group was jointly run by Ruth Stevens (Senior Occupational Therapist), and Phillipa Morreno, (Senior Physiotherapist), who offered invaluable advice on exercise therapy, home adaptations, disability, energy conservation and the exercise programme which we were trialing. Evaluation of this group by those who attended showed it to have been useful in many aspects, such as improvement of knowledge and reduction of anxiety, and I therefore plan to organise similar sessions in the future.

I share a dedicated room on 'C' floor at LGI with Elizabeth Tyas, Clinical Nurse Specialist for patients with SLE. We have a small private area where we can see patients out of clinic times and this has proved an invaluable space for quiet conversation with both patients and their families. This also provides a base for the educational material provided by the Association, which I distribute to patients, groups and provide to the outpatient areas around the Leeds Hospital sites. Another key area which I have identified and developed since beginning in post is proactive work with the local hospices for the small amount of patients who have needs for shared care between ourselves, community staff and the hospice. This follows discussion with patients and families and has been a very needed and well received service by patients who find hospice day care a particularly helpful way of fulfilling their personal needs during times when travel to hospital is difficult for them. I have been delighted by the support and care offered by the hospices and I would like to express my thanks to them for their invaluable support for this small groups of patients who are able to retain an element of choice and fulfilment due to a planned approach to shared care.

I am based at the Leeds General Infirmary and am available for patient consultations on both a planned and 'drop-in' programme during the weekly connective tissue outpatient clinics held there. Further to this, I have links with the outpatient service based at Wharfedale Hospital at Otley from where patients are referred for support and education. I am available during the Connective Tissue Clinic based at St James's Hospital for planned or drop in consultations with patients. The telephone helpline remains very well used by both patients and professionals. I have an answerphone so if you leave me your details I can ring you back. This service is open to anyone who wants advice or support. I continue a programme of education about Raynaud's and scleroderma. This happens with patients and families but also other professionals in the hospitals and community who are involved in your care and may want some more knowledge or support.

I am happy to come and speak to groups within my area, and indeed have already met many interested people who are working hard to raise funds for the work of the Association. We continue to be busy here in Leeds working on research projects to help find out more about the treatments which are available. We are at present keenly involved with the Fibrosing Alveolitis in Scleroderma Trial (FAST), which is a three-year study of the treatments offered for this form of lung disease in scleroderma. Three of our patients are currently enrolled in this multi-centre trial co-ordinated by the Royal Brompton Hospital in London. In addition. we are working on patient education research, and also into the effect of exercise in scleroderma as part of the Leeds Scleroderma Therapy Group. Work towards multicentre research continues with our data input into the National Scleroderma Database, held at the Royal Free Hospital and essential work to provide data for a Scleroderma Disease Activity Index working alongside our American colleagues. We have many exciting plans for next year. This post remains a very rewarding challenge, with huge potential for expansion and I thank the Raynaud's & Scleroderma Association, and the staff and patients in Leeds for sharing their support and enthusiasm.

Naomi Reay

The current role of the Clinical Nurse Specialist in the CTD clinic in Bath

Sue Brown

Specialist nursing practice is described by the United Kingdom Central Council for Nurses as an area of practice where possession of additional skills and knowledge enables the nurse to function with a higher level of clinical judgment, providing expert clinical care, leadership, teaching and support to others. The Clinical Nurse Specialist (CNS) has been described as a role model, where advanced skills are used and expert knowledge is demonstrated in order to assess, plan, implement and evaluate nursing care. Also called an influencer, the CNS advises and teaches patients about their condition, equipping them with coping skills for disease management.

Jackie Hill, a nurse practitioner in rheumatology from Leeds, described in 1992 that the CNS complements the rheumatologist's skills, acting as a professional in his/her own right. Other authors have described the mutual respect that the consultant and rheumatology specialist nurse develop when working together in order to improve both the care and management we offer to our patients.

In terms of patients who attend the Connective Tissue Diseases (CTD) clinic at the Royal National Hospital for Rheumatic Diseases in Bath, we have been able to offer the services of a CNS to Raynaud's and scleroderma patients over the last 4 years. I have been developing my role over this time with all patients who attend the clinic and in more recent times have been partially funded in this role by both the Raynaud's & Scleroderma Association and Lupus U.K. I have been working closely with Dr. Neil McHugh in this constantly changing and developing role, in order to place patients with chronic illnesses such as Raynaud's and scleroderma, centrally to the multi-disciplinary care that is offered in the clinic.

As well as seeing patients in the weekly CTD clinic for nurse consultations, I have recently been involving scleroderma patients in the development of a patient focused education programme in which I have been asking local patients to participate in focus groups where they have been able to discuss as a group in a confidential setting, their opinions and views about the education issues that are important to them. Research in 1985 (Silvers et al) demonstrated that unless patients' views are central to the education process, poor communication and inappropriate treatments have been found. This idea of patients' opinions and views being central to an education programme became stronger with the publication of the USA arthritis and musculoskeletal patient education standards in 1994. Authors such as Neville et al (1995) have reported that in order to improve health outcome in chronic disease, health care professionals have to understand patients' needs, as they can be perceived differently.

In the knowledge of published research such as these, I decided to place patients at the heart of the education programme. By using patients' opinions and views, my aim now is to develop an education programme for scleroderma patients that will reflect the important issues raised in the focus groups. This approach will also allow patients the opportunity to be involved in the multi-disciplinary team that will create the programme. I have now completed the two scleroderma patients' focus groups and am in the process of transcribing the taped recordings in order to feed the group's views into the programme development. One of the ultimate aims of the programme will be to encourage patient empowerment, fostering informed choice that will allow patients to make decisions.

This research will also be used in my current professional development as I am pursuing a MSc in Healthcare Practice at Bath Spa University College. I would like to thank any members of the Association who were kind enough to participate in the focus groups and also the Association for continuing to fund the post so that such new initiatives can be developed.

Sue Brown, Clinical Nurse Specialist,
Royal National Hospital for Rheumatic Diseases NHS Trust, Bath

Lifeline

This photograph shows the Carlton television crew with staff at our office in Alsager, when they came to make a short film on Raynaud's for the lifeline programme. The 5 minute film was shown twice on Sunday 24th September 2000. Two of our members, Kay Tasker from Oswestry and Louise Charles from Sandbach were filmed at their homes, showing how they cope with day to day life.

Percy Pics

Percy meets Mickey Mouse in Disneyland.

Percy sozzled in Madeira!

Posing in the Forbidden Palace in Bejing.

Percy in the Amazon rainforest.

Percy Penguin with member Joan Goulden

This photograph appeared in the Blackpool Gazette during Awareness Month. Joan recently celebrated her 80th Birthday and sent donations totalling £250 to the Association in lieu of presents.

Many thanks Joan!

Millennium Conference

New Venue

Our new venue in Chester proved to be popular for our Millennium Conference. The weekend began on Friday 29th Septemter with a Seminar for Health Professionals. Professor Carol Black, together with Sister Helen Wilson and Sister Sarah Dawes, provided in-depth information on the team management of Raynaud's and scleroderma to 50 nurses, physiotherapists, occupational therapists and G.P.s. On the Friday evening. following an excellent dinner, delegates were entertained by Laura O'Connor, one of our younger members. Laura gave a brief talk on how scleroderma had affected her and then went on to sing to the audience. Laura has a great talent and we are sure that she will achieve her ambition to become a singer.

Speakers' Presentations

The Conference Chairman for the day was Mr Kevin Lafferty who as usual kept the proceedings to time and entertained the audience with his great sense of humour. Sir Donald Wilson said a few words to open the Conference, commenting on how the Association had grown over the past few years. He felt that the appointment of the nurse specialists was a very important development. The first speaker was Professor Mark Winslet who described the problems of the bowels with good humour and a straight forward approach. Professor Carol Black talked about where we are today in relation to Raynaud's and scleroderma and how far we have progressed since the days when all anyone knew was that Raynaud's involved cold hands. A session where the audience asked questions to the nurses proved to be very popular. This was followed by David Wilkie MBE who presented some of the preliminary findings on the Dundee study of Seredrin (high strength Ginkgo biloba with Phytosome). In the afternoon, following Sir Robin David's introduction, Professor Ron du Bois based his talk on the question "How do I know if I have lung disease?". Tonia Moore and Dr. Marina Anderson described the tests which are carried out at Hope Hospital and Frank Webb talked about the problems of Raynaud's and scleroderma in the feet.

Laura O'Connor

The following is a summary of Laura's talk

Hello, my name is Laura O'Connor and I am 15 years old. I would like to tell you how scleroderma has affected me but from a positive viewpoint. Obviously losing part of a limb is not something you can take lightly, it is drastic and traumatic. However, I have been brought up to concentrate on life's advantages and minimise the disadvantages, for example I only have to wash one foot, I only have to cut the toe nails on one foot and I only have to worry about new shoes being tight on one foot. The ups and downs I have had in my short life have made me more determined and resolute. People often say to me that I am brave; I appreciate the sentiment, but I believe brave people carry out good acts on instinct and by choice. I had no choice therefore bravery does not come into it. I took a calculated decision to have a below the knee amputation because I wanted to be more mobile.

I am often asked how I cope considering that losing part of a limb is bad enough, let alone the added complications. I am always encouraged to turn disadvantages to my advantage and I try to see the good side of everything that happens to me. My mum and dad always say that the cure for adversity is optimism and that your happy memories are your cushion in life. I spend a lot of time on various cushions, lying in bed after operations etc. so I ensure that I have lots of happy memories. Every time I believe I am on the up, life has a habit of knocking me down, but this life is going to get tired of knocking me down before I get tired of jumping back up. You may find this hard to comprehend but very few people know that I have a prosthesis. The majority of the children in my school have no idea and some of them that do only know because one of my prosthesis was a loose fit. One day in the classroom I decided to jump up and sit on a desk and my leg fell off. I can tell you there were some shocked and puzzled faces until we had a good burst of spontaneous laughter.

I am pleased to discuss with people matters surrounding having a false limb particularly if they are prospective or new amputees, as I feel that hearing it from someone who has experienced it makes it easier to accept. Since my amputation I have been able to lead a much freer, normal life and I can do most of the things my friends do. Being mobile has allowed me to pursue my greatest love and that is singing and I have a burning ambition to be famous. I know it will be hard to achieve that ambition but when I succeed I want to succeed on my ability and not because people feel sorry for me. Nevertheless if anyone has got any openings for a one legged singer I am available. I have recorded with Boy George at Abbey Road Studios in the studio that the Beatles recorded in and I have been fortunate enough to team up with a song writer who writes songs that I enjoy singing. They are songs with a message which brings to the fore injustice, prejudice and feeling for our fellow human beings. I am hoping to record a charity record but first of all I have to get a record company interested. I have written to TV shows but to date I have received no offers so I am waiting for them to employ someone who can spot talent.

If you ask how has scleroderma affected me I can sum it up by saying it hasn't, because I have not let it. What it has done is present me with a constant challenge and a war of attrition but as far as I am concerned, it is no contest because I know that I will win the battle. There is so much that I want to achieve that I do not have the time or the interest to be sidetracked.

Laura O'Connor

Opening words

The following is a summary of the opening words by Sir Donald Wilson at our conference:

Professor Carol Black and Sir Donald Wilson.

The first task in forming an Association is to make sure that the public understand what it is about - it has an identity. This is not an easy task when you have many prominent Associations established over many years, richly endowed, with a lot of people raising vast sums of money and the public readily understand their work. But you had to start out on a course of identification, needing staffing and resources and that was your first task. Having set it on the right road research was obviously a vital component. You have been going barely 18 years and in that period you have raised over 4 million pounds for research. Much of it has come in penny pieces, a lot of it has come from small sales, but it is a vast sum of money when you think of the small group of people who initially carried this forward.

How vital is research? You are lucky in that you have clinicians, doctors, professionals at all levels who have come along and helped you but it is always very important in this field to think of the nurses. They are the people who are close to the patients, they know what the patients want, they can furnish you with ideas on what is really going on. Research is a long, hard task to face but I suspect probably just over the hill there will be drugs, new ideas, new perceptions, new treatments which will give to many of you an opportunity for a fuller life and that will be funded and provided by research, and money is the very sinew of that research. Another aspect of your work is to make available to many what you are doing, what you are about and what you are achieving. Your newsletter is very successful but it is often through word of mouth, conversation and hearing what other people do that counts. There may be some of you here today who have been recently diagnosed, who are looking at the future with some considerable concern and there will be others who have suffered pain and anguish over many years. They will give strength to those who have recently become identified as they have got through it and other people will see how they have overcome their difficulties. This I believe is the great strength of Associations such as this. All of this is for your future, a very welcome future to provide for many, relief from anxiety and pain. I am sure that you will go away from this conference, renewed and invigorated. You will appreciate the hard work of your officers, your director and many others. You will have learned much, made friends and I wish you every success.

Gastrointestinal manifestations of systemic sclerosis

Professor Marc Winslet

Professor Winslet's lecture focused on our current understanding of gut involvement in systemic sclerosis with particular reference to diagnosis, clinical manifestation, treatment and prognosis. Bowels are not something that are commonly talked about in polite society and just like they are socially relegated, they are medically relegated and perhaps nowhere more so than in the condition of scleroderma. Nonetheless, to ignore the bowels is to overlook what can be a major debilitating problem for patients. Professor Winslet took us on a slightly irreverent journey around the gastrointestinal tract, its investigation and management in scleroderma.

As many of you will know, there are several types of scleroderma, some of which have almost no involvement of the gut at all, such as the morpheas and others in which there is significant involvement such as those patients with diffuse cutaneous disease. It is not a condition commonly discussed but approximately 50% of patients who have systemic sclerosis will have some form of gastrointestinal involvement. It can involve any part of the gut but the commonest sites are in the oesophagus where it presents with difficulty swallowing, heartburn and reflux, or in the anus where, unfortunately, it frequently presents with incontinence. Many of you have a vague understanding of what scleroderma is about and those who suffer can actually see the pathology frequently on their skin. The same phenomena that occurs in the skin, occurs in the gut tissue as well and we get damage to the gut from deposition of collagen, damage to the nerves and damage to the blood vessels as well as damage to the associated immune system.

The disease progresses in a very step wise manner, occurring first in the gut where the nerves become involved at a level which you can't see, often even with a microscope and the changes are very insidious and very difficult for doctors investigating patients to pick up and identify. Nevertheless, in the early stages if identified early, we can produce a reversal of the patient's symptoms. In many however, the disease may be progressive and will move on from nerve damage to muscle damage. 90% of the gut is a muscular tube and once the muscle itself starts to become damaged, we then start to produce irreversible problems in the gut which manifest themselves in their impact on the patient's day-to-day living.

Swallowing food is an amazingly complex mechanism involving co-ordination of nerves and muscles. The first thing that happens is that food gets flicked to the back of your throat, after which you have no conscious control over how it gets down to your stomach but through marked co-ordination of muscles in the gullet it is propelled in an active manner downwards. We can record the propulsion of food through the gut, using modern investigative techniques. The way we do it now rather than using an old-fashioned X-ray, is to pass a very fine catheter through the nose with pressure transducers on it and we can measure these contractions in people's gullet from top to bottom. So having passed this tube into someone's gullet, we can measure pressure waves that build up in the gullet as the food passes on its way down to the lower end of the gullet where a muscle relaxes and allows it into the stomach.

Scleroderma patients' swallowing, is on the whole, much weaker initially in the disease and therefore it is more difficult to get the food down and that presents as food sticking or even regurgitating. In early involvement in the gut, the main problem is in the nerves of the lower two-thirds of the gullet. As the disease progresses there is increasing involvement of the gut and frequently people can actually have an inability to swallow their food at all. Looking at people with scleroderma early on in the disease process, when they have their wet swallow there is contraction, with peaks in the waves which are unco-ordinated and don't resemble that of the normal group. This unco-ordination then becomes a total lack of contraction.

In someone with severe gut involvement, they can swallow hard but nothing happens anywhere in their gut, the food is sitting statically in their oesophagus for many hours before gravity will take it through into the stomach. People with scleroderma not only have trouble getting food down, but they can have trouble because the food keeps coming back up and approximately 40% of people suffer from significant reflux symptoms. Normally there are several things which protect us from the contents of our stomach, mainly a one-way valve to keep food in the stomach but unfortunately, in people with scleroderma this muscle doesn't work and the one-way propagation wave down into the stomach doesn't occur and the flap valve is held rigidly open by muscle fibrosis. We can objectively identify people who are suffering from significant reflux by passing fine catheters into their gullet and measuring their acid levels.

A technique used by Professor Black for many years to assess people's gullets is scintigraphy whereby people are given a radioactive drink and then the radioactivity is observed as it goes up and down the gullet and hopefully into the stomach. Whilst this is not bad as a relatively crude indicator, no-one had ever actually evaluated it against the gold standard of these pressure measurements, which we can take through the nose. One of the first pieces of research Professor Black and I did together, was to evaluate this technique and we have been able to show that in expert hands scintigraphy which merely involves swallowing some pineapple purée rather than having something forced down your nose, is actually as accurate as our current techniques, provided that the transducer experiments are first performed as a base line. So we now use this to follow patients up having identified the problems they have in their gullet and we can grade them on a scale of 0 to 4. After you've taken your radioactive pineapple purée, we pop you under a little camera and we can measure the radioactivity as it goes down.

In the majority of scleroderma patients, the purée remains as a static lump in the oesophagus even after several minutes have passed and one of the things that I was initially interested in was comparing whether there was a relationship between involvement of the gut and other manifestations of scleroderma, probably the most obvious one being skin. I was also interested to see whether from some of their blood tests, we might be able to predict whether people might get gut involvement. We studied 256 patients who had scleroderma and all of those patients had undergone assessment of their skin in a prospective manner and were scored from 0 to 60. They then had two oesophageal scintiscans done approximately one year apart to see whether their oesophageal involvement was static, improved or got worse and whether we could identify those people who were going to get worse and treat them at a stage before they developed their symptoms.

Overall we found that if we just looked at the skin, there was both improvement and minor deterioration in peoples' skin changes over a years review. Unfortunately however, we could find no correlation between progressive skin disease and the development of oesophageal changes as seen on scintiscan. So just from clinical examination we were unable to predict people who might run into trouble with their swallowing. We then looked at whether these fantastically intricate blood tests carried out by Professor Black might be of help for us as surgeons, in predicting gullet involvement. In the same 256, we were able to pull out all the results of their blood tests over a 2 year period and again compare that with their scintiscans. We showed that there was marked variation in the results from the blood tests in those who had limited disease or diffuse disease with a wide variation from 1 in 5 to 75% of people being positive for that blood test. Unfortunately, however, if we compare their gullet results over a year from whether they got better, stayed the same or got worse we could find no predictor that would allow us to identify the group who were going to develop gullet problems and therefore at present we are unable to intervene prior to the development of symptoms. The next major part of the gut that can be involved in scleroderma is the stomach and small bowel and this is relatively uncommon compared to gullet or bottom involvement but is nonetheless severely debilitating when it occurs. There are three methods you use to evaluate whether people have small bowel or stomach involvement and we can measure pressure or emptying.

The next major part of the gut that can be involved in scleroderma is the stomach and small bowel and this is relatively uncommon compared to gullet or bottom involvement but is nonetheless severely debilitating when it occurs. There are three methods you use to evaluate whether people have small bowel or stomach involvement and we can measure pressure or emptying. The standard one that has been used is intra luminalmanometry. That again involves having a catheter placed through your nose down into the gut. The only down side of this catheter is that it is 1.2 metres long and most people, not surprisingly have slight problems getting the whole tube down. At the Royal Free, we developed two new methods of assessing people who might have scleroderma involvement of their small bowel. The first is called electro gastrography which is another way of assessing the heart beat of the gut, except we do it in exactly the same way as we assess normal heart beat. Three little sticky pads are placed over someone's stomach and we just measure the electrical activity. This is a completely non-invasive way of identifying abnormalities in the stomach and proximal gut and we can complement that by doing ultrasound. Normally this is an investigation used for pregnant ladies and those who might have gall stones but with current computing techniques we can actually measure the rate of stomach emptying.

Probably the most understated area of involvement of the gut in scleroderma, but potentially the worst, is people who have involvement of their anus and rectum because this has massive impact on the individual's quality of life. They frequently feel totally isolated not only from their friends but are limited in their ability to go out as they have to plan each journey with a strategic precision to find out where the public loos are. Most patients are even reluctant to discuss it or even mention it to their doctor. The common fact of life is that 60% of people over 60 years of age suffer from faecal incontinence, so it has either happened to us or it is going to happen to us. I want to talk you through a little bit about the problems of scleroderma in the bowel.

Basically there are three muscles that control your bottom. There is a little thin one on the inside which is called the internal sphincter. This is a muscle for which you are all going to be eternally grateful because it is the one which keeps you continent without you having to think about it. We then have another muscle on the outside which is a bit thicker and this is the one we can all use if we get caught a bit short and have to go into overdrive to maintain our continence and that is the one we can control with our brain. We then we have a third muscle which is like a little sheet which acts like a catapult in the rectum, again to keep us continent. All three of these muscles can be involved in scleroderma. The catapult because its nerve can be badly damaged and the other two because they are so thin they can get fibrosed with collagen and other connective tissues. Like in the gullet, this is an extremely complex mechanism of co-ordinated muscle and nerve impulses which we rely on every minute of the day but totally disregard otherwise unless it is damaged.

In people who come to us with incontinence, by the use of modern techniques we can now assess both the muscles of someone's bottom and the nerves of their bottom and we can define their problem and then do something about it. The two tests are ano-rectal physiology, where balloons are passed into the rectum and they give us different information, or we can do an ultrasound just like the ones on someone's stomach. With the balloons we put in people's bottoms, we can measure the minimum amount of motion that someone can sense. That is very important because some people can hold litres and not even know about it and then they have an accident and wonder why and it is because their brains are not connected to their bottom and we can diagnose that. Other people have such a sensitive bottom that they have to go every time that they have 10/15 mls of fluid or stool in there and are always rushing to the loo and again, we can identify them. We can then measure the pressures that the bottom can produce both when it is in its resting state and when it is in action and diagnose any underlying defects. When we measure these pressures and put them on a computer we get various little blips which will tell us whether that patient is someone who has to rush to the loo or whether it is someone who might just be incontinent without even registering it, so defining their underlying problem and helping us to treat it.

We undertook a study to look at the problems of incontinence in 69 scleroderma patients to see if they were the same as the general population. All had balloon tests and we compared them with 58 people who had incontinence as well. Urge incontinence is where you have to rush out of the room but can control it for a few minutes: passive incontinence is where it just occurs and you have no idea it has happened. We found that we couldn't discriminate between people who suffered from urge incontinence in scleroderma and those who were just incontinent but otherwise their colon and anus was normal. In people who had passive incontinence however, we found that there were marked differences, in that one particular muscle, the internal sphincter, seems to be the problem. That had major implications for us because as a surgeon I am used to stitching muscle together but I'm not used to stitching things one millimetre across - its a bit like trying to join up wet tissue paper.

In conjunction with one of the major pharmaceutical companies we have now developed a cream which you can apply to tighten that muscle and we are currently using that in clinical trials in patients with scleroderma to improve their incontinence. It is applied twice a day as a little paste just around the anus and to date we have used

16 people and have produced marked improvement in 14. Marked improvement being that they are able to leave the house without a nappy or a pad and enjoy their social life - a huge human and social impact that one little dot of cream can have. Please note that this cream is not yet available as it is still on trial but looks to be a promising treatment for the future.

We were interested in whether involvement of the bottom correlated with involvement of the gullet. In other words, if you got gullet involvement, did you get bottom involvement later on, because patients want to know what the future holds in store for them. We found that if you had gullet involvement, there was actually no correlation with involvement of your bottom. So just because you have problems swallowing did not necessarily mean that you would ever suffer from problems with your bottom in the future. A very important fact for anyone who does have problems swallowing. We also found, however, that if you did have bottom involvement, you always had problems with the gullet as well. So the reverse did not apply.

As well as doing tests to look at how the muscles function, we can actually do tests to see what the muscles of the bottom look like. In some patients we found that they had a tear to the sphincter during childbirth when the head of the baby was delivered and this is something we can physically stitch back together and restore continence. That obviously doesn't apply to all scleroderma patients. Ultrasound is routinely used in assessing people with incontinence to see whether there is a defect in the muscle and we also use this in patients with scleroderma. We were horrified to see that up to three-quarters of the patients seemed to have a defect in their muscle. At the same time as doing this assessment, we also managed to obtain a new piece of equipment called an MRI (magnetic resonance imager) which is basically a huge magnet which can take pictures both from the outside and the inside. We started using the MRI to access 12 patients with scleroderma to see exactly what this damage was and to our amazement we found that on MRI there was no hole in the muscle shaped like a polo mint and what we had picked up on ultrasound was an artifact peculiar to patients with scleroderma. It showed as a little black area which is a gap of air and only occurs in people with scleroderma. The routine use of MRI in assessing people with scleroderma will prevent unnecessary operations trying to correct this defect which doesn't actually exist.

I hope you have enjoyed the little journey from just beyond the tonsils down to the area where no-one speaks its name and I hope I have shown you that as well as trying to look after people we are trying to take things forward.

Professor Mark Winslet, Royal Free Hospital

Raynaud's & Scleroderma Where are we now?

Professor Black aimed to try and tell us where she thinks we are today, which also meant that she had to look a little at where we were in the past. She started with Raynaud's and stated that it used to be that everything that caused cold hands, or blue hands, was called Raynaud's. So often patients came along saying "I have Raynaud's" when they really had chilblains, acrocyanosis or erythromelalgia, ulcers or even gangrene. One of the main things that has happened over the last fifteen years is that we have much clearer definitions which are important as you need clear definitions because they have implications for prognosis and treatment.

You all know if you have Primary Raynaud's you are very unlikely to get a secondary disease. If you have antibodies circulating in the blood and they are of the kind found in Connective Tissue Diseases (CTD), then you are much more at risk. I thought it was important to mention erythromelalgia because I have patients who have both erythromelalgia and Raynaud's. Erythromelalgia is a strange disease in which your hands might seem cold but your feet are burning hot. Some people get this problem in their hands as well. Patients do not easily understand this because they know the treatment for their Raynaud's is to dilate their blood vessels so they think that it will be impossible to treat both the hands and the feet. The treatments that often help erythromelalgia, are drugs like Iloprost and calcitonin gene-related peptide, which dilate blood vessels. It may sound strange but often the trouble in erythromelalgia is a rather slow blood flow and we can dilate the blood vessels to improve it.

I think we understand the mechanisms of both Raynaud's and scleroderma much better than we did 10 years ago, when Raynaud's was only described in the fingers and toes and then the nose and ears but in fact we now know that it happens in the internal organs. Patients will often tell me they feel cold inside and indeed it has been shown again by research over the past few years, that in vaso-spasm, a Raynaud's type phenomenon can happen in the arteries in the heart, the kidneys and probably the lungs. Many years ago, we did not have any knowledge about the inside of the blood vessel and therefore the structure and the function of the blood vessels was not really very well known. If you think about these tubes, inside them are cells called endothelial cells and outside those cells are muscle layers. What we now know is how important these lining cells are. The endothelial cells are 'factories' introducing many substances that effect blood vessel tone. All this comes from research done over the last fifteen years. Some of the important modulators are produced by both the endothial cells and the muscle cells that surround the lining cells. There has been a vast amount of research for example trying to understand compounds such as Endothelin which causes the blood vessels to constrict. We now have in development, drugs that antagonise endothelin. Once we know the substances that cause structural damage to blood vessels or cause severe constriction, we can try to oppose them or dampen them down or modify them in some way.

When Raynaud's was first described and for many subsequent years, patients did not know that it was important to go to their doctor as they were unaware that Raynaud's may develop into something else. We can now predict which patients with Raynaud's are at risk by just looking at the very small blood vessels at the base of the nail and by measuring the proteins in the blood called antibodies. An important piece of work that we have recently done at the Royal Free is to look at 569 Raynaud's cases to see who would develop a CTD. We looked at patients' screening tests in a computerised database that went back 6 years with over 1500 patient years of follow-up on our database. What we normally do for a Raynaud's patient is to see them yearly to check their capillaries and antibodies. When we looked back to see what had happened to all our Raynaud's patients, only 8 of these 569 had progressed on to a connective tissue disease, which is a very small number. The ones who progressed were patients whose capillaries became worse or who had circulating anti-nuclear antibodies. Patients who present with no antibodies and no capillary changes, have very little likelihood of developing any of these abnormalities. We can therefore concentrate on relieving their Raynaud's symptoms but at the same time reassure them that they are probably going to be healthy.

In the past, we treated Raynaud's with nifedipine which was the one drug we all knew about but now there is a much greater choice. I would now like to turn to trials because increasingly we are trying to test things in properly designed trials. You may be asked to go into different sorts of trials. Sometimes we just try to look retrospectively at our patients. There are always problems with this because there will be bias when you just look back into your 'old cases', and this is not the best way to do it. What you want to do is to look forward so you that have a retrospective trial and you might have it as an open trial so that you know what drug the patient is taking but it is much better if the trial is blinded. The best way to test a new drug is to have a randomised controlled trial where neither the patient nor the doctor know which drug the patient is receiving until the end of the trial and the code is broken. Sometimes it is hard for patients especially when a placebo is used as they worry and think that they might not be receiving a real drug. However, if we are to discover whether a drug is any good, then we have to do it this way. There is no shortcut to getting good information. We often do studies on a small number of patients, called pilot studies, to see whether or not something is going to work, or might work, then we put it into trial in a properly powered study where we need many more patients to give a proper answer.

Why do we need to continue to find new drugs?

Many of the treatments that we use for Raynaud's are inconvenient. They have to be given intravenously and many patients do not want to have them this way. They are imperfect because they suit some patients and do not suit others. There is a variable response often with side effects. What we want to do is to develop a range of drugs so that every patient will find a drug that helps them. I am often asked if a drug prescribed for Raynaud's would be good for scleroderma or is it just for the Raynaud's. The answer is that there are some drugs which will help both conditions.

We now have drugs that act on both the endothelial cells and the muscle cells. One of them is a drug called Losartan which is an angiotensin 11 receptor blocker. This is a very useful drug for patients with Raynaud's and does not have as many side effects as nifedipine. For patients who have very bad Raynaud's with ulcers, subcutaneous heparin is useful especially in patients who cannot tolerate Iloprost. Of course we are always looking to find new compounds. Another useful drug is fluoxetine, (the other name is Prozac) and although you think of it as an antidepressant, it is actually a very good drug for patients with Raynaud's. Fluoxetine reduces 5HT which is a very powerful constrictor of blood vessels. It was interesting that fluoxetine worked better in women than men in our trial. The fact that patients respond to one drug does not necessarily mean they will respond to another so it is important when you are discussing drugs with your doctor that you should have the opportunity to try several drugs. I think that doctors often give up too quickly!

Another great development in the last fifteen or twenty years, has been to realise that scleroderma isn't one disease, it has lots of subsets. There are overlap diseases and then there are diseases called undifferentiated connective tissue diseases. In the family of scleroderma diseases, the one that we think about as being the most dangerous, is of course, systemic sclerosis. Localised scleroderma is quite different and affects children more than adults. This is a very different disease from systemic sclerosis but we treat it as part of the family of diseases.

We also know that scleroderma can be caused by environmental agents such as vinyl chloride. Silica can cause scleroderma and some drugs can also cause it. Silica induced scleroderma which coal miners get is the 'induced disease' which is most similar to scleroderma itself. I am often asked about mixed connective tissue disease (MCTD), the undifferentiated diseases and overlap syndromes. They often look like scleroderma. I do not believe MCTD exists but on the other hand some doctors believe in it. I believe most patients with MCTD develop a defined connective tissue disease.

Several years ago scleroderma was considered an uncontrollable disease. Today we have treatments that improve the disease and its prognosis. There will sadly be a few patients for whom we can do very little but fortunately they are very few. These days, by staging the disease and seeing patients as early as possible, we get a very good idea of what sort of problems people are going to have and how we can treat them. We can divide the disease up into patients with lots of skin involvement and patients who have minimal skin changes. Patients have different internal organ problems and they have antibodies which help us predict the organ which may become involved. That is exceedingly important and has made it much easier to manage patients. We used to concentrate only on the skin and that was obviously the wrong thing to do because people are going to have trouble with their heart, their kidneys and their lungs and therefore we have to be proactive. This is one of the most difficult things to explain to colleagues who are not particularly interested in the disease or to General Practitioners. Doctors must think about what is going to happen to a patient and try to prevent problems, or at least treat them at the very beginning. If you take the lungs, it is no use waiting until you are so breathless and coughing so much that really there is nothing we can do. We want to treat you when there is only inflammation in the lungs and not lots of collagen which is very difficult to treat.

Our biggest problem is the fibrosis of scleroderma. When it is severe I think it is our biggest problem today. Sheets of collagen are laid down in the skin, we can't get rid of it and that really means looking very carefully at what is driving this fibrosis and how we can stop it. This type of research is very basic and also exceedingly expensive and I know patients get very impatient feeling that research is slow. Therefore, I just wanted to try and explain to you as simply as possible, just what we need to understand. We all have lots of genes and you can inherit a disease directly e.g. Huntingdon's Chorea or you can have genes that predispose you to a disease. Scleroderma is this type of disease. You could carry the genes that predispose you to a disease but need other initiating factors to permit the disease to be expressed. One of the genes which is over expressed in systemic sclerosis is the gene which produces collagen. When you get pulmonary fibrosis this gene is being switched on in the cells in your lungs and if you get kidney fibrosis it is being switched on in your kidneys. The really important thing at the moment is to understand what is driving the area of the gene which promotes and enhances its transcription so that we can modify this process.

Systemic sclerosis is a general medical problem but I just want to mention the lungs because we are particularly concerned about the blood vessels in the lungs and the problem of pulmonary hypertension. The prognosis used to be very poor. Patients had a shortened life span and we have been trying to make the treatment of pulmonary hypertension better for patients. Because of recent advice to the Government I believe the facilities for care for patients with PHT will improve and patients will be able to be treated early on with the best treatments for that condition. If any of you have the condition or are frightened that you are ever going to develop it, you can now be reassured that the treatments have improved. In a recent study in America, 111 scleroderma patients were treated for 12 weeks with prostacyclin therapy and it was shown quite clearly that the patients' exercise capacity was much better, that their hearts were functioning better and that they had a better quality of life. The heart is a mystery - it is a 'black box' and we have not as yet made sufficient progress in this area. We have got better with kidney disease but we need to educate our patients what to look out for. I wanted you to know that in each organ there have been advances and in some, very significant advances but our greatest need is still for basic research.

I would like to acknowledge the great support that the Association has been to me in doing some of this research but it requires huge resources to do these things. My unit and I are extremely grateful for all you do to help towards this. We have got so much more advanced and research is so much more expensive, so the work you do is really terribly important in raising funds to make these things possible.

Professor Carol Black, Royal Free Hospital

Professor Ron du Bois

Why am I breathless?

How do I tell if I have lung disease?

These are questions frequently asked by patients so I have tried to structure this talk with these in mind. I shall also introduce some of the concepts that have allowed us to understand a little more about what provokes lung disease and how we can assess it more accurately. Breathlessness is worrisome at best and devastatingly frightening at worst and if one's breathing is really bad, particularly if it comes on fairly acutely, it is a terrifying experience.

What makes you breathless?

There is often a presumption that you are breathless because your lungs don't work but that is not always the case. There are many reasons why you become get breathless that lie outside the chest. These include abnormalities of the joints, limbs, muscles or skin, anaemia, and the muscles that are needed for respiration. However, I am going to focus on the lung abnormality that most commonly affects people with systemic sclerosis. Firstly, you need to conceptualise the lungs as a tree upside down and as a trunk with branches becoming smaller until they are twigs. Imagine the tree branching and you can see why it is called the bronchial tree. At the end of these branches are the 'leaves' - the air sacs - and it is these air sacs that are the working end of this machine. This is where you have to get air to, so that it can move through the air sac and into the blood and out into the tissues. If you cannot do that for a variety of reasons, you get breathless. The sac is surrounded by a really fine network of blood vessels and the distance between the red cell and the air on the inside is really very minute. It is a fraction of a millimetre in width, so that allows the oxygen to get into, and the carbon dioxide to get out of the body. It is when these regions get stiffened by the scar tissue that can be part of scleroderma, that this process of oxygenation of the blood is impaired.

I would now like to go on to explain micro anatomy. An electron micrograph is an ultra-magnified image of one of the air sacs. This consists of a convoluted three-dimensional structure which, when it becomes injured, becomes thickened by scar tissue and this is what is happening in scleroderma. The lungs are being injured and our body always responds to injury by producing scar tissue but in the lungs, it makes them function less well. This is the major cause of breathlessness in patients with systemic sclerosis. What will determine how quickly you become aware of lung disease is related to your normal level of activity and what you can no longer do. If you never did anything but sit, lung disease would take longer to manifest. The main symptom that patients will experience if they have lung disease, initially is breathlessness on more strenuous exertion, such as going up a flight of stairs. As disease progresses a slight incline might be a problem and then day-to-day walking on the flat may become more difficult. It is important to stress that many patients can have lung disease and have not yet got symptoms. This is because the process often progresses slowly but we can look at people who are at risk of developing lung disease and try and find it before the symptoms are disabling, which is one of the core thrusts of the research that has been funded by the Association over 10 years.

When patients are first referred, we ask them to describe their symptoms and I am going to focus particularly on some of the tools which we use to try and give us a picture of the pattern of disease. First, we can do a test which everybody feels anxious about but is usually well-tolerated, which is where we pass a bronchoscope into the lungs and wash out the cells (BAL). The pattern of the cells we see tells us something about the type of lung disease a patient may have. Next is a CT scan which is like a chest X-ray where it is possible to image thin slices of the lung from the throat right down to the diaphragm. This gives us a pattern of distribution of abnormality that tells us a lot about patterns of disease. If all of these tools fail to prove a clear picture, we have to take a biopsy of the lung so we can see what pattern of problem is present. This is important in terms of diagnosing the type of lung disease an individual may have. Assessment of severity is much easier. We can do it with CT by scoring the amount of lung that is involved on the scan but the more traditional investigation involves an individual breathing into a variety of pieces of apparatus that measure the function of the lung. Occasionally, we add to this investigation an exercise test on a treadmill to see how well the lungs perform on exercise.

We are learning more and more about patterns of disease that affect the air sacs than ever before. One of the reasons why we are doing so much research in this area is, sadly, for some people, lung disease can have very serious consequences. Some years ago Athol Wells, who was funded by this Association, looked at our population of patients with scleroderma and compared them with individuals who have a fibrosing lung disease, which is similar to but not scleroderma. To all intents and purposes, these patients appeared to have the same disease but people who had scleroderma responded better to treatment than the group of individuals who did not have scleroderma. More recently it has become clear that there are different patterns of lung involvement that produce scarring, which is one of the reasons why a lung biopsy can be important for the individual. The pattern of biopsy has given us the explanation why the two groups of patients differed. Can we do this without a biopsy? Perhaps in the future. Ideally we'd like not to have to do biopsies but sadly at present we cannot always make a precise diagnosis with CT.

Are there any disease patterns that tell us more about whether one individual is more likely to deteriorate than another?

The treatments we use may have side effects and to be able to predict which patients are more likely to deteriorate and therefore more likely to need treatment, is important for each individual. There is a new tool, known as a PET scan, that we hope to be using which is more complicated than our other tests but is the only tool we have at this time which allows us to understand more about the inflammation in the lung in a more dynamic sense. What this test allows us to do is to see the cells as they move into the lung. In some preliminary work we have been imaging the body's scavenger cells, whose normal function is to keep us clear of foreign material but which in scleroderma can cause injury to the lung. The individual is injected with a substance that goes to the lung and it then moves into those cells that are activated. What we can see after roughly 30 minutes, is that the substance localises to the active disease region of the lung telling us that it is in this region of the lung that there is inflammation that could cause damage. In the future this could be of value in teaching us about the earlier, more treatable phase of lung disease.

I have previously spoken about the air sacs that become damaged and scarred but there are other parts of the lung that can become scarred such as the blood vessels. If blood vessels become scarred, you can be breathless. There are therefore two causes in the lung for being breathless - scarring of the air sacs or the blood vessels lining the air sacs. Blood vessel scarring can lead to pulmonary hypertension and the need for iloprost treatment. It is important to distinguish between these two different types of lung disease because of the treatment implications from blood vessel scarring. CT and BAL are most helpful, being normal in blood vessel disease. The combination of these tests differentiate air sac from blood vessel scarring.

What about treatment?

There are several different approaches we can take. We studied the drug Cyclophosphamide, which we believe is probably the best drug available at this time for this condition, in 29 patients. We had the opportunity to study lung function tests available for a three to six month period before and for the same period after treatment was started. On average, patients lost 10% of their lung function during the pre treatment 3 to 6 month period and then after treatment, on average they improved by 4%. Although 4% does not seem to be very much, when you consider it as a turn around from a 10% fall, it is a 14% shift. So one important message to convey is that there is a treatment which can be beneficial for some individuals with lung fibrosis.

What is better than treatment?

Prevention. To prevent disease we need to know why it is that one patient with systemic sclerosis has terrible lung fibrosis and another patient has nothing. It is likely to have something to do with our genes. We have 23 pairs of chromosomes, half of them from our mother and the other half from our father. On each of these chromosomes there are a number of different genes. Chromosome 6 happens to be one of the more important chromosomes in scleroderma because all of the genes that are important for immunity reside here and scleroderma is an auto-immune disease. The body's own defence mechanisms are a central part of causing the problem. A lot of the funding we have received from this Association over the last five years has focussed on trying to work out what it is about us that makes us more likely to get lung scarring. This has functional consequences. As I am sure many of you know, proteins of our body are the products of our genes. These proteins fold up into complex three dimensional patterns and it is this pattern of folding as much as what constitutes these proteins, that is recognised by our body defence systems. A single protein is made up of amino acid building blocks and just one amino acid change can cause this whole three-dimensional structure to change shape.

What does this mean in terms of function? Does this protein then behave differently?

We are currently exploring this concept. I think you can begin to sense that by looking at our genetic makeup, finding differences that may change the shape of proteins that may then behave very differently, can have very important functional consequences and if we can find such key consequences in scleroderma, we may be able to develop less toxic therapies or better preventative strategies to work out who is more at risk.

Francis Gilchrist, funded by the Association, has used a type of DNA fingerprinting technology to analyse genetic factors that influence the production of the Scl 70 autoantibody. She found differences between patients who have lung fibrosis from those who do not. We are therefore moving towards being able to address the question of susceptibility - why are some genes more likely to result in lung scarring? - but we are still a long way off the final answer. The biggest difficulty is that you are all different. You start differently with different genes exposed to different environmental factors. The inter-relation is complex mathematically and this is what makes the problem so difficult.

Professor Ron du Bois,
The Brompton Hospital

Raynaud's investigations in the Vascular Laboratory

Dr. Marina Anderson and Tonia Moore

I want to explain to you about investigations in the vascular laboratory at Hope Hospital. We have a special interest in circulation and a specific interest in patients with Raynaud's Phenomenon. When patients are referred up from the clinic they go through a standard set of tests in the vascular laboratory. The first test is the doppler test to check the circulation in the main arteries. The circulation is like a tree with the main trunk dividing into smaller blood vessels and each one of those smaller blood vessels dividing into a smaller one. What we want to do is to make sure that the circulation is intact before we start doing any other investigations. We do this by a doppler test, which uses sound waves transmitted from a transducer and reflected back off moving red blood cells in the blood vessels. The machine will pick up any changes in the sound waves that are emitted, producing a wave form that will indicate whether or not there are any problems with the circulation. When patients come for this study, we measure the blood flow and blood pressure in the arm, just above the elbow and then move the blood pressure cuff just below the elbow so we have a measure of the flow down the arm and establish if there is any reduction in blood flow. If so this would be treated accordingly.

If the blood flow in the arteries, as with most of our patients, is normal then the next test that we do is a cold challenge test and what that does is establish the patient's response to cold in order to give us an idea of how severe their symptoms are. The thermal imaging camera works just like a video camera but it picks up differences in temperature which are shown on the screen as different colours. The vascular laboratory is temperature controlled and the cold challenge test is done at a thermally neutral temperature of 23 degrees. We have a large air conditioning unit which helps to maintain that temperature so we try to standardise any external conditions. We ask patients not to have any caffeine or nicotine for four hours before the test because they can act as a vasoconstrictor and that can affect the results. Patients are asked to wear comfortable clothing and they will acclimatise for twenty minutes. What we tend to find is that with normal circulation, you wouldn't expect to see any temperature difference between the fingers and the back of the hand. An area is defined on the dorsum of the hand and compared to the temperature of the tips of the fingers. What we tend to see with patients who have Raynaud's Phenomenon, is that the fingers, at a normal temperature of 23 degrees, are a cooler temperature than the back of the hand counting anything of more than one degree as a significant temperature difference.

When patients have acclimatised for twenty minutes, after we have taken the first image of the hand, we cool the fingers down by immersing the hands in cold water at 15 degrees for one minute (which is the equivalent of cold tap water) having asked them to put on gloves to keep the hands dry. After the patients have had the hands cooled down, I fix the hands onto a polystyrene board with double-sided sticky tape so that they can't move and I focus the camera onto the hands and record the temperature for 15 minutes. I measure the temperature at the tips of the fingers every couple of seconds and plot a graph of how quickly the fingers rewarm. Under normal circumstances, the fingers start to warm up fairly quickly, in fact almost immediately, after taking the hands out of the cold water. However, in patients with primary Raynaud's that increase in temperature is often reduced and the delay in the re-warming is quite marked. In secondary Raynaud's we tend to see no re-warming within the fifteen minute period which means that the fingers are still as cold at the end of the fifteen minutes as they were when the fingers were taken out of the cold water. I then warm the room up to 30 degrees and let the patient acclimatise for a further twenty minutes and take another image of the hands. In a primary Raynaud's condition the fingers should warm to the same temperature as the back of the hand demonstrating the reversibility of the condition. In a secondary Raynaud's condition the temperature difference is persistent, demonstrating the more permanent structural effects of the condition. We use the cold challenge test to try to differentiate between a primary and secondary condition.

Another test that we use is nailfold capillary microscopy. If we go back to the circulation and picture it as a tree, the main arteries divide into smaller arteries and each one of those divides until you get to the very, very tiny branches and these are the capillaries. They are the smallest of all the blood vessels and they are actually about one red blood cell wide so the red blood cells have to squeeze round the blood vessels in single file. Normally these capillaries are at right-angles to the surface of the skin and you can't actually see the capillaries but you can just see the loop at the top. In the area just behind your cuticle in the skin of your fingers and your toes, the capillaries line up parallel to the surface and you can actually see the appearance of the capillary, like a hair pin. This is one test that is very important in differentiating between primary and secondary Raynaud's Phenomenon.

The microscope uses green light which is absorbed by the red blood cells so it shows the capillaries a little more clearly. The microscope is connected by a video camera to the computer, which then records the images. The magnification that I use is 300 times and that gives us a good representation of the capillaries. Your capillaries are quite a uniform shape but it is not unusual to find capillaries that are crossed or that are an abnormal shape. I would say that we tend to see about 7 capillaries in 1 millimetre distance. When we look at the capillaries of a primary Raynaud's sufferer what we tend to see is a normal pattern. Previous studies in our department have shown that if you take the largest of all the capillaries, we tend to see slight differences between normal controls and patients with primary Raynaud's. They tend to be a little bit larger but that has really only been with looking at the largest capillary taken from across the row. Generally they seem to be similar in appearance to normal capillaries, whereas in secondary Raynaud's we tend to see quite marked differences. The capillaries tend to be enlarged and we quite often see bizarre shapes.

In the department we take all these tests and the results of the blood tests together with a description of the patient's symptoms, to make the diagnosis of either a primary or a secondary Raynaud's condition. The equipment at Hope Hospital is quite specialised and is not standard equipment. You will find most rheumatology departments have to rely on a description of the symptoms and they will have developed their own set of tests. We are always developing new techniques for looking at circulation and getting new pieces of equipment for the department.

Tonia Moore

Nailfold capillary permeability in Raynaud's

I am also based in the vascular laboratory, in the Rheumatic Diseases Centre at Hope Hospital with Tonia Moore and I want to tell you very briefly about a research study, funded by the Raynaud's & Scleroderma Association, looking at nailfold capillary permeability in primary Raynaud's Phenomenon and systemic sclerosis. This overlaps a little with what Tonia has described already about the nailfold capillary microscopy. Tonia has explained that capillaries are the very smallest blood vessels in the body and that they occur throughout the body in every tissue. What Tonia didn't mention to you is that these little blood vessels are extremely important as the capillaries are the site at which there is transfer of substances in and out of the blood stream. The oxygen and nutrients go from within the capillaries out into the tissue, and waste products that have formed in the tissue are transferred back into the blood stream at the capillaries, so that these waste products can be taken away and excreted. It is obviously very important that these capillaries function normally for maintenance of healthy body tissues. There are characteristic changes in the shape of the capillaries that occur in systemic sclerosis and these occur very early on in the disease process, but furthermore, there has been work to suggest that the way in which these abnormally shaped blood vessels work is also abnormal.

We can develop capillary microscopy to give us more information with the use of dyes. If we inject a dye into a vein it circulates all the way round the body and will appear in all of the capillaries. We can watch the appearance of the dye at the capillaries of the nailfold with the capillary microscope. We can then watch how the dye moves out of the capillaries - this is called the 'permeability' of the capillaries. The capillaries control how the dye moves out into the tissues surrounding the capillaries, telling us about the permeability of the capillaries and thus how the capillaries function. We use a fluorescent dye, injected into a vein, which then circulates round the body and appears at the capillaries. The fluorescent dye then moves out of the capillaries into a halo in the tissue surrounding the capillaries and we can watch this using a specially adapted microscope. We can measure the intensity of fluorescent light around the capillary at different time points after the dye has moved out into the tissue. The higher the fluorescent light intensity, the more dye has got out. That tells us about the permeability of the capillary and how the capillary is actually working.

There have been a few centres in the world which have used the technique of fluorescent nailfold capillary microscopy. They have generally found that fluorescent dye passes out of the capillaries much more quickly in systemic sclerosis. The halo of dye around the capillary in systemic sclerosis is also much larger and much less well organised than in normal control subjects. The reason why this technique hasn't generally been used more widely, is that it is quite a cumbersome technique and it is very time consuming. Previously video cameras have recorded results onto video tape. This then necessitates playing the video tape back on a video recorder and using light intensity meters to assess fluorescent light intensity at points measured on a TV monitor by a ruler. Our main aim with this study has been to improve upon the technique.

We have attached our video camera directly into the digitiser board of the computer so that there is immediate input of data into the computer, allowing more accurate and automated use of information. In this study we also used the technique to examine the effects of a substance called L-arginine. L-arginine is thought to have the potential to increase blood flow and help the way the blood vessels work. We have studied 7 subjects with primary Raynaud's Phenomenon and also 16 systemic sclerosis subjects. The 16 systemic sclerosis subjects went on after the first nailfold capillary permeability test to have either L-arginine for 28 days or no treatment at all. We then repeated the test after 28 days.

For each test, we put the subject's finger under the microscope and take small overlapping individual pictures right the way across the nailbed. The computer software is such that it can match up the overlapping regions and link up the individual pictures, producing a panoramic view of the nailbed. We then choose a specific area of the nailbed to look at the capillaries and focus on that. Dye is then injected into the vein at the elbow and we observe the dye's appearance at the capillary. The fluorescent dye takes only 30 seconds to 2 minutes to circulate and appear at the capillaries. The dye then moves out of the capillary into a 'halo' in the surrounding tissue. We then watch what happens for 30 minutes and take serial recordings.

We observe the time it takes for dye to appear at the capillaries. As you might expect, this time is increased in people with Raynaud's and scleroderma due to reduction of blood flow to the finger capillaries. We are also looking at the fluorescent light intensity at points around the capillaries at different times after the dye has appeared in the capillary. This gives us a measure of permeability and how the capillaries are actually working. Generally once the dye appears at the capillary the light intensity just outside the capillary rises very quickly. It remains much the same for about 30 minutes and then the dye is re-absorbed by the capillary and excreted, resulting in a drop in light intensity.

So far we have collected a lot of data and are in the process of analysing this. Dr. Danny Allen is the most important member of our team at present. He is a physicist working at the University of Manchester Biomedical Physics Department and he is currently working on the optimal way to handle the results. Importantly, this procedure is exceedingly well tolerated. It can cause mild nausea shortly after the dye is injected and three of our subjects have experienced this nausea, which lasts for about 15 seconds.

I would like to thank the Raynaud's & Scleroderma Association for making this study possible.

Dr. Marina Anderson

Frank Webb

Foot Problems

One of the things that has become very apparent as far as feet are concerned with scleroderma, is that there is very little information about the problems patients with scleroderma (systemic sclerosis) have, so it was decided that we should carry out an 'observational study' of patients at Hope Hospital to see what is going on.

Who was involved?

We had the consultant, specialist registrar, specialist podiatrist, vascular technician, specialist nurse and consultant radiologist. Overall we probably have about 150 patients at Hope Hospital with scleroderma of which we chose 50. All patients were invited to attend, when they came for their annual screening. Of the patients 42 were female, 8 male, with an age range average being about 52. They were given a questionnaire and one of the questions was 'did they, had they, or did they think that there was a likelihood of patients with scleroderma developing ulceration, calcinosis, poor circulation or joint pain?'. Fairly simple questions we thought, but actually found a considerable number were unaware that in scleroderma, their feet can ulcerate or develop calcinosis. We found this quite alarming, because as practitioners we always thought that patients really understood what was going on and the problems that affect the feet.

Types of problems

ULCERATION - an ulcer can be fairly small and probably one of the most striking facts with scleroderma is the amount of pain a small ulcer can cause. I have unfortunately known colleagues who think that because the ulcer is small, it is insignificant and yet the amount of discomfort that this causes to patients is considerable. The other big problem we have is that they do not heal quickly but can last for months and, unfortunately, even for years.

CALCINOSIS - what do we mean by calcinosis? This is deposits of calcium in the soft tissues, the skin, or in fact anywhere in the soft tissues in the body. We have all had a stone in our shoe which is uncomfortable but at least you can take your shoe off and flick it. The calcium deposits start to work towards the surface of the skin and can then break the surface and ulcerate. The other problem we see is where the patient has had inappropriate treatment. An example is a patient who had calcinosis at the end of her toe, had it debrided and ennnucleated, as you would with a corn. Three days later she returned to the hospital in absolute agony and we ended up having to admit her to the ward for 10 days for IV antibiotics because she had a gross infection. Another question asked was "did they have any problems and if so, what?".

We found that about 14% of the patients had ulceration and 12% had a history of calcinosis on the foot; 78% reported problems with their circulation, with colour changes, cold feet to the point that it was actually causing them discomfort and others mentioned corns, callus and dry skin. An example of the colour changes we are talking about is where the foot has gone very white due to peripheral shut-down and then blue with cyanosis due to stasis (deoxygenated blood).

Patients with Raynaud's and scleroderma will sometimes present to the clinic when they get a chilblain type reaction on the toes which again is painful. Often we find topical applications help e.g. Lasonil, but sometimes patients need systemic treatment as well, such as nifedipine. They can go on to a pre-ulcerative state which if not treated soon and if the pressure isn't relieved from that area, will cause the patient problems. They often break down in winter when it is cold and their Raynaud's is worse. Trying to get them healed in winter months is very difficult.

Patients were asked about the changes in the toe nail. "Had they noticed that the nails which were previously normal, were now starting to cause problems?". This is due to the ends of the toes changing shape because the bone is reabsorbed. Consequently, the toe changes and the nail shape also changes, because it is partly dictated by the shape of your toe as to what shape your nail is. Nails can start to dig in at the side and become painful. Hard skin on the foot isn't necessarily that thick but the patient may need to come in every three weeks due to considerable discomfort, which again is worse in the winter months. It is easy to think a patient has purely a digital problem, in other words the circulation to the toes is poor, but miss that they also have a problem in the leg or thigh. I stress that something can often be done, such as surgery, to by-pass a blockage, an occlusion or may be angioplasty (where they stretch open the arteries), if the circulation in the leg or thigh is bad. We cannot do that for toes, so we need to make sure that if the pressure in the patient's toes is dropping, it is purely in the toes and not the larger vessels in the legs or thighs.

Patients complained of other symptoms

8% had a history of previous foot surgery such as an amputation or removal of a toe nail or a toe or even major surgery such as removal of a leg. 86% reported colour changes usually going through the red, white and blue stages, 82% reported considerable discomfort or pain, and 26% reported previous ulceration or active ulceration.

Radiological findings

What we were looking for here was whether there were areas of calcinosis in the skin of the feet and in actual fact, we only showed it in 17% of the patients. There was arterial calcification in the vessels, where the vessel walls start to calcify and that makes them hard. Then we saw erosions and loss of bone, which is what causes the changes in the shape of the toes, in 26% of patients. The feet were then examined so we now had the patient's interpretation of their problems. On examination, 18% of the patients had calcinosis, which is in keeping with the X- ray findings, 10% had active ulceration at that time and 34% had a pre-ulcerative state. If you take into account the 10% with ulceration and the 34% with a pre-ulcerative state, that is a significant number of patients.

The study was done in the winter months so it was the worst time of year. 62% had nail changes which may not seem that significant, but if the nail starts to dig in, causes ulceration and breaks down, we have a real problem. There are a large number of patients with this condition who end up losing parts of a nail or all of the toe nails. What this study told us is that there is a significant number of patients with scleroderma who have problems with their feet and only one patient who had no foot symptoms. It is not all doom and gloom; just because a patient has ulcerations isn't the end of the story and it doesn't mean that we are going to have repeated problems.

One final message - we only get given one pair of feet, we can't do transplants! Medicine is advancing very rapidly but feet still cannot be transplanted. At the end of the day they are your feet and you must look after them. We are here to help you if there is a problem but we can't chase you around to find out if you have a problem and so we rely on you to tell us. The only thing I would stress is because scleroderma isn't that common, people tend to ignore it or don't understand it and I have lots of colleagues who are unaware or not fully aware of the condition. Do not be afraid to tell people how the condition affects you and the problems it causes you and your concerns. I must stress, that sometimes it is down to you to educate the people who are treating you.

Frank Webb, Podiatrist, Hope Hospital

Jean's stem cell transplant

Jean Blakeley

I have been suffering from scleroderma for about 8 years. For the first 12 months I underwent various tests and took several medications. I repeatedly asked to see a rheumatologist and was finally referred to a consultant at Pinderfields Hospital at Wakefield. He was concerned by the rapid progression and admitted me for two weeks of tests followed by several infusions of prostacyclin to help my circulation. I was then approached about taking part in a blind trial where I would be injected with alfa interferon or a placebo. When the results came back it was found that I had actually been given the active drug and it was continued to be administered under supervision for a further 18 months. After this time it was found that there was no improvement and the idea was then put to me of trying a stem cell transplant. I was in fact to be a 'Guinea Pig'.

After considering the pros and cons the one thing that really scared me was the fatality risk due to picking up any infection during the period of my immune system being non-existent. At this point and after discussing the procedure with my partner John, my questions with regards to long term prognosis were answered by my consultant. In his opinion this would be about two years so I had nothing to lose but what on the other hand, had I and the research team to gain? It was with the love and support of my partner, family and friends that I agreed to go ahead with the transplant. On the 1st December 1996 I had my first infusion of chemotherapy followed by a week in isolation in hospital, with daily injections of hormones to aid the recovery and increase of my stem cells. My stem cells were then harvested through a machine which was hooked into a main artery in my groin. After this procedure my cells were frozen and I was allowed home.

I felt weak for a few weeks so had to take things easy. I had never felt more tired, sick and depressed in my life. I owe a lot to my partner John who was always reassuring me, kept me thinking positive and encouraging me to eat. It was also heartening and comforting to receive cards, letters and numerous phone calls from everybody. The following February I was re-admitted and taken to theatre for a Hickman line to be inserted. This was to make blood tests and infusions much easier to be obtained and administered. The chemotherapy was given and 24 hours later my stem cells were given back via a blood transfusion. I had to stay in an isolation ward for three weeks and had constant care and attention from my family, friends, doctors and nurses. When I left hospital it took a while to recuperate due to intense tiredness, loss of appetite and of course getting used to having a hard boiled egg look where my hair should have been! I found it easier to cope by laughing at myself and making a light joke about the situation. At this moment in time I am still stable and able to have some quality in my life. I still have to have regular lung function tests, blood tests etc. and regular visits to the hospital. My gratitude is eternally with the team at Leeds General Infirmary and I consider myself very lucky to have been a 'Guinea Pig'.

Jean Blakeley

Five million pound target reached

At the start of 2000 our aim was to have raised £5 million pounds in total since the Association was founded in 1982. We were delighted to announce that this target was reached during December.

Our thanks to everyone who helped to raise this money. Large donations are few and far between and the majority of our funds come from fundraising events and small donations, for which we are most grateful. Research and welfare projects are only made possible with your support.

Thanks to everyone who helped us to reach this significant milestone.

Raynaud's Questionnaire

The aim of this questionnaire was to try to find more clues as to the causes of Raynaud's. Do you have any idea why your Raynaud's started? Has anyone else in your family had Raynaud's? If you have scleroderma, did you have Raynaud's before scleroderma developed? Answers to these and many other questions could prove to be invaluable.

In order to create awareness and publicity for this questionnaire, posters were designed for displaying in hospitals, health centres, libraries etc.

Our thanks to Schering Healthcare and South Cheshire Health for their support towards this project.

Raynaud's Celebrity Swim raises over £10,000

After months of planning, the day drew near - would everyone turn up? Phone call upon phone call to get two teams together for the Raynaud's Celebrity Swim was probably the greatest challenge. We began with David Wilkie, Carol Black and myself but decided that in order to get maximum publicity at the start of our Awareness Month, we needed to expand the number of celebrities. I approached my local MP, Mrs Ann Winterton, to get two MPs - one Labour and one Conservative - who would be prepared to take part. To get MPs to reply was virtually impossible but I was delighted when Andrew Robathan MP for Blaby was the first to respond positively. The three

In the photograph from left to right: Andrew Robathan MP (Blaby), BBC Weather Girls Isobel Lang and Sarah Wilmshurst, Sharron Davies, David Wilkie, Anne Mawdsley (with Percy Penguin mascot) and David Tredinnick MP (Bosworth).

Kate Hoey, Minister for Sport starts the event.

Labour MPs suggested were otherwise engaged but David Tredinnick, MP for Bosworth stepped in. Ken Livingstone telephoned the day before, giving his apologies. However, we were delighted that Kate Hoey, Minister for Sport, agreed to start the event. David persuaded Sharron Davies to swim and to add a seasonal touch during this cold spell, we invited two of the BBC Weather girls, Isobel Lang and Sarah Wilmshurst. Can anything go wrong? I had invited some of our members who live near to London to come along for support.

Wednesday evening, after a very busy day in which I had given several interviews both to journalists and on radio, I left the office for my journey to London. At lunchtime, I realised that one thing I had overlooked were T-shirts for the participants to wear on the photographs, so I rang a local company in Crewe and said "I have a slight problem which needs urgent attention". Geoff, the manager of Zero Ads said, "I knew there had to be a crisis - there always is when you ring!". "Please can you print me 6 T-shirts by 5pm and I'll collect them on my way to the station?". No Problem! I left the office, drove to Crewe, collected the T-shirts, pushed them into my bag and headed for the station. I stayed the night at the venue which was the Dolphin Square Hotel, who had not only agreed to let us use the pool at no cost but also gave me a complementary room. They were absolutely brilliant - helping in every way and in particular Ronnie Page and Joanne Connolly who I had liaised with prior to the event.

February 1st 2001- I could hardly believe the day had come. I got up at 6.40am to have breakfast at 7am as I hadn't had time to eat much the day before. Down on poolside at 8am and Ronnie Page helped to put up the banner and make sure everything was ready before the first guests arrived. There was a lull of about 10 minutes to get my breath back and gently panic! Everything then seemed to happen quickly. Spectators and photographers arrived followed by Sarah Wilmshurst, closely followed by Isobel Lang, who came in carrying the saddle of her bicycle, having chained her bicycle to a tree outside the hotel! I showed them to the changing room and then went back to the poolside where David Tredinnick had just arrived and was talking to David Wilkie. Professor Black appeared and next Kate Hoey, a delightful lady, who was most interested in our work, as she has a friend in Ireland who has scleroderma. She took time to talk to everyone present before we had some photographs taken with David and Percy Penguin. Andrew Robathan came and we were complete with the exception of Sharron Davies. Something had to go wrong - a phone call from Sharron to say that she was driving from the Cotswolds and it was foggy - she was on her way but would be late - how late? Professor Black had patients to see, Andrew Robathan had a busy schedule and time was pressing on. We had more group photographs (including those taken by Hello Magazine), and decided to start. As we were running late we had 4 swimmers each swimming 10 lengths in rotation. We had, or so I thought, decided to do breast stroke for the first few lengths. Kate Hoey started the event, we dived in and as I surfaced I saw David and the two MPs each doing front crawl and I was breaststroking! I was about half a length behind so decided to front crawl the next length, which exhausted me, so I had to return to breast stroke for the rest. The next four in were Professor Black, Isobel Lang, Sarah Wilmhurst and my good friend Noelle Orton who fortunately came as reserve and swam in Sharron's place at the start. We repeated the exercise, each doing another 10 lengths. I was tired but this is what all the training had been for and I was not going to give in. We finished and within a few minutes Sharron arrived. I went along to the changing room to tell her where we were up to and to brief her on Raynaud's, as she was giving an interview on Radio 5 Live following the swim. She told me that she had one finger which went dead and her hands often went very cold especially when skiing.

By this time, David decided that we would finish by doing a relay race to inlcude Sharron. Professor Black had to leave but Noelle was still there and the MPs and weather girls were happy to race once again. My heart sank - my legs were like jelly, but we had waited long enough and the photographers were eager to get their shots. Sharron came onto poolside amongst clapping and cheering from spectators and photographers. Looking very tanned and wearing a white swim suit she looked stunning - but then so did David! Photo after photo with cameras clicking - it was then time for the race. I was asked to be starter for David and Sharron - she actually left the poolside before David! They were on their way - we were doing 2 lengths each with David and Sharron finishing with two extra lengths. Having started the race, wearing my Raynaud's T-shirt, I then had to dash to take off my shirt, put on my goggles and get ready to swim. The MPs went in next, followed by the weather girls. Sarah was a strong swimmer so had taken quite a lead over Isobel which meant I had to try and gain some lead - front crawl was my only option but could I do two lengths flat out? Yes, - I made it! David took over and we only lost by a few yards. More photos, floating bottles of champagne and it was all over.

Showered and changed we then had a buffet lunch before a Press Conference to discuss the results of the Seredrin Trial conducted by Jill Belch in Dundee. Bad news -

Jill was fogbound in Edinburgh so could I give details of the study? Dr. Paolo Morazzoni from Italy was due to speak after me but his laptop PowerPoint presentation wasn't working! As luck would have it, David Tredinnick had stopped for lunch and was interested in complementary medicine and indeed was on a committee involved in Parliament to try and regulate complementary therapies. We asked him to speak and he agreed. Having come to swim for an hour, he left after four and a half hours!

I had the opportunity to try and get across to journalists the fact that we needed to create awareness and asked for their support with our questionnaire. Eventually everyone left but not before Noelle had donated a cheque for £250 from Glenwood Laboratories (the company of which she is General Manager in the UK). Members present - many of whom had already sponsored me, gave further donations for the swim.

Packed up and ready to leave, I collected the banner, loaded up and left by tube for Euston. Fortunately, when I got on the tube, I met up with member June Timpanaro who travelled with me to Euston while we caught up with news and she waited with me until my delayed Virgin train arrived. "Never again" I cried - but that's until next time!

Anne Mawdsley

Percy Pics

Percy meets his brothers and sisters in Antarctica

Percy in Hollywood

Percy's favourite Pic!

Percy at he Valley of the Kings

Percy and the Sphinx

Newly Awarded Grants

At a Trustees meeting held in November 2000 the following grants were approved at a total cost of £355,988. Non-invasive determination of macrophage behaviour in Scleroderma patients at risk of fibrosing alveolitis. £171,677.00 was awarded to Professor du Bois and Dr. Hazel Jones in collaboration with Professor Black over two years.

Royal Free Hospital - The role of TGF-B-producing Th3 T cells in Immunopathogenesis of Scleroderma. £132,910 was awarded to Professor Carol Black and Dr. David Abraham over three years.

University of Bath - Hypoxia and oxidative stress in scleroderma fibroblast activation: Investigation of a role for xanthine oxidase. £51,401 awarded to Dr. V R Winrow with Professor Black, Dr. Stevens and Professor Blake for one year.

These are in addition to many other projects currently being funded by the Association.

Amy

Amy Best

In 1995 we published a photograph of Amy (see page 132) together with details of how scleroderma was affecting her. Now six years on, Amy's Mum has sent us an update:

"When we first found out that Amy had scleroderma, we were left in the dark. It seemed as if we were told what she had and were just left to get on with it. We felt so alone. It is a big shock when first you are told your young daughter has growing pains which are nothing to worry about, and then to find out she has a rare disease for which there is no cure. I used to phone the office a lot then and I really don't know what we would have done without you. We felt so alone and on our own. I still find that the doctors don't really listen to me. I have spoken to other parents and they say the same - that doctors think you are either making it up or you are making a fuss about nothing.

Amy was diagnosed as having scleroderma in August 1995, when she was four. She first started to complain of her legs when she was three and we were told it was growing pains. Then her leg started scarring as if she had been burned. Our local hospital sent us to Great Ormond Street and Amy was put on D-Penicillamine, but it had to be stopped as she complained of bad stomach pains. She then went onto methotrexate which was fine at first, but then we had terrible trouble with her taking the drug. We tried tablets and liquid, but then had to have it injected, which she really didn't like but that was the only way to get her to have it. After a while the methotrexate stopped doing its job so they tried iloprost which was given to her by infusions. Next, it was decided to combine both methotrexate and cyclosporin but that was stopped after a while.

Amy is now on cyclosporin, but her disease has started to progress over the last few months so her medication has been going up and down like a yo-yo. It would be nice to know from other parents of children taking cyclosporin, if they have experienced any side effects. Amy has always complained of stomach pain, ever since she started her first medication. She suffers a lot with headaches, feeling sick and has very bad dreams where she is too afraid to go back to sleep. The latest one is tingling and tightness in her face and also she is having a lot of problems with her teeth and gums. Her gums seem to be growing through and over her teeth and she has three abscesses at the moment. I really don't know if this mouth problem is caused by the medication or the disease. She has been having problems with her arms, shoulders, neck and hands but I have been told scleroderma is not the cause. When I ask what is causing these problems, I don't get an answer. We have been going to Great Ormond Street every two months to stay and at the same time, we go over to the Royal Free where Amy has her thermography done.

Her disease started in her right leg and I was told that it would only affect that leg. Now her right leg is very wasted. She has scarring running from her foot all the way up to her stomach. Her right leg is shorter than her left and she has lost the arch under her right foot, her right shoe has to be built up and she also uses insoles. During the past year, her left leg has started to go like her right. We still get no local physiotherapy for her as we are told they are short staffed on paediatric physiotherapists. She has about half an hour a week in the hydrotherapy pool and also started having connective tissue massage but for some unknown reason that was stopped after two sessions.

We were told that the scleroderma could go into a remission after five years but Amy has had this for six years, so now we are told it could go into remission after ten years. More than likely when she has had it for ten years, we will be told fifteen! Sadly the damage has already been done.

Once again, thank you all at the Association for being there when we needed someone to talk to. Time has gone so fast since I last sent you a photo of Amy so I have enclosed a recent one taken at Christmas - she is now just turned ten. Her headmistress always says "she is a happy little girl in spite of all the problems she has".

Julie Best

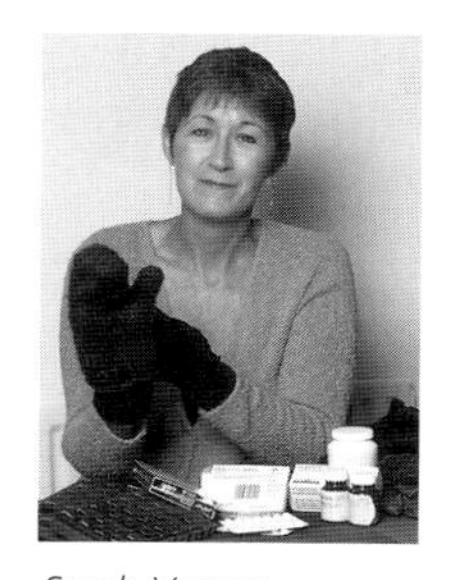

Sarah Vernon

Sarah

Our thanks to Sarah Vernon for taking part in an interview to create awareness. The following article appeared in TV Quick.

"You need to wash your hands, they're filthy," Sarah Vernon's friend said, as they walked into the school canteen. Sarah stuck her hands in her pockets. "They're not dirty, just cold," she retorted. Once the cold weather started, 14-year-old Sarah's hands became blue and painful. A few weeks later, Sarah went to the doctor with an infection in her finger. He gave her some antiseptic cream, but when the infection persisted, Sarah went back and saw another G.P. "You have Raynaud's," he said. "Cold causes the blood vessels supplying your fingers to contract. Your finger has become ulcerated and infected because of the poor blood flow." He advised Sarah to keep warm and wear thick gloves. But, although she followed her doctor's advice, she suffered more ulceration in her hands and the Raynaud's affected her feet.

"My fingers were so ulcerated that I would walk around with them permanently bandaged to protect them from infection," remembers Sarah. "Apart from the fact that it looked awful, it was painful. If someone knocked my finger, it felt like they were driving a nail through it." Sarah was even cold in the summer. She was given vasodilator drugs, to improve blood flow, but they didn't help - and everybody got used to her swinging her arms around trying to get her circulation going. When she was in her early twenties, she noticed lumps on her fingers. Her doctor assured her that it was just a side effect of the Raynaud's but a few years later, when Sarah was in hospital being treated for another problem, the doctor noticed the lumps and he immediately summoned a rheumatologist who diagnosed scleroderma. The lumps, caused by calcium deposits, are one of the symptoms. Sarah had no idea Raynaud's could develop into something more serious.

Over the next 10 years, she struggled to cope with the effects of the two conditions with calcium deposits on the undersides of her feet making walking painful. "My feet hurt so badly that I could only wear trainers," says Sarah. The skin on her hands became thick and shiny and her fingers became stiff. She also had joint pains and fatigue. Now 43, Sarah has calcium deposits on all her pressure points, she hasn't been able to work regularly for 10 years and has to keep her stress levels down because it makes the problem worse. "Life is restricted because of my physical problems and fatigue," she says. "Even moving into the shade on a sunny day will turn my hands blue but, on the plus side, I have a wonderful, caring partner and I always manage to laugh at life. It's the best medicine - if you can't laugh, you can't live.'

Newly Awarded Grants

At a Trustees meeting held in March 2001 the following grants were approved, totalling £96,800. This is in addition to the Association's commitment of £1,271,854.00 over the next 6 years.

A two year grant - 'DTPA clearance in systemic sclerosis: its pathogenetic significance and potential role as the optimal method of predicting outcome' was awarded to Dr. Athol Wells, at The Brompton Hospital.

A further one year grant has been awarded to Hope Hospital to fund Kerry Griffin, the Raynaud's & Scleroderma Nurse Specialist.

To Dr. Sarah Dallas, at Manchester University, a small equipment grant was agreed, to supplement funding which she received from the ARC, for a project entitled - 'Interactions between TGFB, fibrillin- I and latent TGFB binding proteins in systemic sclerosis'.

Placebo controlled study of Seredrin

Study Winter 1999-2000

Following the positive results obtained from the pilot study carried out by the Association it was decided to carry out a randomised, placebo controlled study of Seredrin at Ninewells Hospital, Dundee. This took place over the winter months between Autumn 1999 and Spring 2000. Twenty-one volunteers with primary Raynaud's Phenomenon consented to take part. The Volunteers were randomly allocated to receive either Seredrin or placebo (dummy).

All the volunteers were required to keep diaries recording the length and frequency of Raynaud's attacks. They also recorded an overall daily severity score. These diaries were kept for 2 weeks prior to commencing study medication and then for a further 2 weeks after completing the 10 week course. Only patients who averaged 5 attacks a week or more were recruited into the study. .

The volunteers attended for study visits regularly during the course of the study to have their diaries checked and to be asked about any adverse effects of the medication. Prior to commencing any medication, research blood tests and blood flow measurements were performed. Two volunteers were withdrawn from the analysis due to documented non-compliance with the medication. There were no side-effects attributable to Seredrin.

The study showed a statistically significant reduction in the number of Raynaud's attacks experienced after receiving Seredrin. The number of attacks in the group treated with Seredrin reduced by 56% and in the placebo group 27%. There was also a reduction in the duration of attacks by 63% in the Seredrin group and 29% in the placebo group.

In summary, it would appear that Seredrin may be of benefit to Raynaud's sufferers. It is particularly encouraging that none of the volunteers suffered side effects. A much larger study now needs to be carried out to confirm the results.

Percy Celebrates at Head Office

In the Spring Issue of Hot News, we announced that the Association had reached a target of 5 million pounds. This photograph appeared in our local paper and shows the staff celebrating with Percy Penguin. In the photograph (by kind permission of the Crewe Chronicle), from left to right - Karen Littley, Pat Poulson, Anne Mawdsley, Jan Scott, Helen Slattery and Percy.

Losartan helps Raynaud's

A recent report from the Royal Free Hospital in London describes some hopeful clinical tests on the drug losartan for Raynaud's. The twelve week trial compared losartan with the vasodilating drug nifedipine. Although the trials did not proceed under a double blind protocol the differences between the two therapies were large enough to suggest they exceeded any placebo effect. The 52 patients involved took daily doses of either nifedipine or losartan and made weekly reports of symptoms and side effects. There were also regular measurements of blood flow and blood chemistry to aid in the assessments. Half the subjects had primary Raynaud's (not associated with scleroderma), the other half had secondary Raynaud's (scleroderma patients).

One of the primary goals was to assess the tolerability of the drug. This outcome was positive. Compared to nifedipine, losartan produced considerably fewer adverse reactions. The headaches, nausea, and swelling associated with nifedipine occurred in 39% of the group taking this drug while 12% of the group taking losartan reported occasional dizziness.

Reduction in the frequency and severity of Raynaud's episodes proved significantly better in the losartan group, particularly in the primary Raynaud's patients. The biochemical markers suggested a better result for losartan as well, but the conclusion of the report was that these may be suspect and deserved closer study in the future.

(Dziadzio, M. et al. Arthritis Rheum 42:2646-2655, 1999)

Clinical Trials

What is a Clinical Trial?

The factors that allow someone to participate in a clinical trial are called inclusion criteria and the factors that keep them from participating are called exclusion criteria. It is important to note that inclusion and exclusion criteria are not used to reject people personally. Instead, the criteria are used to identify appropriate participants and keep them safe. The criteria help to ensure that researchers will be able to answer the questions they plan to study.

What is a placebo?

A placebo is an inactive pill, liquid or powder that has no treatment value. In clinical trials experimental treatments are often compared with placebos to assess the treatment's effectiveness. In some studies, the participants in the control group will receive a placebo instead of an active drug or treatment.

What is a control or control group?

A control is the standard by which experimental observations are evaluated. In many clinical trials one group of patients will be given an experimental drug or treatment, while the control group is given either a standard treatment for the illness or a placebo.

What is a blinded or masked study?

A blinded or masked study is one in which participants do not know whether they are in the experimental or control group in a research study. Those in the experimental group get the medications or treatments being tested, while those in the control group get a standard treatment or no treatment.

What is a double-blind or double-masked study?

A double-blind or double-masked study is one in which neither the participants nor the study staff know which participants are receiving the experimental treatment and which ones are getting either a standard treatment or a placebo. These studies are performed so neither the patients' nor the doctors' expectations about the experimental drug can influence the outcome.

What protections are there for people who participate in clinical trials?

The government has strict guidelines and safeguards to protect people who choose to participate in clinical trials. Every clinical trial must be approved and monitored by an Ethics Committee in the U.K. to make sure the risks are as low as possible and are worth any potential benefits.

What is an Ethics Committee?

This is an independent committee of physicians and lay people that ensures a clinical trial is ethical and the rights of participants are protected. All institutions that conduct or support biomedical research involving people must have an Ethics Committee that initially approves and periodically reviews the research.

The above article has been copied from the NPDG (UK) newsletter with the kind permission of the Niemann-Pick Support Group.

The U.K. Scleroderma Study Group

Who are they and what do they do?

This is a group of doctors and nurses who are particularly interested in scleroderma. The group has grown over the past ten years and now includes the specialist nurses and as with many branches of medicine, there is an appropriate team approach to patient care.

Several exciting new trials are due to start during the coming year. For patients with limited disease, there will be a trial of Quinapril, a drug which dilates and possibly remodels the blood vessels. There will also be three trials for early diffuse disease. One uses a drug called Beta-Interferon, the second trial will be a European trial on bone marrow transplantation and the third will be of anti TGFB antibodies in fibrosis. A fourth trial, starting later this year, is using oral iloprost and will target patients who have problems with the large blood vessels.

Nina

Nina Ingold

I have always had cold hands and feet, and suffered misery with chilblains in childhood, but I do not remember having Raynaud's attacks until much later in life.

In September 1983, when I was 46 years old, we were fell-walking in Derbyshire when I was taken ill with a mysterious illness, which was later diagnosed, as Sarcoidosis (large painful erythritic nodes on arms and legs, swollen joints and bloodshot eyes, TB-like lung X-ray). All the doctors in the hospital were asking if they could look at my legs and take photographs! It was two months before I could return to work, after treatment with steroids. At about this time I had my first Raynaud's attack, when working outside in the cold and my fingers turned white, then blue and numb. When I warmed them they slowly turned bright red, spreading from base to tip, and were very painful. My G.P. eventually prescribed a vasodilator drug (Adalat), which had severe side effects, but did not help the Raynaud's.

I happened to see a small article in a magazine, about Anne Mawdsley and the Raynaud's Association so I joined - I had found some fellow sufferers, at last. By the late 1980's I was suffering other symptoms as well, such as difficulties with swallowing, shortness of breath, and digestion problems, and calcinosis of the hands and feet, and red spots were appearing on my face, but I did not know at that time that they were linked to the Raynaud's. On Anne's advice, I asked my G.P. to refer me to Professor Carol Black's clinic at the Royal Free Hospital, where I learned that I had limited scleroderma, of which Raynaud's is just one of the symptoms. This is quite rare as most people have just Primary Raynaud's. I still attend that clinic today, and have taken part in several trials of various treatments to relieve the Raynaud's symptoms, The most successful one for me was an infusion of CGRP (Calcitonin Gene Related Peptide), given in hospital over five days. Following this the attacks were much less severe for nearly three years. I also tried low-dose heparin injections, over the coldest winter months, which do give me relief, and I do the injections myself. I also take Seredrin Ginkgo Biloba, which seems to help too.

I trained as a biochemist, and back in the 1950's and 1 960's there were no Health and Safety Regulations for laboratories, so I used many dangerous and carcinogenic chemicals including vinyl compounds. I have also worked close to both Gatwick and Heathrow Airports, both factors which have been linked with the condition. I had to give up my job in pollution control which I loved, as this involved being out on site in the cold much of the time. Now that we are retired, I should love to be able to go fell-walking again, instead of just going to hot places.

Nina Ingold

Carrie Steen

Carrie

Carrie was just two years old when we first noticed the small patch of silvery hard skin begin to form in the small of her back. My wife Jayne took Carrie to the clinic, where the nurse told her not to worry - it was just a patch of eczema. Not really being satisfied with that answer, we decided to take her to see our local G.P. who said it was probably a fungal infection and proceeded to prescribe medication. After a while there was no improvement so we stopped the medication and asked our G.P. to refer her to a specialist, which he agreed to do.

Another observation we noticed prior to the mark forming on Carrie's back was that her MMR vaccination which was injected into the top of her right leg was not healing properly and the inflammation seemed to be getting hard to the touch. Eventually we got an appointment through from the hospital to see a consultant dermatologist, but during this time the mark on her back had widened to over an inch and elongated round the right side of her waist. The consultant diagnosed Carrie as having the rare condition known as morphea. At that examination we were told that morphea was an incurable condition and that there was no effective medication or treatment and a cortisone cream was advised to alleviate the tightness in the skin. We were then told to make a follow up appointment for 6 months later, then after a while it became once a year.

Over the next year I tried to find out as much as possible about morphea by going to reference libraries and consulting medical books, but they only seemed to confirm what had already been said. As time went by three more lesions began to appear on Carrie's back, the furthest one reaching the base of her neck. Also the mark where her MMR injection had been given began to travel in a linear direction down her right leg. We have our suspicions that the MMR may have been a catalyst in Carrie's condition, but our theory has been dismissed by the local consultant. By the time Carrie turned twelve years old a few more lesions had appeared, one under her right arm and the other on her right ankle. It had also become apparent that muscle tissue had wasted away on her waist causing a significant indentation. The same pattern of underlying tissue damage is now forming on her right leg. It wasn't until last year that I managed to get access to the Internet and found a wealth of information about other sufferers and their various treatments. In the last 10 years Carrie has had only visual examinations once or twice a year, with two sessions of medical photographs taken for reference at the hospital.

While I was researching on the Internet I found the address for the Raynaud's & Scleroderma Association. Upon phoning the Association we were greeted by a very friendly and understanding staff who gave us advice and told us about Professor Carol Black and her work at the Royal Free Hospital. We managed to get Carrie referred last year for an examination at which it was advised because of the amount of coverage of morphea she should start on Methotrexate. We did not decide straight away about the medication, but returned home to come to terms with our options. Meanwhile an appointment was due to see our local consultant, so we thought it would be a good idea to get his opinion and local support. On seeing him he told us that there is no evidence that the treatment will work and that the side effects could cause serious alternative problems. We now had a total conflict of interest of what is best for Carrie and we didn't know what to do now. After reading the latest spring news letter of the Raynaud's & Scleroderma Association we decided it would be very helpful if we could get in touch with other parents to hear their views about the medication and their experiences with this disorder. So the Association helped us get in touch with other parents who gave us their views, which helped to ease our minds.

The morphea under Carrie's right arm has rapidly progressed down to her elbow in the last six months, so arrangements were made with the Royal Free for Carrie to have her first infusion on the 21st March. I would like to thank Helen Wilson and Sam Fox for their help, patience and understanding during our time of deciding to put Carrie on medication. Carrie has recently turned thirteen and over the years we were told that the morphea tends to stay in a localised area where it usually goes into remission over a period of time. In Carrie's case this has not happened, because a more generalised pattern is now emerging.

For a few years when she was going to junior school, the morphea did seem to be slowing down and almost going into remission. Over the last year though Carrie has been going through puberty and the morphea has become more active again, with dormant lesions beginning to erupt. Since getting access to the Internet I have realised what an invaluable tool it is. If it wasn't for the chance use of a PC at our local library with Internet access, we would not have the professional medical help that we do now for our daughter. Carrie feels very lonely and isolated because of this illness, and she would like to be able to communicate via the Internet with other child sufferers of localised scleroderma to help her know she is not alone.

We are very much looking forward to the family weekend organised by the Association in February 2002 and meeting other parents and youngsters. The Raynaud's & Scleroderma Association was a positive turning point for us and I would like to thank them for their help and support.

Brian Steen

Gabriella

Gabriella Verzi

Gabriella Verzi is now 17 but was just 15 years old when she was diagnosed with scleroderma. It took her around 18 months to accept her illness and to realise that her life will never be the same again. At first she was in denial but has now come to terms with it and gets on with her life, which has changed completely. It is not easy for a youngster who had planned to join the police force, but now has to spend long, enforced periods in hospital, and is at present struggling to revise for her 'A' level in business studies, while in hospital. Gabi had always had bad circulation but first realised there was something wrong with her when her hands went blue and stiff while she was out in the school playground. Just before she was diagnosed, she had to battle with doctors to see a specialist because as far as they were concerned it was "chillblains and nothing else to worry about". They said "seeing a specialist would have been a waste of time!" Not satisfied with the G.P.s initial diagnosis of chilblains, she insisted on being seen at her local hospital by a specialist who carried out tests which showed she had Raynaud's phenomenon, sometimes a precursor to scleroderma.

Gabi would however, like to thank Dr. Charles Li and Dr. Rapti Mediwake who over the past two years have been amazing with her and have seen her not only in clinic but also out of clinical appointments. When Gabi was referred to a consultant, scleroderma was diagnosed straight away. She was put on a course of drugs to help with her skin, which had become very hard and stiff and was restricting her movement. She went back to school but found it difficult.

"It makes me feel awkward when I am walking around in school or out in the street and I have people looking closely at my fingers, because of the ulcers. No matter how many times I have told my teachers and some of my friends, I don't think they actually listen because if I tell them I cannot write, they think it's an excuse and start making jokes about it, so I sit down feeling humiliated. One teacher in particular who simply didn't understand scleroderma was sarcastic about my lengthy periods of absence and illness, and made my life difficult. I hide myself away from the outside world because when I'm around people I feel abnormal as they do things I can't".

Gabi has since come to terms with her illness and is determined to raise awareness. She is currently helping the Association by putting up posters in her area.

Heather Semple MBE

Heather's Award

We were delighted to hear that Heather Semple who runs our Northern Ireland Group, had been awarded an MBE for services to the community.

Since 1972 Heather has been involved in many aspects of voluntary work and for over 30 years she has worked as a volunteer on mental health committees, rehabilitation and befriending work. She is involved with many other committees including her local church and all this is in addition to the work which Heather does for our Association in Northern Ireland!

Well done Heather on a well deserved award.

Radio Stars

Our thanks to member Nina Ingold and Sue Brown, Rheumatology Nurse Specialist at the RNHRD for taking part in a radio programme on Southern Counties Radio. This was to promote the work of the Association and to publicise the Questionnaire 2001. It was the first time on air for both Nina and Sue and we are most grateful to them for helping the Association in this way. They both said that they enjoyed the experience!! The Association is also grateful to members who spoke to reporters from newspapers and womens' magazines, in helping to highlight Raynaud's and scleroderma.

Cheshire Woman of the Year

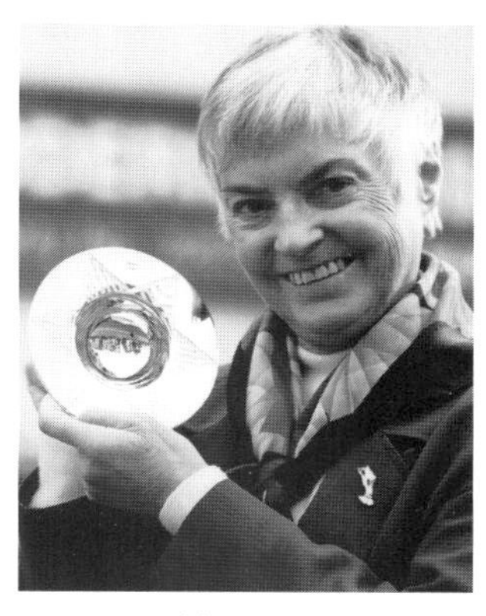
Anne Mawdsley MBE

Anne Mawdsley MBE, Director and Founder of the Association was voted Cheshire Woman of the Year, at a luncheon at Chester Town Hall on 21st March. The event was organised by the NSPCC and sponsored by Cheshire Life Magazine, who presented her with a cheque for £1,000 towards the work of the Association. Anne also received the silver Spirit of Chester Bowl which portrays aspects of Chester. She was delighted to receive this award and hopes that it will help to raise greater awareness of Raynaud's and scleroderma.

International News

Denmark

Anne Mawdsley and Professor Carol Black were invited to speak at the Danish Conference held in Copenhagen on March 30th. This gave them the opportunity to encourage patients and doctors to establish a closer relationship. At the patient meeting, Chairman Niels Sorensen presented Anne with a cheque for £500 from the Danish Raynaud's & Scleroderma Association, as a gesture of thanks for the support given to their organisation.

Dublin

In April Anne spoke at the Irish Raynaud's & Scleroderma Society Annual meeting in Dublin. Once again she enjoyed the Irish hospitality and was delighted to meet so many friends. Dr. Suzanne Donnelly was also invited from the U.K. and gave an excellent presentation on scleroderma.

Nobody Knows How it Feels

Dr. Mark Flapan

Living with scleroderma can be a lonesome experience. Even in the presence of caring family members and friends, you feel different and set apart. What's happening to your body is not happening to theirs so how can they possibly understand what they have never experienced? You would like to share your feelings and concerns, but this isn't easy. You don't want to sound like a complainer, and you certainly don't want to bore others with repetition of your ailments. But more important, you don't want to upset or frighten those who are worried about you already.

You also know family members would like to hear you're fine. They wish it would all go away, as you do; and if they could, they would like to forget you have an illness. But you can't forget it. So you're torn - between wanting to reassure them everything will be alright - and wanting to tell then how you really feel. To help you feel less alone, and to help family members better understand your feelings and concerns. I'll portray, in this article, some of the physical ailments and emotional reactions experienced by persons with scleroderma. I must remind you, however, scleroderma is an exceedingly variable disease, and no one will have all the physical effects and emotional reactions I'll describe.

Physical Ailments

At times, you may feel aches and pains in every joint or muscle of your body, or you may just feel sick all over. But more often, you're bothered by such specific ailments or discomforts as the following:

TIGHTNESS

The most unique physical experience of scleroderma results from tightening of the skin. The skin on your face may feel two sizes too small, and when you turn your head you may feel a pull on the skin of your neck. When you reach for something overhead or bend for something on the floor, you may feel like you're stretching rubber tubing.

COLD

Winter temperatures, as well as summer air conditioning, make you uncomfortably cold. Even a Spring or Autumn breeze may chill your hands. In fact, if your Raynaud's is severe, your hands and feet may feel numb or painful when exposed to even moderate temperatures.

FATIGUE

Whether physically active or not, you live with fatigue. At times, fatigue may be so vague as to make you wonder whether you're really tired or you just don't feel like doing something. At other times, you're so exhausted you have to take to your bed. But even after a full night's sleep, you may wake up tired.

WEAKNESS

Sometimes you feel weak - too weak to climb a flight of stairs or get up out of a chair. Lifting an arm may require more strength than you can muster. What's more, if your joints or muscles are aching and stiff, physical movements may be difficult and painful.

DRYNESS

Dryness of the skin and mucous membranes causes various discomforts. Dry skin may result in rough and painfully cracked fingers. Insufficient nasal secretions make nasal passages dry, caked and stuffy, and the absence of vaginal secretions make sexual intercourse uncomfortable. Eyes, if lacking moisture because of Sjögren's syndrome, feel gritty and irritated. And your mouth may be so dry that tongue, teeth and lips stick together, making whatever you eat taste like cotton.

EATING DISCOMFORTS

Each phase of eating and digesting may be a source of unpleasant sensations. Chewing may be hard work, and swallowing difficult. Swallowed food may feel uncomfortably stuck in the middle of your chest, while heartburn may be the aftermath of eating. And depending on the movement of food through your digestive system, you may feel uncomfortably bloated or suffer from either diarrhoea or constipation.

PAIN
Pain comes from many sources. A painful muscle spasm in calf or foot may awaken you in the middle of the night, and itching skin may be excruciating day or night. But the most unremitting pain of all comes from infected ulcers which never seem to heal. And no matter how careful you try to be, you are constantly bumping ulcerated fingers, resulting in piercing pain. Whether you have few or many of the bodily ailments which I have described, pains and discomforts are somehow more bearable if family members and friends have a compassionate understanding of what you're going through.

Emotional Reactions

In addition to physical ailments, you also have emotional reactions to the effects of scleroderma.

FRUSTRATION
You're frustrated by difficulties in doing the ordinary activities of everyday life. Buttoning a shirt or blouse, unlocking a door, handling change, stepping up on a bus - are all frustrating experiences. And you may express your frustration in irritation and anger.

ANGER
Anger, however, has many sources. You may be angry about getting scleroderma, and in anger have asked, "Why did this happen to me?" You would like to blame someone, but whom can you blame - God, fate, the whole world? You may, of course, blame yourself. Did you do something that caused your illness? Is your disease a result of poor health habits or leading a stressful life? Or is your sickness God's punishment for some wrong doing? You may be also angry at doctors. After all, they don't have a cure for your disease and may not even be able to stop progression of your symptoms. Then they either don't explain enough or say things that upset and frighten you. But what hurts and angers you even more, is when they view you as just a case or, on the other hand, when they don't seem really interested in what's happening to you.

HURT
You may also feel hurt and angry at family members and friends who are insensitive to your feelings or don't show sufficient interest or concern. They're not always as helpful as you would like and they sometimes expect you to do things without considering you have an illness.

SHAME
If you view illness as a weakness, you may be ashamed of being ill. And if you're the kind of person who needs to be independent, or needs to be doing things for others, you're especially ashamed if you need others to do things for you.

SELF-DEVALUATION
You may feel inadequate or useless if you're unable to do what you used to do. What's more, if you're a perfectionist and can no longer live up to your high self expectations, you may disparage and even hate yourself.

GUILT

You feel guilty if you can't fulfil your responsibilities as a wife or husband. Your guilt may be unbearable if you're a mother who can't do all you think you should for your children. Guilt is intensified if you feel you're a burden on others - if you need help for such everyday tasks as opening jars, picking up dropped objects and getting something off a shelf. If you need help for such personal tasks as getting in and out of a chair, bathing, and dressing you may not be able to live with yourself. And should you sense resentment on the part of family members who do things for you, you not only feel guilty, but feel hurt and resentful besides.

SENSE OF LOSS

You feel a sense of loss if you're unable to engage in activities which you once enjoyed. or unable to use abilities and skills in which you took pride. If, in addition, you have given up life plans without developing other realistic and meaningful goals, you may feel so sorry for yourself, you become depressed.

FEAR

As much as you put the thought out of your mind, you still live in fear the disease will progress. You fear changes in appearance, becoming disabled, and being dependent on others. But worst of all, you fear dying before your time, particularly if you think of scleroderma as a terminal illness, rather than a chronic disease. You also have fears related to your family. If you have young children, you worry about what will happen to them if something happens to you? If you're dependent on your husband for personal care - you can't imagine how you'll manage if something happens to him. Although you know it's unlikely, the thought has nevertheless occurred to you - what if he gets tired of taking care of you and leaves? What will you do then?

ENVY

You may envy family members and friends who do things you're no longer able to do. In comparison to them, you feel cheated and treated unfairly in life. Living with scleroderma fills you with emotional reactions as well as physical pains and discomforts. You wish somebody could live inside your body for a week or even a day, just so they'd know what life is like for you. But that isn't possible. What is possible, however, is for you to share your inner world with those close to you to try to understand what fills your heart and mind.

You may not be able to get all the emotional support and understanding you need from family members and friends alone. They're too directly affected by your illness. They feel frightened and helpless themselves and don't always know what to say to you. So you may feel you're making the journey of illness alone. This doesn't mean they don't care about you and love you. It just means they're separate persons from you and their suffering is not your suffering.

The above article was written by Dr. Mark Flapan, a scleroderma sufferer for 9 years. When Mark died his articles were put together in a book edited by Marie Coyle, entitled 'Perspectives of Living With Scleroderma' and published by the Scleroderma Federation in the USA.

Genetic Features of Scleroderma

Dr. Maureen Mayes

Did you get it from your parents? Can you give it to your kids?

Patients frequently ask whether they can give this disease to their children. The short answer is "No". While there may be a genetic susceptibility to scleroderma, for over 99% of patients no one else in the family has scleroderma. But let's take a closer look at who gets scleroderma and why.

Genes and Scleroderma

Diseases are classified as being genetic (inherited) or acquired. Inherited diseases are the result of an abnormal gene that gets passed down from one generation to the next. Acquired diseases are caused by exposure to some triggering factor that occurs at some point after birth. Some diseases occur through an interaction between an external trigger and an internal genetic predisposition.

Examples of diseases that are totally genetic (that is, passed down from one generation to the next) are sickle cell anaemia, haemophilia (a bleeding disorder), and Huntington's disease (a nerve disorder). In these conditions, the only thing necessary to develop the disease is to inherit the gene. Usually these diseases become apparent in childhood, but sometimes (as in Huntington's disease), the first symptom does not occur until middle age. However, in all of these cases, there is a family history of other relatives being affected; sometimes several children in one family will be affected.

Other diseases are clearly acquired, like the 'flu. Several people in a family are affected at the same time. Since the time period is short between exposure and illness, it is clear that there is some 'bug' or infectious agent that the family members are spreading among themselves.

Scleroderma is considered an acquired disease, that is, people are not born with it but develop or acquire it later in life. This means that they 'catch it' somehow, from being exposed to something in the environment, perhaps a virus, a bacterium, a chemical, or an allergen (an allergy-causing agent).

Many diseases are caused by a combination of genes and environment. High blood pressure, or hypertension, is a good example, as is the tendency to have heart attacks. Hypertension and heart disease frequently run in families. But even if people have the gene, they do not have to get the disease if they are careful with their diet, exercise, medications to keep blood pressure and cholesterol levels normal, and other sorts of measures. Many of the diseases in modern life fall into this category.

Is there a gene for scleroderma?

The answer from what we know now, is that there probably is a susceptibility gene or several susceptibility genes, without which people could not get scleroderma. However, just having the gene is not sufficient; there must be some additional trigger to make the disease happen.

What is the evidence that there is any role for genes in the development of scleroderma if most individuals have no family history of this disease?

The evidence comes from an unlikely source: a group of Native Americans of the Choctaw tribe in Oklahoma, who have a much higher than expected prevalence of scleroderma (almost eight times the prevalence in the rest of the country). These individuals have an unusual combination of immune regulation genes that non-Choctaws in Oklahoma do not have. One of the problems with labelling this gene complex as the 'scleroderma gene' is that there are Choctaws who live in the southeastern U.S. who have this same unusual combination of immune-regulation genes but do not have this tendency to get scleroderma. The answer to this riddle is either that there is another gene (as yet unidentified) that the Oklahoma Choctaws have and the southeastern Choctaws do not have, or that there is something in the environment in Oklahoma that has triggered scleroderma in this group. The search is on for the gene, but this may give us only half of the story. Of course half of the story is a lot better than none of the story, which is where we are now in our understanding of the cause of scleroderma.

An additional line of evidence for a genetic link comes from the few families in which more than one member is affected. Among the more than five hundred scleroderma patients I have seen, there are two families with scleroderma in two related individuals. One is a brother and a sister - he has diffuse disease and she has limited disease. The other family has two sisters affected. In both these situations, the diagnosis was made years apart, and long after these people had left home, so they had not shared the same environment for years.

Could this have occurred by chance alone?

This is pretty unlikely. Could this have happened not because of having a 'scleroderma gene' but by being exposed to a particular virus or bacterium, which then stayed dormant in the body for years before emerging as scleroderma? We just don't know. We do know that viruses can remain in the body for decades and manifest years later as a disease that is very different from the original one caused by the virus. This is the case with chicken pox and shingles.

One way to distinguish between the role of genetics and the role of the environmental factors is to study twins. If a disease is strictly genetic, then both members of a set of identical twins should have the disease. If the disease is strictly due to exposure (exposure here can mean a viral or bacterial infection, as well as exposure to a chemical or toxin) and if the exposure happened after the twins grew up and left the shared home environment, each twin should have only the same chance of getting the disease as the general population.

A study of twins, both identical and fraternal (nonidentical), was done by Dr. Timothy Wright and his colleagues at the University of Pittsburgh. They gathered blood samples from as many twins as possible, at least one of whom had scleroderma. What this group of researchers found is that the identical twins, who have identical genes, were no more likely to both have scleroderma than the non identical twins, who are no more closely related than any other brothers and sisters, but that this likelihood among all twins was higher than the likelihood in the general population. To put numbers on this, the likelihood of both twins in a twin pair having scleroderma was 6%, which is higher than what occurs in the general population, but nowhere near the 100% that would be expected if the disease was purely genetic. The conclusion from this, as from the pattern of the disease among Oklahoma Choctaws, is that there is some genetic component in scleroderma, but that there is something else in the outside world that a person must come in contact with in order to get the disease.

The above article has been taken from The Scleroderma Book by Maureen D Mayes MD. ISBN 0 19 511507 4. This is an excellent book written especially for patients and their families and can be ordered from most good book shops.

Ulcers

What are ulcers, what can I do to prevent them and how can they be treated?

These are questions regularly asked by Raynaud's and scleroderma patients.

Ulcers are erosions or holes in the skin which can be tender and very sore. They are often caused by an inadequate blood supply and sometimes in people with scleroderma, particularly those with limited disease (CREST), by lumps of calcium building up under the skin. These may break through the skin surface forming ulcers which are slow to heal.

If you are prone to develop these on your fingers and toes, care should be taken to maintain a good circulation by keeping your hands and feet warm. It is also essential to keep the trunk of the body warm. Make sure that your hands are kept as clean as possible and do not be too aggressive when manicuring your cuticles.

Once an ulcer has formed it needs medical attention

To heal, dead tissue needs to be removed, infection needs to be cleared and circulation needs to be improved. Unwanted crusts and dried pus can be removed by soaking the ulcer in luke-warm water for approximately five minutes. The area should then be allowed to dry before applying a dressing. There are several good dressings available but they need to be used properly to get the best results. Treatments available from your doctor may include antiseptic or antibiotic ointments. Sometimes a dry dressing is best such as gauze or a non adherent dressing or one of the hydrocolloid adhesive preparations. Alternatively you may be given a calcium alginate dressing derived from seaweed. These dressings have the great advantage that they can be removed from the ulcers by washing with saline solution.

Ulcers should be covered by a loose bandage over which a plastic or metal splint can be fitted during the daytime to prevent the finger being bumped. The splint should not be worn continuously because the joints of the finger need exercise to keep their mobility. If the entire finger become red and swollen, deep infection may have occurred.

Treatment

Antibiotics can be prescribed by your G.P. and you will probably need a longer course than normal. You may need a high dose initially then a half dose until healing is well established. If the infection is deep seated, one or two months of antibiotic treatment can be prescribed. Flucloxacillin is generally recommend as being the first antibiotic to try. Vasodilator drugs are useful for helping to improve the circulation and, in severe cases, patients may be offered an iloprost infusion which is given intravenously in hospital. Iloprost is a potent vasodilator which has proved to help healing.

Ulcers are slow to heal but almost always eventually close. Nothing works rapidly or consistently enough to convince all patients and doctors that the best single treatment has been discovered. The cure for ulcers will be that which can restore normal blood supply to the fingers. In the meantime, with good common sense and patience these ulcers will generally heal.

Should I have any tests for Raynaud's?

The following information is provided as a general guide for patients with Raynaud's who may need to visit their doctor.

Classic symptoms occur when the fingers turn white and/or blue and red. This happens on exposure to the cold or to sudden but slight temperature changes, or stress. The extremities most likely affected are the fingers and toes but the ears and nose may also be affected. There may be accompanying pain, numbness or tingling.

Raynaud's is generally a benign, primary condition which is no more than a nuisance and by following advice on keeping warm and maintaining constant body temperature, most patients can cope.

The condition may also be severe and if the attacks are getting worse it is worthwhile visiting a doctor who may prescribe drugs to improve the circulation. There are many drug treatments for Raynaud's and no one drug suits everyone, so you may have to try several before you find one which suits.

The type of treatment given will depend on the severity of the attack and the underlying condition, if one is present.

What tests are available?

Your doctor may suggest the following:

a) Taking a blood test to look for antinuclear antibodies. The blood test is the easiest and most important test to do for most doctors. If it is abnormal he/she will almost certainly wish to seek further help by referring you to a specialist centre.

b) Looking at the capillaries at the base of your nail with an opthalmoscope to look for abnormal patterns in the nailfold.

Remember, Raynaud's is usually diagnosed by the patient's symptoms. A blood test will not give a diagnosis of Raynaud's but may help to eliminate or confirm any underlying conditions.

Welfare Support

For a chronic condition with no cure, self-help, support and advice play a crucial role in the care of patients. This is particularly so for Raynaud's and even more so for scleroderma. It can be distressing and frightening for the patient as well as for family and friends, who have great difficulty not only in coming to terms with an 'orphan' disease but also coping with life on a day to day basis.

The Raynaud's & Scleroderma Association prides itself on the welfare side of its work, which aims to help patients through these difficult times by offering support in a variety of ways. The largest proportion of time spent on welfare involves communication by telephone. Support may be for sufferers but can also apply to relatives and often to bereaved family members. When medical questions are posed, if these are outside our knowledge and understanding, the caller is referred to one of the Nurse Helplines. These nurses have proved to be an invaluable source of information, reassurance and comfort to callers.

A personal interest in someone with scleroderma by a person who understands their problems can be a real tonic. Many people are looked after by doctors who may only see one patient in their lifetime and are therefore not familiar with the feelings of frustration and fear which can be experienced. People who live on their own can become isolated because their friends 'don't understand". Many fears can be alleviated once talked through. To know that we have made a difference to the lives of many, is very rewarding to those involved in the welfare of sufferers.

Our thanks to all the companies and charitable trusts who made donations towards our welfare work and special thanks to Roger Jefcoate CBE for his invaluable advice.

The Scleroderma Register

Scleroderma is an uncommon disease and many patients feel very isolated and because scleroderma is rare, doctors and nurses may be unfamiliar with the disease. Treatment has been considerably improved by the 'specialist centre' approach but even so, the variable nature of scleroderma means that each centre may only care for a relatively small number of cases with various patterns of disease. This would not matter if we knew everything about the disease and its treatment but sadly we do not - far from it.

A 'Scleroderma Register' of patients has been established under the auspices of the U.K. Systemic Sclerosis Study Group. This register will help rapid recruitment to proper studies of new drugs so that effective treatments can be identified as soon as possible for the benefit of other sufferers. The register is of course strictly confidential and the information will only be used for legitimate research.

Doctors based in many centres in the U.K. comprise the U.K. Systemic Sclerosis Study Group. If you have scleroderma, check with your doctor to see if you are on the register. It does not commit you in any way to taking part in trials but should appropriate treatment become available it may be in your interest to know about it.

Professor Carol Black
Royal Free Hospital

Is there a doctor in the house?

This photograph was taken when Kathryn Thomas (left) and Anne Mawdsley joined Dr. Mark Porter in Norwich to record two items for a television programme called Doctor in the House. One item was on Raynaud's and a separate one on scleroderma. Percy came along too!

Newly Awarded Grants

At a meeting of the Trustees, the following grants were awarded:

Studies of Calcinosis in Systemic Sclerosis - Two year funding awarded to Dr. Ariane Herrick at Hope Hospital.

An extension of a grant being carried out by Professor Carol Black at the Royal Free - title 'Identification and cloning of CTGF receptors expressed by scleroderma fibroblasts".

An extension for Dr. Viv Winrow at the University of Bath, to finish her project. Title of project 'Hypoxia and oxidative stress in scleroderma fibroblast activation - An investigation of a role for xanthine oxidase".

Professor Corris at the University of Newcastle - entitled 'Endothelial function in patients with pulmonary arterial hypertension complicating systemic sclerosis.'

Sue Brown in Bath, Ros Robb in Dundee and Naomi Reay in Leeds have also had an extension to their positions as Raynaud's & Scleroderma Nurse Specialists funded by the Association.

The above grants have only been made possible by the generosity and fundraising efforts by members and supporters of the Association to whom we extend our thanks.

Annual Conference Chester 2001

Professor Peter Maddison

New Approaches

Some really exciting things have been happening over the last few years and I think that this is going to continue into the future. I have always found scleroderma a very challenging condition to treat. However, people with scleroderma develop very troublesome and sometimes quite serious complications. Added to that in the wider medical community there has been a rather nihilistic attitude towards scleroderma. I think we are getting better at diagnosing scleroderma at an early stage, perhaps by identifying people who are more likely to develop particular types of scleroderma and in particular, complications. At last we are getting a much better idea of some of the underlying processes leading to scleroderma and this in turn is leading to quite important targets on which to focus therapy for the future.

I am going to use the term scleroderma but scleroderma technically applies to rather a wide spectrum of clinical disorders in which thickening and hardening of the skin is a common feature. I shall talk about systemic sclerosis, calling it scleroderma, in its various forms. You will see as we go along, that scleroderma comes in many different shapes and sizes. I want to emphasise that I am going to be largely talking about drug treatment and the challenges of drug treatment, which is just part of a treatment package involving different inputs from different health professionals.

One of the reasons why the medical profession have generally felt a bit pessimistic about drug treatment, is that up to now it has been difficult to demonstrate, without any doubt at all, that treatments actually work in scleroderma. Many treatments are now subjected to scientifically designed trials to try and ensure that any therapeutic response is a real response related to that medication and not just a response due to chance. Many of the drug studies in the past have been limited because scleroderma is quite an uncommon condition. In northern Europe the doctors specialising in scleroderma would expect to see twelve to twenty new cases of the diffuse form during the year and twice as many of the milder form. You can therefore imagine some of the difficulties if we are designing medicines which are needed to treat people with early scleroderma.

We really haven't got our act together as a medical profession in identifying ways of carefully assessing the progress of scleroderma and defining outcomes, which we need to change with our treatments. Clearly if we want to cure this condition we want to catch it at its earliest stage. One of the important aspects of treating scleroderma successfully is being able to assess progression very carefully and we are now getting the tools to do that. As doctors interested in these drugs, we've got to work with our colleagues and that is beginning to happen. Many people, when they first come to the clinic have features which could be easily recognised as scleroderma and the diagnosis is not so difficult, but there are still a lot of people who might present with Raynaud's Phenomenon alone. Raynaud's as many of you know is a feature which is not necessarily a symptom of scleroderma. but can occur by itself. However, if somebody comes with Raynaud's Phenomenon and rather puffy fingers - is that person likely to develop scleroderma? In most scleroderma clinics, clinicians will be looking to what we call nailfold capillaroscopy and also looking for the presence in the serum of patients, of particular antibody proteins which are very frequently associated with scleroderma.

We can say now that with a careful history and clinical examination and a combination of these techniques that we can identify: at least 90% of patients presenting to the clinic with Raynaud's Phenomenon. who are likely to go on and develop full-blown scleroderma. That is a very major advance.

In nailfold capillaroscopy we are looking at are the little blood vessels around the nailfold and we do that by using magnification which actually shows the flow of blood in the little blood cells around these vessels, so we can see abnormalities in blood vessels at a very early stage of scleroderma. The other progress we have made to complement that investigation is looking for the presence of antibody proteins. Scleroderma loosely falls into a family of what we call auto-immune diseases and many people with scleroderma have the presence of auto-antibodies. Antibody proteins which are of a particular rather characteristic type, are present right from the very beginning and that is why they can be helpful in assessing somebody with minimal clinical features. There are lots of different antibody proteins that we can find in the spectrum of scleroderma and are now using techniques to detect about seven of these antibody proteins, some of which may be present in one person, another may be present in another person. We are able to classify by what we call serology, about 85% of people who are destined to develop full blown scleroderma, which is again a big advance.

Scleroderma is a broad spectrum of conditions and we see people with different manifestations, different progression and different outcomes

It has been very difficult for drug trials to subclassify scleroderma into meaningful sub-sets. The traditional way of doing this is to subdivide scleroderma into two broad categories depending on the extent of skin involvement. To some degree, the extent of skin involvement mirrors what is happening in the internal organs. So we see two broad sub-groups, one which we call diffuse cutaneous scleroderma in which the scleroderma process, that is thickening and tightening of the skin, involves not only the extremities but most of the limbs and perhaps the trunk, and the degree of skin involvement is rather more extensive. In this situation we tend to see rather more early manifestations of scleroderma in other internal organs. In contrast to this are people with limited cutaneous scleroderma where the scleroderma is restricted to the extremities and in this situation we much more rarely see early signs of inflammation in internal organs. However we do see some involvement of internal organs rather later on in the course of the condition - usually about ten or twenty years - typically after the development of Raynaud's Phenomenon.

There has been nihilism about the effectiveness of drugs in this condition but the fact is that most people with scleroderma at some stage can benefit from drug therapy.

Clearly all of us are working towards the cure but we are not there yet. In the last few years there has been a huge advance in identifying particular complications of scleroderma, in particular internal organs. The key to that sort of approach, using the organ involvement approach to treatment, is that we may be able to identify involvement in these organs at the very earliest stage and then have the means of being able to assess whether or not there is progression. Here are three examples of organ system based treatment and where it is really making a very big difference. The first is involvement of the oesophagus, the gullet which is commonly involved in the course of scleroderma. The very first thing that happens is that the motility, the contractability of the lower part of the gullet, is reduced. There is a tendency for reflux of the stomach contents, development of severe heartburn problems and if that is not checked, the possibility of actual scarring and narrowing of the lower part of the gullet which can prove to be a very major problem. Nowadays we have the means of identifying the earliest form of involvement of the gullet using techniques called scintigraphy and manography We know now that there is a huge advantage of preventing and if necessary treating the very earliest stages of inflammation in the gullet. We can actually help to prevent some of the more serious complications of scar formation and gullet stricture, which has been the bane of the lives of many people with scleroderma. A lot of research is going on into the causes of this earliest phase and it is realised that we have got to have better treatments to actually attack it at this stage. The use of what we call proton blockers has really revolutionised our way of managing some of the oesophageal involvement.

The next example is lung involvement, which is the commonest cause of demise in scleroderma. It has taken over from the serious kidney involvement which can happen occasionally and again, we have to try and recognise the inflammation in the lung spaces before severe scarring takes place. Nowadays virtually every major district general hospital has the tools for pulmonary function tests and high resolution CT scanning for identifying this inflammation at the very earliest stages. The question is when you have identified it, what do you do about it? Well, there is the suggestion from case studies, that there are drugs that may make quite a difference to the long term course of this complication and may prevent the severe scarring from happening. My third example is the management of renal disease as one of the feared complications of scleroderma, the so-called scleroderma renal crisis, which at one time was an almost invariably fatal complication.

Fortunately, the outcome of this has radically changed with improvements in management of blood pressure, particularly with the introduction of what we call ACE inhibitors for controlling blood pressure and for controlling damage in the kidneys and also the revolutions that have happened in actually supporting kidneys that are not functioning properly. Again our emphasis is on prevention and so what we need to do is identify people at a very early stage, who are at more risk of developing this complication. Such people need to be monitored very carefully. We now know that the use of high doses of cortico-steroids is likely to have an adverse effect in people who are at risk of developing this kidney complication, so we tend to avoid high dose cortico-steroids if at all possible and then if we see the earliest traces of kidney involvement we can treat with ACE inhibitors.

Some years ago an organisation of people, doctors and scientists with an interest in scleroderma, got together to form The U.K. Scleroderma Study Group which has proved to be very productive. There are similar organisations that will perhaps have their origins in Europe but also involving people from around the world and yet other organisations which probably started off in the United States but again involve scleroderma specialists from around the world and many of these groups, interact with each other. Setting-up large scale, multi-centre trials is the only way of seeing whether or not a particular agent is effective in this condition. I am going to give you a few examples of some of the things that have happened as a result of these international collaborations. A lot of these tests need to be pretty simple and they need to be everywhere not just in the specialist centres.

One of the things that has been developed is the so-called scleroderma skin score. We know there is a lot to be gained in being able to assess the degree of scleroderma and how that relates to treatment, so the scleroderma skin score is really a very simple means of assessing the degree of scleroderma in different parts of the body, in fact in seventeen different sites on the body, and grading it from a zero to a three. Three being the thickest and the most immobile skin involvement and the highest possible score is fifty-one. We know that in fact the skin score relates to other important outcomes in this condition and this has been a great advance.

Many drug studies are now underway. The FAST study, which is funded by the Arthritis Research Campaign. is testing the hypothesis that the drug cyclophosphamide, is effective in reducing inflammation in the lungs and this is a very important study Another study is looking at oral iloprost in trying to prevent some of the blood vessel damage that happens during the course of scleroderma and this is being very generously funded by the Raynaud's & Scleroderma Association. There are a number of studies of new agents in an attempt to see whether or not they down regulate the scleroderma process. I'm going to concentrate on a pharmaceutical drug company sponsored study looking at an agent which counteracts the effect of a substance called TGF (transforming growth factor), which is quite exciting.

The focus on this particular agent has come through recent research in scleroderma and this is going to be one of the first studies of a targeted therapy. We do not know how effective it will be but it represents the new generation of drugs in scleroderma and it also gives me a chance to emphasise to you that the major pharmaceutical corporations are interested in finding ways of counter-acting this condition, which is very hopeful. This is largely I think through the efforts of Associations like this and also some of the doctors and other health professionals who have been prominent in the field. I think all of us, both seeing people with scleroderma and people who have scleroderma, owe a great debt of gratitude to people like Professor Carol Black, who have really pioneered this area over several years and have made it a respectable area for the drug companies to be dealing with.

I would like to mention a little about the 'QUINS' trial. Most of the drug trials in scleroderma deal with suppressive treatment in people with diffuse cutaneous disease, but here we are dealing with people with limited cutaneous involvement and we are looking to see, whether or not over a period of some time, one of the ACE inhibitors can prevent some of the complications which are due to vascular damage. This group of people, who actually represent the majority of people with scleroderma, have been rather overlooked when it comes to disease suppressing treatment because it has been felt that this has been a slow, perhaps milder form of scleroderma. However, we now appreciate that a proportion of people with limited cutaneous scleroderma, do in fact develop quite serious complications over a number of years.

The aim of this sort of study is to try and prevent these complications from happening. We are using the ACE inhibitor, quinapril, not only because it is effective in the renal complications of scleroderma but because it has been found in other clinical situations to have a calming effect on damaged blood vessels. We have designed a study which is going to involve a large number of people and I have to say that recruitment is very successful and has just started. One of the things we are going to assess is to what extent this sort of treatment can prevent the development of digital ulceration which again can be the bane of some peoples' lives. It is a feature that occurs in about 15 to 20% of people with this type of scleroderma but in many people it can be a multiple problem particularly during the winter months.

I hope I have given you a little feel for what progress has been made. Certainly we are making progress in being able to diagnose scleroderma at an earlier stage. We are definitely getting better assessment tools and also assessment tools which can be used by clinical people in all environments in different countries of the world. At long last we have got our act together and have formed the sort of collaborations to mount much better clinical trials which will be accepted by the scientific community as being robust. I have tried to show you how there is progress in identifying targets for treatment and we are going to see over the next few years I think, some very, very exciting results indeed there is a great deal of hope for people with scleroderma.

Professor Peter Maddison Ysbyty Gwynedd

The above article has been taken from Professor Maddison's talk at our 2001 Annual Conference

Raynaud's Overview

Dr. Douglas Veale

I don't need to tell you what Raynaud's is, but I'd like to explain in plain English, not medical terms, about what we think causes the colour changes. We know fingers change colour during an acute attack often accompanied by excruciating pain. Raynaud's by definition is reversible skin colour change, classically from white to blue to red and there are reasons for specific colour changes. The acute attack is due to vasospasm, common precipitators are cold, emotional factors - stress and pressure, such as carrying shopping or heavy objects. Other factors which induce attacks are temperature change, even slight change, or going into an air conditioned situation.

What exactly do we mean by blood vessel spasm? During a Raynaud's attack the fingers turn white, due to the inside of the blood vessel becoming completely obliterated, temporarily. The smooth muscle constricts down and closes off the blood supply completely, so the blood is just cut off for the duration of that acute attack. When fingers go red the blood vessels have vasodilated or 'opened up'. Sometimes in the same hand, blood vessels open up to try to compensate for those that have closed down. This results in complete whiteness of some fingers and redness of others.

Redness is caused by the increase in blood flow in open blood vessels and blueness is due to blood pooling in the veins. However, in secondary Raynaud's, the muscle around the blood vessel constricts or goes into spasm and in addition, immune cells may form an inflammatory reaction in the same way as a cut on the skin starts to heal. An inflammatory reaction will go red around the cut before it starts healing - forming a scar. This is due to white blood cells going in to repair the tissue, but in systemic sclerosis or other diseases associated with secondary Raynaud's, inflammation is abnormal. These blood cells go in and cause swelling around the blood vessel. Fluid also gathers around the blood vessel and the muscle contracts. So there are three mechanisms in secondary Raynaud's which squeeze the blood vessel.

Classically, Raynaud's affects fingers, toes, nose and ears, however peripheral sites where blood vessels are exposed to the environment or to external temperature can also be affected. We know from some very good studies that spasm can occur in blood vessels in the gut, the tongue, the gullet and also the large or small bowel inside our tummies. It can also affect heart vessels. In certain people spasm in the coronary arteries may occur if exposed to the cold. Raynaud's may affect other internal organs, such as the kidneys, the ovaries and the testes. It is important that these effects are understood as a part of Raynaud's. Migraine is a very common symptom and is frequently seen in patients with Raynaud's.

When fingers are blue, we call it cyanotic Raynaud's. This may be part of a classical white, blue and red attack or on its own. Veins take the blood away from the tissues back to the heart and they are different in anatomical structure from the arteries, in that they have much thinner walls with less smooth muscle, so don't go into spasm as easily. What they usually do in a Raynaud's attack is to open up and cause blood to accumulate in the vein. This blood has had all the oxygen removed, which turns the blood from red to a blue colour. Blood that has oxygen removed by the tissues and used in the normal way i.e. the deoxygenated blood, is left standing in the veins for longer than normal, causing the blue colour.

The connective tissue diseases are associated with secondary Raynaud's - scleroderma and CREST (limited systemic sclerosis) and overlap syndromes - features of scleroderma, rheumatoid arthritis and lupus may co-exist. Some of the antibody tests define specific characteristics more clearly helping diagnosis. We use the term secondary Raynaud's, when there is an identifiable cause, which may precipitate the attack. The most common of those is occlusive arterial disease due to smoking. Cigarette smoking and atheroma, the common cause of heart attacks, is also the commonest cause of peripheral occlusive arterial disease. This can also cause Raynaud's which can occur with occlusive arterial disease.

One puff of a cigarette can induce the small blood vessels to go into spasm, so if you smoke, stop smoking now!

Smoking adds to the damage to the lining of the blood vessel and it also affects the smooth muscle. Smooth muscle is exquisitely sensitive to cigarette smoke or to the chemicals that get into the blood stream from cigarette smoke and it can cause an immediate spasm in the blood vessel. Many things need to be considered when a patient first presents with Raynaud's, to identify simple problems e.g. thoracic outlet syndrome or an extra rib in the neck (even a fibrous rib), which may put pressure on the blood vessel from outside and stimulate spasm. Other forms of compression are nerve compression like carpal tunnel syndrome and reflex sympathetic dystrophy which can cause compression on a nerve giving rise to symptoms very similar to a secondary form of Raynaud's. Vascular injury due to repetitive occupational trauma such as pneumatic drills, welding or other heavy industrial equipment may also cause Raynaud's.

Drugs such as beta blockers, which were widely used in the 1970/80s for blood pressure and to improve survival after heart attack, can induce severe vasospasm (and produce secondary Raynaud's). People who work with chemicals such as polyvinyl chloride can also be at risk of developing scleroderma. There are conditions like cryoglobulinaemia, which cause a thickness of the blood, called hyperviscosity. In this case antibodies precipitate in the blood stream on exposure to cold. When blood becomes thicker and doesn't flow easily, you can imagine that in small blood vessels the blood can clot more easily and therefore mimic Raynaud's. We consider conditions like lupus and systemic sclerosis, Sjögren's, primary biliary cirrhosis and thyroiditis to be first cousins of each other and they are more common within a broad family group. It may not be in your immediate family but you may know a cousin, an aunt, or even a distant relation who may have had one of these other diseases. The unifying factor is they are auto-immune diseases, which direct antibodies to attack various structures within the body. In the case of secondary Raynaud's or scleroderma, that may be the blood vessels, the skin and the other internal organs.

There are definitely genetic factors particularly in pulmonary hypertension and fibrosis, which have been identified more clearly. There are no single genes identified for Raynaud's or scleroderma. However, probably two, three or four genes may be responsible in giving the background which provides the susceptibility in an individual, who may then suffer some environmental consequence which leads on to the Raynaud's or scleroderma.

I am going to describe briefly the antibodies associated with Raynaud's and scleroderma. In primary Raynaud's you don't get these antibodies. We know that the centromere antibody is entirely specific for limited systemic sclerosis. The other thing that we also measure is nailfold capillaroscopy. Regular blood vessels come to the nail cuticle but sometimes these get a little bit dilated and there may be a few little gaps in between the tiny blood vessels. When the pattern becomes more irregular these are features which we now know will define, together with the antibodies, up to 90% of people with secondary Raynaud's. The importance of these tests, is that they answer some of the big questions. If you present initially with Raynaud's you want to know what the future holds. Can we in the medical profession predict what will happen and if we can predict what will happen, can we do anything about it?

We now think of Raynaud's as Primary Raynaud's Phenomenon which is also called Raynaud's Disease and is not associated with antibodies. It is not associated with an abnormal nailfold capillary pattern. Certain features have enabled us to define Raynaud's at an early stage. In most cases when the patient first attends the clinic, we can actually define which type of Raynaud's the patient has, which means we can then direct the most appropriate treatment to each individual.

We know that Raynaud's can occur at an early age and can affect children. In this case it often has a family history so if a young girl comes to see us, we know that her mother may have had Raynaud's and the pattern of the illness at that stage may give us a clue as to whether this will just go away, whether it will stay through the teenage years and then stop in the early twenties, which it often does, or if it is actually going to progress into something more sinister.

Secondary Raynaud's is often called Raynaud's Syndrome and is associated with other diseases like systemic sclerosis, lupus, rheumatoid arthritis and others. Now to the pattern of clinical features. The clinical features of involvement of other areas of the body include the skin, the eyes, the mouth, the gullet, the gut, the internal organs, such as the lungs and the heart and the kidneys. These features often occur later but sometimes there is a little clue when you first see a patient with Raynaud's as to whether or not there is a systemic disease and whether this is primary or secondary. I have mentioned blood tests to look for antibodies and nailfold capillaroscopy. These two tests are really critical at an early stage in defining whether Raynaud's is primary or secondary. I think if anything has helped us in the last ten years to get a better handle on the condition at an early stage, it is these two tests.

To give you an idea of the incidence of Raynaud's in different connective diseases, systemic sclerosis is the most common systemic disease that is associated. 90%-99% of patients with systemic sclerosis will have severe Raynaud's. Mixed connective disease is also commonly associated with Raynaud's, systemic lupus to a little lesser extent and other less common conditions. Another common medical term is sclerodactyly or 'puffy fingers' where the skin over the fingers becomes puffy or swollen. This is often a first feature of systemic sclerosis, whether it be limited or diffuse. Scars or digital pits can be seen in the skin on the finger tips, which occur when the blood supply is cut off for longer than the tissue can sustain, so that the skin and the subcutaneous tissue can't get enough oxygen. For this to happen, the vasospasm of the blood vessel has to be present for a long time or be recurrent. The tissue can't get nutrients and oxygen, therefore cells start to die and little areas of necrosis, digital pitting or ulceration occur.

What we've done in the last 10 years is to look into lots of other blood vessels. All the blood vessels that I've mentioned up until now are really the small blood vessels beyond the knuckles or the toes and of course, as you know, the blood vessels get smaller and smaller as you go to the tip of your fingers or the tip of your toes. It is usually the blood vessels between the knuckles and the tip of the finger that actually go into spasm. What we wanted to do was to look at the larger blood vessels to see whether these had also been affected in some way or another, particularly by the inflammation. What we found was that in the carotid arteries, that is the large arteries in the neck and in the large arteries in the lower legs there was a greater prevalence of disease in patients with systemic sclerosis, compared to the normal population. This therefore was evidence that there is involvement, that is inflammation of the large blood vessels, as well as the small blood vessels. When investigating the risk factors which may be causing the inflammation, we looked at disease duration and incidence of smokers. We already knew that limited disease is more common than diffuse disease. In early disease duration there was no apparent difference in the number of smokers which indicates that smoking as a risk factor did not explain this difference between the incidence of large vessel inflammation in systemic sclerosis and the normal population. So we looked at the other traditional risk factors such as cholesterol, the triglycerides or the level of fat in the blood, whether the patient has a tendency to diabetes or not, as these will have a profound effect on their blood pressure, their risk for coronary artery disease and strokes, and found that these were all the same. We then looked at blood pressure, the mean systolic and the mean diastolic blood pressure and these were similar between the two groups.

So what this tells us is that there are other risk factors which must explain the difference in the inflammation, and therefore the risk of large vessel disease in patients with systemic sclerosis and we have been working on this. It is now quite clear that when there is inflammation in the body, whether it is just affecting the blood vessels or whether it is affecting the joints, that the level of inflammation in the body will have a direct effect on the blood vessels and will increase the risk for large blood vessel disease. Much of our efforts now are focussing on how we can actually change that.

I am going to finish briefly with the advances in therapy. Of the vasodilators, nifedipine still remains the most tested and in terms of effect, efficacy, it is the gold standard but it is also the highest in terms of side effects. Many of you will be familiar with iloprost which is given by an intravenous drip for acute attacks or digital ulcers, usually for secondary Raynaud's, but it can also be useful in primary Raynaud's. The natural therapies can often give some symptomatic benefit and I would say that may be useful in people who can't tolerate some of the traditional drugs or may work well with traditional drugs to have some benefit. The recent trial of Seredrin Ginkgo biloba with Phytosome, was very successful for some Raynaud's sufferers. Just to briefly mention surgery, sympathectomy can be useful for lower limb Raynaud's for legs and feet but is no longer recommended for Raynaud's of the hands or u pper limbs.

I would like to thank the Raynaud's & Scleroderma Association for the help they have given me in terms of our research in the past and hopefully in the future.

Dr. Douglas Veale, St. Vincent's Hospital, Dublin

The above article was taken from Dr. Douglas Veale's talk at the 2001 Annual Conference.

The Heart in Scleroderma

For over 50 years there have been suggestions that heart disease is common in patients with scleroderma, and that when present the outlook is poor. It is increasingly clear that serious heart disease is no more common in scleroderma than in the rest of the population. In the early 90's Folanasbee published his findings in over 1000 patients with scleroderma followed for around 20 years, showing that cardiac deaths occurred at a rate found in the rest of the population. Recent data from Greece support these findings. This is not to say that heart involvement in scleroderma is uncommon or unimportant.

Dr. Gerry Coghlan

The main ways in which scleroderma can affect the heart are scarring within the muscle of the heart (interfering with it's ability to relax), inflammation of the muscle or lining of the heart (causing breathlessness), and possibly increasing the amount of coronary artery disease, thus making angina and heart attacks more likely. In addition, the heart can be affected indirectly by the effects of high blood pressure in the arteries of the body or the lungs – since these increase the amount of work to be done by the heart.

Symptoms of heart involvement

In most people in whom the heart is significantly affected, there will be some problems noticed by the individual. Breathlessness is the most common symptom, but may occur for many reasons. Scarring of the lung is by far the most common cause of significant breathlessness in scleroderma – but lung function tests and CT scans of the lungs should show enough scarring to explain the severity of restriction in these cases. A sudden reduction in your ability to do normal levels of exercise without a change in these tests should lead to investigations of the heart. The next most common cause is high blood pressure in the lungs (pulmonary hypertension) - this affects up to 3 in 20 people with scleroderma, and can usually be picked up by an echocardiogram.

Unfortunately, the echocardiogram cannot confirm the presence of pulmonary hypertension except in a few people with very advanced disease, and can never provide enough information to direct treatment. In some cases it is necessary to pass a tube to the heart (cardiac catheter) under local anaesthetic to make the diagnosis. This is a very simple test and in most cases is very straight forward. It is however, an invasive test and thus very serious complications can occur. It is therefore only done where the benefits in terms of knowing how to act, exceeds the risks of the procedure. Inflammation leading to scarring and stiffness of the heart (myocarditis and restrictive cardiomyopathy) are further causes of breathlessness which can only be demonstrated clearly at the time of catheterisation. Finally, narrowed arteries and fluid around the heart (from inflammation of the heart lining – pericardium) are the other less common causes of breathlessness. Thus, when investigating breathlessness – the lung function tests and X-rays of the chest may provide the answers. However, often an echocardiogram or catheter test are necessary if the heart is thought to be causing the breathlessness.

Chest pain particularly coming on while walking and easing with rest is also a relatively common symptom. This may be due to narrowed arteries in the heart. However, chest wall pain from arthritis of the joints in the rib cage and reflux of acid to the swallowing tube can both produce the same kind of pain. Thus, again investigations may be necessary before one can determine how precisely to treat this symptom. The final relatively common symptom is palpitations (severe awareness of the heart beat). This is usually due to extra beats (which affect 3 in 20 of the population at some time of their lives). It is thought that people with scleroderma may be more prone to problems with the electrics of the heart, and 24 hour taping of the heart rhythm is the most useful test for investigating this symptom.

Why does scleroderma affect the heart?

To date there is no clear answer to this question. Some have suggested that Raynaud's of the heart arteries allows intermittent spasm of the blood vessels around the heart and that this leads to gradual damage and scarring. Others believe that the inflammation which one gets in the skin and sometimes muscles, can also affect the heart muscle. What is known is that by the time people have had scleroderma for 15 to 20 years, one can find evidence that the relaxation of the heart is slowed in about half the population. In addition there are subtle changes in the ECG (electrical tracing of the heart) in about 4 in 10, and in how the heart rhythm normally varies throughout the day. Thus, research to date has shown that small changes in heart function are common. We do not know precisely when these changes occur nor why.

How important is heart involvement?

In a small number of people very serious heart problems occur. Severe inflammation of the muscle can lead to severe breathlessness and interfere with the heart's ability to contract – having taken a sample of heart muscle to confirm the diagnosis, we usually treat this with drugs to dampen inflammation. Inflammation of the lining of the heart can sometimes lead to the heart, being compressed by fluid around the heart, again causing severe acute breathlessness. This is easily removed once diagnosed by echocardiography. Of course angina and heart attacks (coronary artery disease) are at least as common as in the rest of the population and require investigation and treatment in the same way. High blood pressure is more common in scleroderma because of kidney involvement in the condition and this must be controlled to avoid long term strain on the heart. Finally, pulmonary hypertension is less well tolerated in people with scleroderma because the right side of the heart cannot cope with very high pressures over a long period of time. Fortunately we now have reasonably effective therapies for this condition and are developing new treatments every year.

Where is research leading?

A new blood test called 'troponin' allows us to find out when minute amounts of damage are occurring in the heart. We have found that troponin leaks from the heart when the skin disease is active, especially in the first few years of the disease. This suggests that we can find out when damage is actually occurring, and can investigate the mechanism of damage at the right time. We plan to ask people who have evidence of active skin disease to have this blood test and if positive to undergo investigations into the blood vessels and muscle of the heart looking for evidence of vessel spasm or inflammation. Only if we can find out the earliest changes in the heart can we hope to treat properly those few patients who develop serious heart involvement, and improve the ability of the heart to cope with other complications such as pulmonary hypertension. We aim to be able to start this study in about one years time.

The above article has been written by Dr. Gerry Coghlan, Royal Free Hospital following his talk at our Annual Conference 2001.

Launch of New Booklet

The Role of The Occupational Therapist

Anne Johnson, Occupational Therapist in Bath has written a booklet for Occupational Therapists which is now available from the Association. It has been kindly sponsored by Schering Health Care Ltd.

Dermal Ultrasound in Systemic Sclerosis

Last year the Raynaud's & Scleroderma Association very kindly funded us the loan of a dermal ultrasound scanner. Measurement of skin thickness is very important in scleroderma, for example, in clinical trials of early scleroderma. The 'skin score' is usually the main outcome measure because this gives a good indication of disease progression and can be a reflection of internal organ involvement. In the skin score, the skin is pinched to assess its thickness and elasticity, giving a score between 0 and 3 depending on how thick, and how elastic each site is. At present scores from 17 sites are taken, adding up to a total score, which is monitored at each clinic visit. The draw back of this method of examination is that the measure is subjective and may differ between different examiners.

Ultrasound scanning has been used recently as an objective measurement of skin thickness, and previous studies have suggested that ultrasound might be useful in the assessment of sclerodermatous skin. However, these studies have examined skin thickness at only a small number of sites and we thought that by using multiple sites we might increase the potential usefulness of the technique.

We therefore conducted a study measuring skin thickness by ultrasound at 17 sites, more or less corresponding to the sites of the skin score. Thirty-five patients and thirty-three controls had ultrasound skin thickness measurements taken. This involved the patient lying on a couch and having skin thickness measured by means of a high frequency probe and ultrasound gel at pre determined sites over the body. The investigation is totally painless taking approximately 30 minutes. The measurements were performed twice by me (to assess the reliability of the technique when used by the same person), and were repeated by a radiologist to see whether measurements were significantly 'observer-dependent'.

Our results showed that the technique was reliable, (there were only small differences between the readings for each individual). Therefore this 17 site ultrasound scoring method has the potential to be used to follow the progress of the skin thickening over time. We also confirmed (as expected) that skin is much thicker in patients with scleroderma than in healthy controls. We are very grateful to all the patients who gave their time to take part in the study.

Tonia Moore, Hope Hospital, Salford

Frequently asked questions on pulmonary hypertension

Can an echocardiogram (echo) be wrong or give misleading results?

Yes. The best way of determining the pulmonary artery pressure is by Right Heart Catheterisation. However, when an experienced technician does an echo carefully, estimated pressures usually correlate to those obtained during a catheterisation.

With PH do I need to take Warfarin?

Warfarin is a blood thinner. Unless there is a good reason not to, most doctors recommend prescribing Warfarin. When the blood is thinner it is easier for it to pass through the narrowed vessels in your lungs. It is also known that PH patients run a higher risk of developing blood clots in the lungs. Warfarin gives good protection to prevent this happening. Two studies have also found that PH patients who use anticoagulants live longer than those that don't.

Although aspirin is cheaper it acts on the platelets in the blood. Warfarin acts on the fibre-like agents, which also cause clots. The fibre-like agents are more likely to contribute to PH. For safety, you will need to have regular checks to determine how long it takes for your blood to clot. Normally an International Normalised Range (INR) of 1.5 to 2.0 is aimed for although some doctors prefer it to be higher.

Do I need to alter my diet?

The major dietary concern in patients with PH is salt. As your heart finds it harder to pump blood around your body the blood flow to the kidneys is decreased. Your kidneys respond to this by holding onto extra sodium and water rather than getting rid of it. Fluid can build up, leading to swelling in the legs and abdomen and increased breathlessness.

Is it a good idea to limit your salt intake?

TIPS: Don't add salt to cooking or have it at the table within two months - you won't miss it! Experiment with salt free seasonings like pepper, onion, lemon and parsley. Make food from scratch, commercially prepared foods are loaded with salt. Buy or borrow a low sodium cook book or ask to talk to a dietician if you are concerned.

Why does Prostacyclin/Iloprost help PH patients?

Prostacyclin dilates blood vessels, reduces clotting by keeping platelets from clumping together, can improve cardiac output, and can slow down the growth of smooth muscle cells. Pulmonary Artery Pressure and Right Atrial pressure fall, and oxygen saturation climbs. Symptoms decrease or even almost disappear. This change usually takes place from a few weeks to a few months, sometimes longer. In some cases the drug actually seems to reverse the course of the disease. Patients who do not initially respond often slowly get better over time.

How can I relax, deal with anger and depression?

You can do it - you have serious motivation. Stress can significantly aggravate PH symptoms. Many patients get angry - it's not fair they got PH and they don't deserve it. It's important to deal with the anger so you can move forward and cope with the illness. Talking to a counsellor, another patient or joining a support group and helping others can help. Other ideas are: finding a physical outlet such as mild exercise, even cleaning out a cupboard, making a 'things to do list' and completing it, keep a diary of accomplishments and learning as much about the disease as possible helps give a sense of control.

Depression can come hand in hand with the illness: fatigue, lack of oxygen, anger turned inward, some medications and a lot of other things can trigger depression. Luckily, clinical depression is one of the most curable diseases of the mind and body. But the key is to reach out and ask for help. If you think you may be depressed, talk to your doctor. The signs and symptoms are well listed in many books available in shops and libraries. For relaxation try a hobby, meditation, or adult education class, meditation, or yoga.

The above section has been reprinted with kind permission of the Pulmonary Hypertension Association U.K. Newsletter Winter 2001.

'Scleroderma has changed my life....although not all for the worse'

Seven years on since I was first diagnosed with scleroderma and I don't think that my life could be going much better. I am in my last year at school with plans to do 'A' levels followed by a degree in law. I have fantastic friends who have known me all the way through my troubles, as well as new friends who aren't even a little disturbed by my condition. Of course this isn't how I saw things seven years ago. I went for months wondering if I would ever be able to walk again and people at school asking questions and making snide remarks. I think the worst thing was coming to terms with things myself. I was only nine at the time and couldn't understand what was going on around me or why...

After I managed to face up to the facts I learnt to deal with other problems too. I worked hard to be able to walk again and soon found a way of handling the people who didn't even want or try to identify with anyone who was slightly different to their so-called 'normality'.

About a month ago I bought a skirt whilst I was out shopping one day. This was very exceptional for me as I'm usually the last person to go for a skirt, mainly because of the appearance of my leg. Last Friday I convinced myself to wear it to a disco, not because I like skirts or because I wanted to make an impact on anyone but because I could. I proved to myself that even if I opted never to wear a skirt again, I knew that if I ever decided otherwise I could, and that I wouldn't feel uncomfortable or ashamed. Having scleroderma has changed my life in various ways, although not all for the worse. I think that I'm a much stronger person for having to deal with this. In the big picture it's hardly a problem at all and I'm constantly aware that there are lots of people worse off than me. I believe that the recent incident in America has put a lot of things into perspective.

Although I had problems at first, my life is going great and I have the rest of my life ahead of me. I would love to offer support and advice to any children who are going through similar problems. I know that I may not know as much as the doctors, or how much your family and friends know about you, but I've been there, they haven't!

Jennie McMonagle

See article on page 169.

Good news from an erythro sufferer

Gwendolyn Langer

I am positively euphoric with the control over erythromelalgia (in my feet and shins) that 'Neurontin' has given me. I have had to build up the dose gradually since last autumn and since June I have been taking two 300 mg capsules four times a day. Apparently I am very lucky not to have any adverse side effects, unless you count a shocking short-term memory and slight shaking of the hands - but I am seventy-four! I am also very fortunate that I do not suffer from Raynaud's as well.

We all have to battle persistently to get any medical help for this rare condition and I, like others, explored all sorts of alternative therapies. What they all found was damage to the sympathetic nerves. A doctor of radiology, upon seeing my crimson feet when I went for a spinal X-ray, remarked that my "sympathetic nerve had been cut during surgery". The homeopaths believe that it has been damaged by heavy metals (mercury and aluminium both showed up with hair analysis) and an acupuncturist said that she had to treat my sympathetic nerve. My general practitioner had been visibly shocked when I called in after shopping at the supermarket to show him my dreadful feet, so I asked him to refer me to a neurologist. This he did and I met a delightful specialist who listened thoughtfully and read my account of my four years, and the other 'bits and pieces' that I had taken about erythro. Thus emboldened I remarked that sufferers in America had been trying a drug called Gabapentin, to which he replied that that was what he was going to prescribe, and in this country it is called Neurontin.

I have just written to tell him that "I have got my life back" - I have been out to dinner and shopped all afternoon. I now sleep without my fan and I'm going on holiday (to somewhere cool!). For over four years I have been crippled by the afternoon, if not earlier, and so have been more or less tied to my house and garden, where I could use a fan when the burning pain became bad. However, if I have a shock (I concussed myself recently) or have emotional stress the control breaks down. I do wonder if stress can be at least partly to blame for erythro. I have asked the neurologist to write about erythro in whatever publication G.P.s read because none of them have ever heard of it, and I believe that there are many more sufferers out-there. I know how very fortunate I am and wish with all my heart that others could find the same relief, and I honestly feel fine on it. G.P.s might need a neurologist to prescribe it but if you are a sufferer push for it, and don't give up pushing.

Gwendolyn Langer

Sponsored cycle ride raises £4,601

Rosemary Chalk from Fovant, Wiltshire organised a sponsored cycle ride which has raised £4,601. This is in addition to money raised by Rosemary earlier in the year. We are most grateful to her for her fantastic efforts. The photograph shows the cyclists setting off wearing their Percy Penguin T-shirts.

New leaflet on Limited Cutaneous Systemic Sclerosis (CREST)

New in our range of patient information leaflets is one on limited cutaneous sclerosis, previously called the CREST syndrome. This was written due to the number of requests we receive for information on CREST and has been approved by Professor Carol Black.

20 Years of Caring & Sharing 1982-2002

This year we celebrate our 20th Anniversary. We have come a long way since our first newsletter, an A4 sheet of photocopied paper in February 1982. At that time very little was known of Raynaud's and even less about scleroderma. Research into these conditions was barely existent and very little help was available for patients. Over the twenty years the Association has made a difference to the lives of hundreds of individuals through our welfare fund, has invested millions of pounds in research, produced numerous publications and videos and been responsible for promoting educational material for both patients and health professionals. We have also been instrumental in bringing together health professionals. The creation of nurse helplines in addition to our own helpline at Head Office has been invaluable to sufferers. There is now a much greater understanding of Raynaud's and scleroderma, and better treatments are available to alleviate the conditions. We still have a long way to go in educating the general public and our recent questionnaire has highlighted the fact that even more needs to be done if patients are to get an early and accurate diagnosis. International collaboration with doctors and patients alike has contributed to a greater interest worldwide which can only be beneficial for sufferers in the future. The success of any organisation lies with its members and supporters.

Grace Mary & Margaret Smith, Jim Jones and Ann Winterton MP

Congleton M.P., Ann Winterton (left), and Anne Mawdsley, with a plaque to mark the 20th Anniversary of the Association. This photograph was taken at a reception held at Head Office on 1st February and was attended by guests, staff and volunteers. Photographs courtesy of John Cocks, 'Cheshire Life' magazine.

A reception was held at Head Office on 1st February 2002, to celebrate our Anniversary. This was attended by guests, staff and volunteers. I am extremely grateful for the support which I have received and will hopefully continue to receive over the years ahead. It is only by working together that we can hope to achieve our ultimate goal. The doctors, researchers, nurses and other health professionals who work closely with the Association have been invaluable both in patient care and research. Finally, new posters have been supported by Cheshire Building Society, which depict the feeling experienced by Raynaud's sufferers.

Clr. Ron Tyson, Chairman of Alsager Town Council, with Helen Birtles, Jan Scott and Mike Elkin.

Sir Richard Baker Wilbraham (left) with Mayor of Congleton, Clr. Roy Giltrap, and Ann Winterton M.P.

Anne Mawdsley

Congratulations!

We were delighted to hear the news that Professor Carol Black has been awarded a CBE for her research and clinical care in scleroderma and related fibrotic disorders. The Association would like to congratulate Professor Black on this award which is very well deserved and has helped to highlight scleroderma through her lifetime dedication and achievement.

Professor Carol Black

Raynaud's Survey 2000-2001

Raynaud's Questionnaire

Our thanks to the thousands of people who completed the questionnaire.

Below are just a few of the comments given:

"It's the most embarrassing, extremely painful, ignored disability".

"Every person I know with Raynaud's has a Scottish ancestor - could it be a protection to slow blood to the fingers in a cold climate, to stop damage to fingers and joints, or to keep blood near the heart (not to lose heat)? Sluggish blood around the joints could deposit crystals and damage joints - no blood, no damage".

"I have found that as I get older, my symptoms are worse, particularly my feet when at times, I can barely walk with the pain. I consider myself very lucky that I have been able to control effects by taking care not to venture out without adequate protection".

"I find red wine and brandy (regular but small amounts) help, as does taking cod liver oil liquid and eating lots of oily fish (tuna, mackerel, sardines). I also stopped smoking (very important!)".

"I have found that following a strict diet to balance my blood sugar levels and improve my digestion has helped my condition a lot. I also feel that thought patterns (stress) have a very large part to play in Raynaud's".

"I get hands with blue nails, white fingers between second and third joint, even in summer if the temperature falls. In South Africa, I wore shorts, T-shirt, sun hat and gloves!'

"I try to keep as warm as possible in cold weather and find this easier to do living in the country because you can dress for the weather. It's not so easy in the town/city. Wearing sensible shoes and thermal socks helps - so called fashion shoes were a killer!'

"This is a very frustrating condition - I can feel warm in the body but my hands go white or blue and numb or tingle painfully and go very cold. It is usually worse if my toes are cold too".

"I would definitely recommend getting pregnant as a (drastic!) way of improving Raynaud's! Four years on, the improvement seems long lasting".

"Thank you for conducting this questionnaire! I found it so frustrating to be diagnosed and then to be told there was no treatment available. I have had huge difficulties at College and University as my Raynaud's causes lots of problems with writing. Thankfully I have been able to get learning aids through the Disabled Students Allowance.

Diagnosis or misdiagnosis?

One of the main points of concern was the amount of time taken for patients to get diagnosed with Raynaud's. Only 10% were diagnosed immediately, with diagnosis taking over a year for 15% of the respondents. For those with scleroderma only 5% were diagnosed immediately. For 37%, it took up to one year to get a diagnosis and for 10% it took over five years. More work needs to be carried out in creating a greater understanding and awareness in the medical profession and we are looking at ways of achieving this.

Obviously there are many doctors who do diagnose the problem early but from the feedback received from Raynaud's sufferers, we need to do more to highlight the condition. The following are some further comments:

"I am finding it difficult to get a diagnosis as my doctor first sent me to hospital suspecting Lupus (rash on face). Since then I can't get a proper diagnosis and it's driving me mad".

"When the doctor (my G.P.) said he thought I had Raynaud's and I asked what could be done, he said "try ginger and gingko and wearing gloves". I don't think he understands how uncomfortable and debilitating the condition is".

"Doctors are not very helpful and don't tell you much about the illness. I had an operation on my feet when I was 15 and now have nerve damage and problems with my feet".

"When I mentioned symptoms to a doctor during a visit for something else, he said it's just poor circulation, he did not mention Raynaud's".

"My doctor said there was nothing I or he could do about it".

"I had mentioned to my doctor when first experiencing the numbness of fingers, but nothing was done. I was told it was bad circulation - friends have told me it is Raynaud's".

"Until two years ago my hands got cold but my feet were OK. For some reason the situation has reversed. I have told doctors but they have no answers. The right foot always goes numb first".

"I have seen three doctors and one Specialist about Raynaud's and they were not interested or helpful".

"As long as I can remember I have hated the cold weather - as a child I had bad chilblains. Sometimes they got infected and my mother put hot poultices on them - I had to be off school. My fingers have always turned white in the cold (even indoors) and are painful when they are returning to red. A doctor I worked for (not my own G.P.), saw my white fingers once and said "You've got Raynaud's'".

"I have not been diagnosed as having Raynaud's. My doctor doesn't seem interested and just remarks "Oh yes - you've got chilblains".

"No-one has suggested any tests, when I showed the doctor my dead fingers he said "that looks like Raynaud's Syndrome - there's nothing we can do, just keep warm" (this was 40 years ago and I've never mentioned it to my present doctor)".

Family Weekend gets a hearty thumbs up!

The children meet Percy

Comments from the Adults

"It's good to know you're not on your own" That was the comment heard many times during the weekend of February 8th-10th when 14 children and 20 parents or grandparents met at The Moat House Hotel in Chester, for the first family scleroderma weekend. We had travelled from all over England, Wales. Southern Ireland and Scotland to meet the 4 staff from the Association and 3 health professionals from the Royal Free Hospital in London, to get to know more about this rare disease and how other children coped. It was a well-balanced weekend, including learning and fun. We did painting, went to McDonald's, had a beetle drive, swam, had use of the sauna, were entertained by a brilliant magician and had a special visit from Percy Penguin. The girls did a show in the swimming pool and the boys played football. There was plenty of time to chat and ask questions of the doctors and physiotherapist.

Professor Carol Black led our first session and explained that scleroderma is a family of diseases, a connective tissue disease, which is either in a localised or systemic form, and can affect all the major organs. Although genes, the child's environment, trauma or viruses could cause scleroderma, we don't really know why some children develop it. The important thing is to get in touch with good specialists so that the disease can be monitored early. We had the chance to ask many questions e.g. Can hormones affect it?, Is having a TB jab safe?, Do vitamins help?

The physiotherapy talk by Jan Wroblewaz, stressed the importance of exercise but also stretching and resting. It is important to keep the joints moving when the disease is under control to prevent muscle wasting. Sometimes the physio needs to do it with the child, if they refuse to do it for Mum. In our family physio session, using cling film, we had to assert gentle pressure to cause tension in the cling film. ready to practice on the skin! Dr. Geraldine Brough helped us to see how having scleroderma has a great impact not just on the child but also on the whole family. Having a chronic illness from pre-school age to adolescence (Harry Enfield's Kevin!) makes a child face adult issues far too early. Why do I have to take the drugs? Why do I look different?

This was the first family weekend organised by the Association and the children made friends with each other and the parents enjoyed meeting others. Many thanks to Anne and her team for organising it."

Sue Briley

"The hotel and facilities were excellent. I appreciated the literature sent beforehand. Chester is a really lovely location. The pool was great! It was wonderful to meet the staff from the Association and put faces to names - everyone was so approachable and helpful. The talks from the medical staff were excellent and really helpful, very positive and 'normalised' the illness. The activities laid on for the children were just right to maintain interest and provide a challenge. My daughter's comment to Anne "Look, your hands are the same colour as mine!" struck a chord. This is the first time she had seen someone else with blue hands due to poor circulation. The physio session was so useful. The physio my daughter has seen hasn't dealt with anyone with systemic sclerosis and feels rather in the dark, so the comments and exercises have put a better understanding on what can be achieved and why certain exercises are important. It was wonderful to see the children together, playing and chattering away. So many of the children have fighting spirits and I can see so much of my own child's behaviour reflected in the other children. The magician was excellent and a wonderful finale."

Debbie Richards

"A very well organised and beneficial weekend. Extremely helpful to meet and speak with others who have the same worries as ourselves. You have all been very successful in helping us understand scleroderma a little more and made us all feel most welcome".

Michael and Ann-Marie Little

"I enjoyed the weekend. Professor Carol Black's talk was very interesting. I have learned lots about scleroderma I didn't know before. Dr. Geraldine Brough was very reassuring and helpful".

Doreen Aherne

"Thank you very much for the weekend. It was very well organised - no time for boredom! Our daughter enjoyed meeting other children with similar conditions as she had never met anyone with scleroderma before. The hotel setting in Chester was lovely and the food was superb".

Andrew and Carole Lorenz

"Thank you very much for a lovely weekend. It was very beneficial to us all. I found it very helpful and everything went very well. We understood things a lot better in different aspects of the illness".

Colin and Sally Edwards

"Great weekend - very informative as well as reassuring. My son and I have thoroughly enjoyed ourselves and do hope that we are able to see you all again next year. Thank you very much for your hard work".

Barbara Roberts

"This weekend has been most beneficial for us as a family. I have nothing negative to say about it at all. Please can this be an annual event?!'

Marina Orme

"The professional talks were very informative and the opportunity to have a talk with Professor Carol Black and the Royal Free staff was excellent. The arrangements made for the weekend by the staff of the R & S Association were exemplary and well-organised for the children. It was great to talk with other parents and children with the condition".

Mark Steen

"Very informative - Children were well catered for. We were very grateful for the chance to meet other families with similar conditions. I got the answers I was looking for this weekend. Glad my son met other kids with a similar problem. The children enjoyed the games that were laid on for them, the food was good, the rooms were spacious and very warm.'

Katrina Astley

"We learned a great deal and it was very helpful to talk to other parents - no-one else can really understand. As a family we have probably gained a support network for the future. It was particularly valuable for the children as they no longer feel isolated. Hotel, organisation and entertainment couldn't have been better".

Michael & Anita Gray

Children's comments

"I really enjoyed myself this weekend, the games and crafts were brilliant. I thought it was great to meet all the other children. The food was wonderful, I thought it was great the way you could eat as much as you liked at breakfast. I liked the games and magic show we had after dinner, it was really fun".

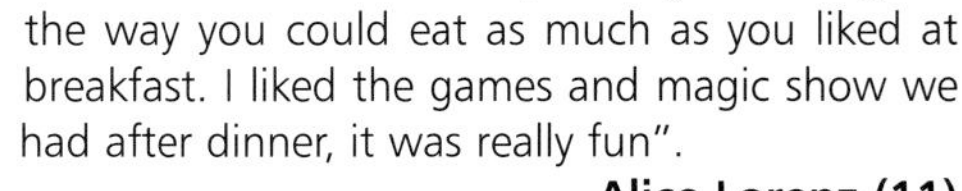

Alice Lorenz (11)

"We enjoyed the games and the food was good. The rooms were spacious and very warm. Let's have more because we need it. I will definitely come again but I will bring my older brother and sister to see how much fun it was".

Ben Astley (5)

"The physio session really helped me know more about my scleroderma and it was a fantastic weekend. I had loads of fun and thanks very much. But I wish I could have stayed a lot longer".

Aine Aherne (10)

"Brilliant. I would love to come again".

Gemma Orme (11)

"I enjoyed it immensely, epecially meeting other children, and knowing that I am not on my own. My brother, Jordan loved the magic show and making friends".

Arnya Edwards (9)

"I thought the weekend was really good fun and good for everyone. It was good for making new friends who know about scleroderma and Raynaud's. Wish it was longer as well, as I enjoyed it so much".

Annwen Gray (13)

"The weekend was good. Could we have a children's section in the magazine just to keep in touch with each other, saying what we're doing at school?"

Nathan (13)

"The best part of the holiday was going to McDonalds and also meeting other children like me. Thank you".

Jenny Richards (7)

"It was a good weekend and I enjoyed it. It was good making new friends and meeting other children with this condition. It was a great fun time".

Carrie Steen (13)

"I like all the new friends I've made and want to see them all again. I was excited to come here and I've really enjoyed myself".

Rees Roberts (5)

"I really enjoyed this weekend. It was so beneficial and I enjoyed talking to other members and people who are affected. I hope you carry this weekend on yearly as judging from this weekend it will be successful. You have all worked very hard and I would like to thank you for that. I have made some friends who I'm sure I'll keep in touch with. Thank you so much".

Emma Little (13)

"Lots of fun and wish it was longer".

Hannah Gray (10)

Help at Hand?

Following an article in The Daily Mail and a piece in Hot News,we received several letters relating to fluoxetine. Some of the comments are published below for your interest.

It looks as if I have found something to take the edge off my pain resulting from Raynaud's. Here is my story.

I am now 44 years old and have suffered from Raynaud's since my early twenties. It started with just the middle finger getting cold/white. Over the years it has progressed to both hands and feet getting so cold that I lose the feeling in them completely and they are turning from white to dark blue with considerable pain involved, especially when the blood decides to return.

I think I must have tried everything alternative, all the usual herbs, ginger, ginkgo, even specially mixed Chinese recipes, acupuncture, magnetic bands and hypnosis. Unfortunately nothing has worked for me. By chance a friend saw an article in the Daily Mail last October, in which it stated that doctors from the Royal Free Hospital have discovered that the mood - changing drug fluoxetine, which controls the amount of the natural hormone serotonin in the blood, reduces radically the severity and frequency of attacks caused by the disorder without any unpleasant side effects.

After approximately 3 weeks of taking one tablet of fluoxetine capsules (20mg) a day, I found that my hands still turned white on occasions, but not so regularly and not so severe. The dreadful pain is nearly gone. It really has taken the edge off it for me and even at this time of the year I can actually get to the car and grip the steering wheel without having to warm up my hands for a while. I do not know what kind of side effects this drug might have, but my doctor said they are minimal. I will have to wait and see, but I felt I had to give your readers the opportunity to try it out for themselves and possibly report back.

I would like to thank you for your varied articles in the 'Hot News' which I always find very interesting, even though some of the stories are quite sad and worrying but it is good to know, one is not alone with this problem.

Rangy Holt

I visited my consultant at The Oaks Hospital in Colchester in October and took along with me the article that had appeared in the Daily Mail. Whilst being sceptical he said that there might be some truth in it and gave me a prescription for the drug. I started off with one tablet a day (about six weeks ago) and within three weeks found that I had not had an attack. The side effects however were not good, as being very small (6½ stone in weight) I found that I was feeling incredibly 'spaced out' and quite frankly a danger when driving etc. so I reduced the dosage to one every other day. I went on holiday to the Far East for a fortnight and stopped taking the drug. On my return to England, having experienced no attacks on holiday despite continually going from hot to cold/air conditioning etc., the symptoms returned a few days after. I have started to take one a day since and remarkably I have been free of an attack for four days now. It is early days but I feel that the side effects are reducing and hopefully once my body has got used to the daily dose I will not be affected by any symptoms i.e. dizziness and inability to drink alcohol in any quantity whatsoever! I must admit to feeling quite euphoric as the continual attacks were getting me down. I began to dread stepping outside the door or even walking upstairs if the temperature was colder from room to room.

(Later) I have now been on the drug for two months. The side affects (dizziness, feeling on another planet, inability to drive properly, low tolerance to alcohol) have now subsided and the results so far are really marvellous. I have not had a proper attack of Raynaud's in 6 weeks in my hands at all. My feet have still been affected but not until I have been exposed to the cold for half an hour or so. Even then they go numb but don't go white and I certainly don't get that exploding feeling when they begin to come back to life so I'm wondering if I have a simple circulation problem with my feet that are exacerbated by Raynaud's. I am really, really pleased. My body core is so much warmer. It's as if my thermostat has been turned up. I don't get the awful shudders running through my body when temperatures change. I have been told to continue with fluoxetine until the summer and then stop taking it to see if the medication has triggered my body thermostat to act in a more efficient manner. If I go back to the way I was then I shall continue taking it for as long as is possible. I actually went for a walk on the banks of an estuary in January and it was freezing cold with a wicked wind. My hands stayed OK and after an hour my feet became numb - such an improvement. I wouldn't have attempted to do that last year.

I will keep you informed as to whether the drug continues to have the same affect or whether or not my body gets used to it and reverts back to how it used to be. I was interested to see that you had mentioned the trial in your newsletter and thought I would respond with my observations.

Annie Hammerton

I felt I must write and tell you how fluoxetine has changed my life during the winter months. I could not go into my fridge during the winter without wearing thick gloves and gardening was impossible. My NHS consultant has been wonderful and knew about this drug that had been recently tested on a trial at the Royal Free, and he prescribed it for me. I have been taking it now for two months with no side effects. I have had no severe spasms of dead white hands and my swollen ankles are much improved. Although I still keep myself warm with boots and gloves, I feel almost normal and I am simply delighted with it.

Dorothy Caughey

Ten Years on...

Jan Scot

My name is Jan and I have worked part time at the Association for the past ten years. I wasn't looking for a job when I first met Anne but she had other ideas!

I was on the PTA at a local primary school at the time and I had taken on the responsibility of producing a summer programme for the School Fayre. I had sold all the advertising space except one and I needed to finish the programme for the printer, so I decided to give the space free to a Charity. To my dismay the Cancer Research shop was shut and Age Concern weren't answering their phone. Suddenly I remembered that there was another Charity with a funny name at the other end of the village. I knocked on the door and Anne answered. When I explained why I had called, she gratefully accepted the space to advertise a forthcoming Teddy Bears Picnic. Little did I know that this chance meeting was going to change my future!

On chatting she told me that the Association was taking delivery of its first Apple computer in a few weeks, so I offered to come in and help her set it up. I had only just started using a computer myself but I wasn't going to admit that - I hoped that by the time it arrived I would be a bit better! I visited the Office on several occasions, helping

Anne get the computer up and running. I enjoyed every minute but my youngest child had only just started school and I was looking forward to spending some time at home without the children - apparently Anne had other plans!

One day I received a phone call to ask if I could type and would I be interested in working just a few hours a week. How could I say no - especially to Anne!

So now ten years on I am still here - working four days a week. For a little part time job in the village it has been quite an experience. Unfortunately due to family commitments I haven't been able to make the most of all the opportunities that came my way but I have met some incredible people and been totally inspired by sufferers of these devastating conditions. Anne's wicked sense of humour usually ensures that most days we have a laugh and it has been a wonderful ten years. My son is now at university and my daughter at sixteen is becoming more independent every day. As for spending time at home - well Anne says I would be bored anyway!

Jan Scott

A Chairman's Farewell

Alan Golding

The year 2002 sees the celebration of two anniversaries - the birth of the Raynaud's & Scleroderma Association twenty years ago and my birth seventy years ago. I make no comment on the relative importance of these two events.

The story of the creation, (of the Association, I mean), has been told frequently but a good tale cannot be repeated too often. A young woman, Anne Mawdsley, living somewhere in the wilds north of Watford had an operation and awoke from the anaesthetic aware that some of her fingers were white, numb and painful. Eventually, Raynaud's Disease was diagnosed and the doctors, when asked if any treatment or cure existed, knew of nothing that would help. Most people faced with this situation would have taken up bird-watching or knitting - no, knitting could have been difficult with those fingers - and this story would not have been written, but as we all now know, Anne Mawdsley is not 'most people'. Within a few years she had decided to found a support group which would also raise money for research into a serious illness about which so little seemed to be known. By now, I also had been diagnosed with Raynaud's and a friend showed me a newspaper cutting about Anne's efforts. I contacted her and very soon the Association, registered as a charity, was up and running and Anne and I were two of the first trustees.

At this time, Anne was working part-time, devoting only forty or fifty hours a week to the Association's activities, but when she began to get into her stride it was decided that she should be made the Director, and another trustee was appointed. At the beginning, Anne worked from home, and this continued until the increasing piles of books, files, papers and general records on the landing reached such proportions that, if rumour is to be believed, it was only possible for the Mawdsley family to retire to bed by climbing the outside wall of the house and entering through a window! At this stage it seemed reasonable to consider alternative accommodation and the present premises were purchased. Needless to say, Anne raised the money for the purchase.

Very reluctantly, I have now decided that after twenty years it's time I went. I have no wish to become a useless old fogy who dozes through meetings and has to be constantly reminded where he is - although Anne says I've been like that for years - and I am retiring at the 2002 Annual Conference.

Traditionally, this is the stage at which people look back and recall the early days, so why should I be different? Twenty years ago, most people when told they have Raynaud's or scleroderma, knew virtually nothing about their illness, and it is a sad thought that neither did most doctors. At the time, I looked up scleroderma in a 'Be Your Own Family Doctor' book, and the entry read "Scleroderma means 'hard skin'. It can affect both internal and external parts of the body. There is no cure - death will follow". Unfortunately, the first part of the prognosis is still true and the second part always will be. Some time later, the medical correspondent of a national daily newspaper explained scleroderma briefly and added that death usually followed within five years of diagnosis. Little wonder that the Association's first annual conferences were rather depressing affairs. The experts - and there were precious few of them - told us frankly that they knew of no cure and too many members were clearly very ill. I do, though, recall two young doctors - a Dr. Black and a Dr. du Bois - giving us hope, even while explaining graphically the effects of scleroderma on human lungs. (Whatever happened to those two?!).

The fact that recent conferences have been far happier events and that so much of the depression that used to exist has gone, is due to the magnificent research carried out by a relatively small number of doctors. The Association has funded many of their projects and while there is still no cure for either Raynaud's or scleroderma, there is much that can now be done to alleviate symptoms and ensure that the quality of lives of patients is enhanced. Drugs have been discovered that are effective for many, even if not all patients, and conditions can now be anticipated and helped well in advance. The Raynaud's & Scleroderma Association has done a great deal to educate medical practitioners about the illness and members themselves are much more aware of options open to them. The Association has also increased public awareness of the disease by constant articles in the press and radio and television broadcasts.

The Association has now raised more than six million pounds for research and this is due to hard work by many people, but be in no doubt about the contribution of Anne Mawdsley. There are few people with the drive, motivation and sheer cheek that she possesses. Where the interests of the Association are concerned, she believes that paying for anything is a sin and combines this belief with a charm and skill that enables her to obtain as a gift, almost anything the Association needs. Anyone doubting this should enquire when she last paid for computers, carpets, telephones, stationery or heating equipment. Many years ago I was puzzled at not being able to find a record in the accounts of payments to office cleaners and I asked Anne where she had hidden them. It was one of the few times I saw her embarrassed. "We don't have a cleaner', she confessed. "I clean the offices myself - we can't afford to pay a cleaner". It was only when I threatened her with assault and battery that she relented. Since then, I believe that we do have a cleaner but I have my suspicions!

I am lucky to have been closely involved with the Association's activities for the past twenty years and I realise more than most, the debt we owe to three groups of people. Firstly, of course, all those doctors and nurses who encouraged us from the beginning, who were never too busy to talk to our members and help in any way we asked, as well as organising and carrying out the research that has done so much to assist Raynaud's and scleroderma sufferers. Secondly, our members for their tireless work in raising huge amounts of money and for never saying "no" when Anne bullied them into helping in many other ways. And thirdly, Anne and all her colleagues in the office who never knew the meaning of normal office hours, who were invariably warm and courteous to all who telephoned or visited them in trouble, and whose efficiency was impressive. As far as the future is concerned, even if, as I hope, we do one day soon find a cure for Raynaud's and scleroderma, there will still be much work to do. The need for help, advice and information will always be present, and nobody provides that better than the Raynaud's & Scleroderma Association.

Alan J Golding - Chairman of the Trustees

A Nurse's Perspective

Feeling The Freeze

The painful effects of Raynaud's phenomenon can make daily tasks impossible. Caroline Swinburne visits a unit that helps sufferers.

"To begin with, I just felt extremely cold in my hands, feet and ears," says Aileen McGregor, who has suffered from severe Raynaud's phenomenon for more than 20 years. "I would wake at night absolutely freezing, despite having an electric blanket and hot water bottles, as well as extra heating on. And the pain in my hands and feet was excruciating. "These days, I find it's sudden changes of temperature that bring on an attack - I always have to have the heating on full blast, even in summer. Otherwise I can easily be caught out, and find myself gradually getting colder. I think it must be like that for people going into hypothermia, just finding yourself gradually losing concentration".

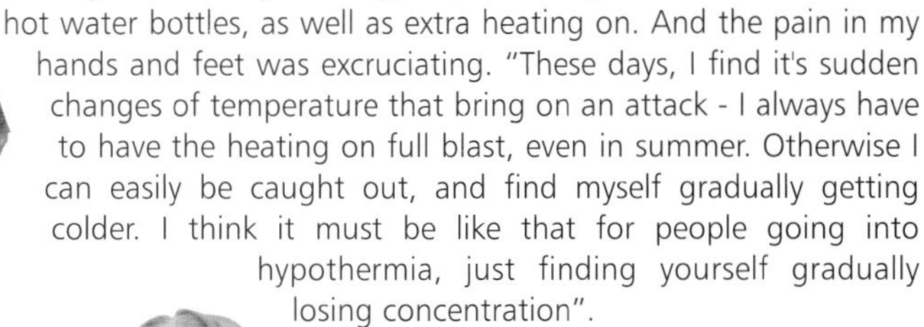

Raynaud's phenomenon affects around one in ten people in the U.K. Ninety per cent of them are female and young women are particularly susceptible. The condition is caused by a fault in the blood vessels, which leads them to constrict. One warning sign is cold hands and feet, which eventually turn white or blue and are extremely

Helen Wilson with Aileen McGregor

painful. At best, the condition is highly inconvenient; at worst, as in Ms McGregor's case, it can dominate life. Daily tasks can be very difficult. And a small but significant percentage of sufferers will develop an even more serious condition scleroderma, meaning literally 'hard skin'. Scleroderma affects about 7,000 people in the UK, again mostly women, and occurs when the body produces too much of the basic structural protein collagen. This is contained in the connective tissue between the skin and internal organs.

In this condition, the tissue becomes fibrous, and the person's body gradually becomes encased in hard and tightening skin. Hands (and even feet) are often so stiff they become clawed. In around 4 in 10 cases the condition spreads over large areas of skin and eventually moves inside the body to cause fibrosis in the lungs, heart, kidneys and gut. Lynn van Varik was diagnosed with scleroderma a year ago. "To begin with I just had swollen hands and things gradually got much worse," she explains. "Now it is in my hands, wrists and feet, and I have sharp pains up my arms. My skin has become really hard and I cannot really move my arms much. I have also put on a lot of weight." Since being diagnosed, Ms van Varik has had to give up her job. "I have always worked in administration", she says. "But with my hands like this, I obviously cannot use a computer and I find it very hard even to write.

Also, I have no energy. I used to be very fit - I was a professional swimmer when I was younger. Now I am extremely breathless and I just feel really ill all the time". Ms van Varik has also had to move house to be near family members who can help with daily tasks. "There is just so much you use your hands for, from personal hygiene to cooking. It is essential for me to have help - I can't do simple tasks like opening things and taking money out of my purse, because I can't turn my wrist. But the worst thing is the pain. I take painkillers when things get too bad".

Genetic link

Her condition was first diagnosed by Professor Carol Black, at London's Royal Free Hospital, where the Rheumatology Department specialises in the treatment of Raynaud's and scleroderma. Professor Black is currently researching the causes of fibrosis, and has long been trying to work out why people like Ms van Varik suddenly become so ill. "We really don't know exactly what causes either condition', says Professor Black. "But we do think that people are probably genetically predisposed to scleroderma, and we think there are lots of genes that might influence its development. We know there are certain chemicals that can actually initiate the disease. Also, the fact that more women are affected, usually in the child-bearing years, suggests hormones play a part. The disease can worsen during pregnancy. But there is a lot we still don't know".

Clinical nurse specialist Helen Wilson, a colleague of Professor Black, runs regular clinics, helping with a wide variety of problems. "Many patients have ulcers that need treatment', she says. "In scleroderma they may have lumps of calcium in the hands or elbows or any other joints that stick out. People also suffer from joint contractures and aches and pains. The internal organs can be affected from the heart to the lungs to the bowels. Many will have clawed hands, so I teach them hand exercises and waxing techniques to help them manage their own condition. There are also techniques for people having problems with swallowing". When Helen is dealing with a Raynaud's patient - and if the condition is mild or the person is young - she encourages them to avoid drugs such as vasodilators. "The problem with vasodilators is they are used to treat high blood pressure," she explains. "Obviously, they have side effects such as nausea and headaches. Many of our patients are young women and they often tend to have low blood pressure anyway. If you lower it even further, they can start to feel dizzy".

Instead, Helen suggests practical measures patients can take to help themselves, such as quit smoking or keep warm. She also tells them about natural therapies. "Vitamins E and C, evening primrose oil, and other things like ginger and ginkgo biloba, have all been found to be useful". However, many sufferers with severe forms of the condition, such as Ms McGregor, end up taking vasodilatory drugs. "By the time I was referred to Professor Black in 1995, my general health had deteriorated very badly - I had virtually no nails", she says. "She immediately suggested that a vasodilator might help. From the first treatment there was a dramatic improvement. My nails started growing again for the first time in 15 years. I have not had any ulcers in my hands since then, and my general health has improved a lot". Another option for patients with severe Raynaud's is sympathectomy. This involves injection with nerve-blocking chemicals, cutting nerves or administering laser treatment. If successful, this can provide relief for some years. But there is as yet no known cure for Raynaud's or scleroderma.

New drug

However, Professor Black is excited by the prospects of a new drug, currently in development, which acts as an antibody to the growth factor TGF beta 1. "TGF beta stimulates fibrosis and we do know that patients with scleroderma are making too much of it', she says. "This is a targeted therapy to try to suppress the growth factor so that the body is not producing so much of the collagen that will cause fibrosis. The drug needs more trials and it is not yet licensed, but eventually it could be one of the best hopes". Drug trials are part of Helen Wilson's highly varied role. "I work as a clinical specialist, offering expertise on specific or rare aspects of the conditions, which patients can't easily access elsewhere', she says. "We do research and I am involved in clinical trials for pharmaceutical companies. I also act as an educator in the outpatient and the inpatient setting and we run a telephone helpline. We also run a children's clinic. Some children get what we call localised scleroderma, which can affect an area of skin and the tissues immediately below, rather than damaging internal organs. This may also take the form of linear scleroderma, which is when just one side of the body is affected. This can cause growth problems which can be quite serious - for instance, a limb that doesn't grow properly. Obviously those children need to be encouraged to exercise and do a lot of physio to increase their growth".

The above article appeared in The Nursing Standard, Vol. 16, No 24, Feb-March 2002.

Towards the Future

RESEARCH NEWS 2002

Royal Free Hospital

Lay summary of current research funded by the Raynaud's & Scleroderma Association

The current research programme at the Royal Free Hospital focuses on laboratory experiments that are aimed at increasing our understanding of the main problems of scleroderma; The inflammatory process, the blood vessel problems and the connective tissue fibrosis.

Our major thrust is in the area of translational research. This, in the broadest terms is using the information gained in the laboratory as a guide to develop and assess treatments for scleroderma. In practice the basic research provides fundamental scientific information on the scleroderma diseases process using a number of model and laboratory systems, many using samples derived from patients themselves. This information is then used to assist in the rational assessment of new targets for therapy and in the development of therapeutic agents.

We are trying to understand how the white blood cells in the body are involved in the early phases of the disease process and how they may be important as culprits in driving the initial changes in the tissues that eventually lead to the fibrosis or scarring. Work in collaboration with Professor Richard Bruckdorfer of the Department of Biochemistry at the Royal Free Hospital, has shown changes in the blood levels of a number of factors that are important in controlling blood vessel size and shape. These studies have suggested potential new avenues of study for Raynaud's Phenomenon and early scleroderma. In particular they have formed the foundation for future studies aimed at examining the role of reactive oxygen species in scleroderma and the use of potential anti-oxidant therapies.

Funding from the Association has also been instrumental in the studies on a new and important factor, found in the blood and in tissues from patients with scleroderma. This factor, called connective tissue growth factor appears to be very important in the connective tissue fibrosis or scarring. Our studies in the laboratory have been to find out what controls the amount of this factor in tissues and how the cells in the skin and other organs respond to CTGF in a way that makes them produce more connective tissue. These studies have been ongoing for just over two years, and we are making good progress in identifying the proteins on the cell that interacts with this growth factor.

It is true to say that research supported by the Association is at the forefront of this exciting and productive area of research. Moreover, studies from the Royal Free have been pivotal in the organisation of a clinical protocol using an agent that inhibits the effects of CTGF. This study of anti-CTGF therapy in scleroderma is at present in the planning stages for a clinical trial (phase I/II study) and will hopefully reach the clinical stage over the next year or so, initially in the US and eventually in the United Kingdom.

Extremely exciting studies are also about to begin in collaboration with Professor Ron du Bois at the Brompton Hospital. These studies are aimed at examining the genes that are involved in and possibly control the progression and extent of scleroderma. Experiments are planned over a period of time, that will allow us to carry out an extensive and unparalleled analysis of almost all the genes that are in the human body to see if there are any striking differences between people who have scleroderma and those that do not. These ongoing and future basic science studies are very important to our increased understanding of scleroderma and to the collaborative efforts between scientist and clinical colleagues, that will lead to better ways to assess, manage and treat scleroderma.

Professor Carol Black & Dr. David Abraham
Department of Rheumatology

Congratulations

We were delighted to hear the news that as from August 2002 Professor Carol Black has been elected President of the Royal College of Physicians. She has been vice president for the past three years and we send our heartiest congratulations to her on this most prestigious appointment.

Hypoxia and Oxidative Stress in Scleroderma Fibroblast Activation:

Vivienne R Winrow

Investigation of a Role for Xanthine Oxidase

In recent years, our group at the University of Bath has made some interesting discoveries that are changing the way we envisage certain disease mechanisms. Scleroderma or systemic sclerosis and its associated spectrum of diseases, characterised by thickening and hardening of the skin (overproduction and deposition of collagen), provide excellent examples.

Briefly, we have been investigating a well-known human enzyme called xanthine oxidoreductase (XOR). In health, this enzyme is involved in the metabolism of certain nucleic acids (the building blocks of DNA) but also has a more general role in generating reactive molecules capable of signalling to cells and, in excess, of causing cellular damage. We have discovered that, in low oxygen environments, this latter ability is enhanced. The skin in patients with scleroderma provides such an environment since low levels of oxygen are found there: It is often the case that scleroderma follows episodes of ischaemia or poor blood supply associated with Raynaud's phenomenon (numbness and whitening of the fingers). The cell responsible for keeping the skin healthy is the fibroblast and we propose that a low oxygen environment alters the normal functioning of this cell, stimulating the overproduction of collagen through factors released by XOR.

Firstly, we looked to see whether XOR was present in skin biopsies from patients with scleroderma. Using an antibody to the enzyme, we detected increased amounts of XOR in both lesional and non-lesional skin, when compared to normal healthy skin. One of the factors released by XOR is the molecule nitric oxide (NO). This species can be identified by its ability to damage proteins. Again, we looked at sections of skin from patients with scleroderma and found evidence of NO damage, which co-localised with XOR expression. This provided good evidence that NO was being released from XOR in situ.

Next, we turned our attention to the effects of hypoxia (low oxygen). Skin biopsies taken from patients with scleroderma and healthy controls were placed in culture to allow outgrowth of fibroblasts. The cells were then transferred to small flasks and allowed to multiply until they just covered the area of the flask (confluent). The flasks were then placed in a low oxygen environment (1% oxygen) or in anoxia (0% oxygen) and removed at various time intervals from 30 minutes to 24 hours. Cells were examined under the microscope for shape changes and then processed for protein or gene expression. The results showed, that in healthy skin fibroblasts, basal levels of XOR were undetectable but hypoxia was a good inducer of XOR and also induced collagen degrading enzymes. Fibroblasts from patients with scleroderma expressed high basal levels of XOR and these were not increased further following incubation in a hypoxic environment. This suggests that XOR is maximally activated in scleroderma fibroblasts.

In conclusion, we have good evidence that the enzyme XOR plays a role in the progression of systemic sclerosis. The mechanism is not fully elucidated but, by mimicking conditions in the scleroderma lesion, our results suggest that a low oxygen environment is the trigger for XOR activation in skin fibroblasts, leading to the overproduction and deposition of collagen.

Vivienne R Winrow, Cliff R Stevens, *Carol M Black & David R Blake
Department of Medical Sciences, University of Bath, BA2 7AY &
***The Royal Free Hospital School of Medicine, London NW3 2PF**

Studies of calcinosis in Systemic Sclerosis

The Raynaud's & Scleroderma Association has kindly funded a two year project grant to enable clinicians and scientists at the University of Manchester to undertake studies of scleroderma-related calcinosis. Many patients with scleroderma develop calcium containing lumps in and beneath the skin. These calcinotic lumps can be very painful and unpleasant, and currently there is no effective treatment. To date there has been relatively little research into calcinosis, yet this is badly needed so that we can understand the underlying disease process and develop effective treatment strategies.

We believe that calcinosis results from alterations in the biology of the skin and of what are termed the subcutaneous tissues (the tissues underneath the skin). Our hypothesis is that abnormalities in the small blood vessels lead to poor blood flow, this in turn leads to a lack of oxygen which 'drives' the calcinosis. We have recently begun a series of studies examining patients with and without calcinosis, as follows:

1. Blood flow studies

We are studying the very small blood vessels (called capillaries) in skin and skin blood flow, using the techniques of nailfold microscopy, laser Doppler imaging, and thermography, all of which are available at Hope Hospital. We hypothesise that the small blood vessels may be more abnormal in patients with calcinosis than in those without. These studies have only recently begun - in May 2002 - but already a number of patients with scleroderma attending Hope Hospital have agreed to take part.

2. Microscopic examination of skin tissue

In order to further investigate scleroderma-associated changes in the small blood vessels of the skin, we are examining small samples of skin taken from the forearm of patients with various degrees of severity of scleroderma, both with and without calcinosis. To enable us to track changes in the microvessels (small blood vessels), markers (antibodies) are employed that recognise specific components of the tissue. To date, 60 skin samples have been cut into thin slices, and currently, four markers that target growth factors thought to be important in skin maintenance, are being applied to the slices using a special staining procedure. At the end of the process the markers are dyed so that their pattern of distribution in the tissue can be assessed under the microscope. Any changes in the occurrence of the markers will then be evaluated with respect to the progression of the disease.

Our studies should be complete towards the end of 2002.

Investigators: Dr. A Herrick, Professor AJ Freemont,
Dr. M Jeziorska, Dr. JA Hoyland,
University of Manchester

Non-invasive determination of macrophage behaviour in scleroderma patients at risk of fibrosing alveolitis

Introduction

Oxygen reaches the blood through the lungs when we breathe. The oxygen in the air crosses through very thin membranes deep in the lungs into the blood, which then carries it round our body to where it is needed. If this membrane becomes thickened, the oxygen cannot cross into the blood as easily. There are many cells present in our lungs, which maintain a normal healthy structure and protect us from particles that we inhale including microbes that cause infection. Following most lung insults such as infection the beneficial action of these cells means that we suffer no permanent damage. Unfortunately in some people this process does not work perfectly and can result in permanently thickened membranes due to scarring (fibrosis) of the lungs and the lungs can no longer transfer oxygen effectively. Some patients suffering from scleroderma produce an antibody which makes them particularly susceptible to developing lung scarring which can cause devastating loss of lung function, with increasing breathlessness, resulting in loss of time from work and even premature death. We do not yet understand how these diseases are controlled and it is difficult to measure the lung inflammation that is happening during the patient's life as the disease activity is deep in the lung.

Macrophages are cells that are crucial to the lungs defences but are believed to be of major importance in the development of fibrosing alveolitis secondary to systemic sclerosis (FASSc) and are present in large numbers in the lungs of patients with FASSc. There are several ways by which these cells can be assessed. Firstly, we can measure the presence and behaviour of these cells deep within the lung while the patient lies in a special scanner. We inject a radioactive tracer, which binds to macrophages in the lungs. We then scan the patient and obtain images, which show us the location and number of these cells in the chest. The behaviour of macrophages in patients with a predisposition to lung fibrosis is being compared with that in normal volunteers. This technique gives us an opportunity of determining the behaviour of these key cells at the site of the disease, with very little discomfort for the patient. We will be able to see which treatments are having the greatest effect on macrophage behaviour and whether this improves the condition of the patients.

These macrophages may also be assessed by sampling them using bronchoscopy (a procedure where a camera is passed down the breathing tubes into the lungs and washings of the lungs taken) or lung biopsy but these are relatively invasive tests and therefore cannot really be repeated at frequent intervals. We have therefore been looking for a new way to find out what mischief these cells are up to in FASSc with a test that has minimal discomfort for the patient but that allows us to obtain cells from the lungs. There are several phases of our research.

Phase 1

The first phase of investigation is now fully completed. We have looked at lung washings of a series of patients with FASSc to assess which of the harmful chemical agents that macrophages produce are detectable in our group of patients. These results proved to be very interesting and showed a clear relationship between the levels of one of these chemical agents (called MCP-1) and the extent of fibrosing alveolitis seen on the CT scan.

Phase 2

Macrophages can be tagged with a substance called PK11195 that allows them to be monitored within the lungs by a machine called a PET scanner (positron emission tomography). We have previously shown that the PET scans in patients with FASSc are very different to those in people with healthy lungs. These early studies gave very interesting results, which suggested that the macrophages in FASSc are quite different to those in normal healthy lungs but they did not tell us why they were different. We are therefore scanning a larger number of patients with FASSc than in the pilot study but this time we are following the PET scan with a sputum test. The macrophages in this sputum will be analysed to see how much of the PK11195 is tagging on to them – we suspect that it is abnormal and that this is why the initial scans were abnormal. We have recruited all the patients for the PET scans, and are nearing completion of this phase of the study. These PET scans will be completed in June 2002 and will be analysed within 2-3 months after completion of the scans. The detailed analysis of the sputum work will take a little longer to complete, as part of the sample will be analysed in conjunction with phase 3 of the research.

Phase 3

We are examining the usefulness, in FASSc, of a test called sputum induction, which involves breathing a misty salt solution that stimulates people to cough up sputum. This sputum is then tested in the same way as lung washings and the results of the 2 tests are being compared. We are interested in the macrophages, as we know there are different subtypes of macrophages in the body. We are aiming to find out if any particular subtype of macrophage is different in FASSc compared to normal. We will also be analysing the chemicals produced by the macrophages to see if they differ between FASSc patients and people with normal healthy lungs.

We hope to show that similar information can be derived from both investigations. Whether this will mean that less people need to have bronchoscopies remains to be seen.

Conclusion

We have finished phase 1 of the research and this has been presented and published in the USA. The most critical part of our studies (PET scanning) is nearing completion and we are about to start the final phase of this research project. We anticipate that the project will be fully completed by March/April 2003.

Howard Branley,
Hazel Jones,
Ron du Bois
Brompton Hospital

What is Raynaud's?

The following has been taken from the text of a new G.P. booklet currently being written for the Association by Professor Carol Black.

Raynaud's phenomenon is a common, episodic circulatory disorder. Raynaud's is most usually found in females. It affects between 3-20% of the adult population worldwide and there may be as many as ten million sufferers in the U.K. It is different from chilblains, acrocyanosis or permanently cold, blue or white hands. The algorithm below may be useful in reaching an accurate diagnosis.

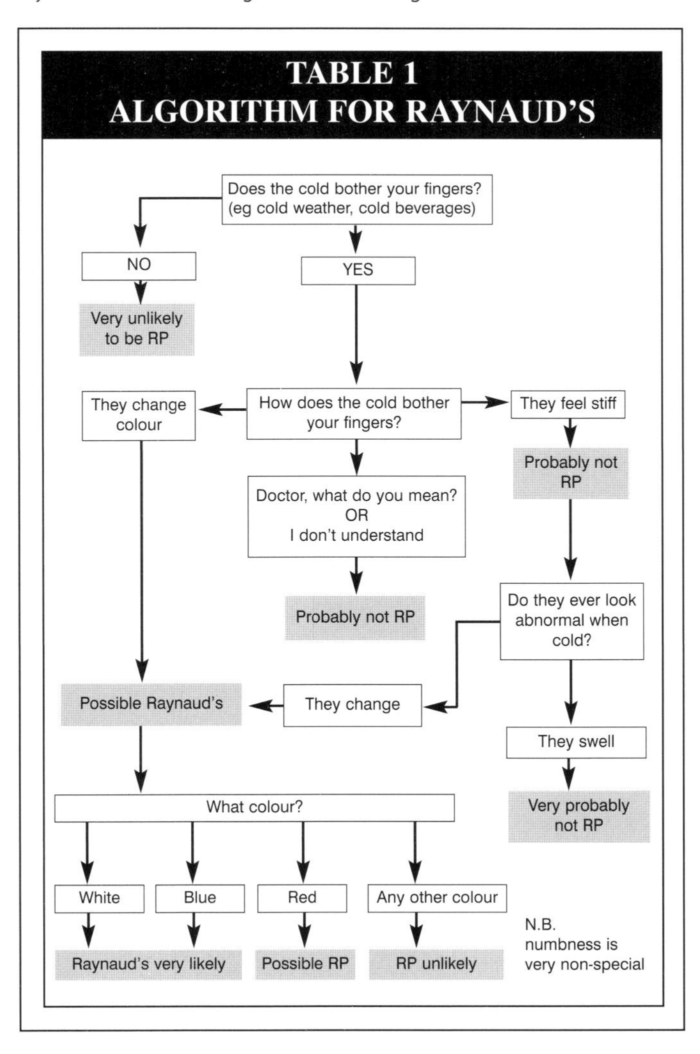

The hallmark of Raynaud's is a biphasic or triphasic colour change of the extremities. The digits turn white, and/or blue and red. This happens on exposure to the cold, or to sudden but slight temperature changes, or stress. The extremities mostly affected are the fingers and toes, whilst the ears and nose may also be affected. The patient may also complain of pain, numbness or tingling. It can affect children, adolescents and adults.

It is generally a benign, primary condition, patients needing advice only on ways of maintaining a constant body temperature. Primary Raynaud's usually begins in the teens and early 20s and represents an exaggerated response to cold and other stimuli. However, the condition may also be severe and indicative of an underlying disorder. The development of RP at an older age (30+), in males or associated with other symptoms and signs, suggests that it is secondary to another condition.

Secondary Raynaud's, although less common, is being increasingly recognised and the list of associated conditions continues to expand. Because many of these associations are serious, a careful history and examination should be taken on each patient and a referral made to a specialist centre if necessary.

Prompt recognition and treatment of underlying problems can do much to modify the condition and improve the quality of life for sufferers who, in very severe cases may have persistent ulcers, infection and ultimately gangrene, with the possibility of amputation.

British Rally Co-Driver Supports Raynaud's

Member, Claire Mole tells us how she became involved in Rallying and how Raynaud's has been a problem to her.

Claire has suffered from Raynaud''s since her early teens but she has not allowed it to stop her from pursuing her passion for Co-Driving. In 2000, together with her Swedish Driver Mats Andersson, Claire secured the British Ferodo Super 1600 Rally Championship crown and gave Proton second place overall in the Manufacturers championship. The partnership of Mats and Claire is well respected within the rallying world.

"My family have always followed rallying and family holidays were often spent trudging through forests watching rallies. When I was old enough to drive myself I took more interest in motorsport and became a Co-Driver. I have had a lot of lucky breaks in the sport and have never looked back. Having Raynaud's has had its draw backs. I have to plan carefully for each event especially when competing in cold climates. Turning down the chance to compete on the Arctic Rally has probably been the biggest disappointment brought about by having Raynaud''s. Competing in minus 40° would not be possible.

Claire Mole

Knowing how Raynaud's can affect many of our members, I want to do as much as I can to raise awareness and raise funds for research.

Claire Mole

Greetings from Northern Ireland

Dr. Aubrey Bell FRCP & Heather Semple receive a cheque from Violet Bloomer raised by the Social Evening and Mini Auction, which she and her family organised in gratitude for the care she received from Dr. Bell and his rheumatology team.

I have been urged by Anne to write about what we do over here in our group so here are some thoughts. Back some nine years ago two Raynaud's and Scleroderma patients met in a rheumatology ward and the thrill of finding someone else who had similar problems and didn't make one feel a complete oddity was wonderful. By word of mouth, letters to our main Rheumatology hospitals, a radio announce-ment, encouragement from our nurse specialist at the Out Patient Clinic and names of Northern Ireland members sent to us by the U.K. Association, we got the nucleus of a group to meet and about 15 more to join making 25 in all.

In 8 years we have doubled our membership and meet seven times a year. Most meetings include a speaker, podiatrist, physio, pharmacist, physiotherapist, demonstration of armchair exercise, reflexology, camouflage make up, etc. Meeting together and friendship during the welcome 'cuppa' is very important. Every member gets a synopsis/report of meetings and notice of the next meeting in the form of a mini poster for public display. We try to get invitations to conferences of health professionals where we can have an information stand. Through these we have added to our mailing lists. We have looked at complimentary medicines, food supplements, magnetic bracelets, organic wheat bags and aromatherapy.

By good fortune one of our first members was a fashion model who offered to run a fashion show to raise funds and also to create awareness. Each year in varying venues, our chairman Patience, has generously committed herself to holding a fashion event. She has a wonderful team of models, some related to members, usually one or two with physical disabilities. These are shows with a difference - they run like clockwork, no panics for her committee and now she raises funds through fashion shows for other organisations, where we have a stall or raffle. Many individuals have held events to help funds and awareness such as sponsored runs, flag days, social events and a mini auction. A sales and information trolley is permitted in the main rheumatology in-patient ward in Belfast. For the last two years we have been represented on the BLAR (British League Against Rheumatism) group in Northern Ireland and this has given contact between the rheumatological support groups and where patient problems can be raised.

I must pay a very warm tribute to Anne and her team in Alsager for all their help and friendship. I look forward to meeting my friends on the mainland every year and the many friends this work has blessed me with. I would encourage any patient to urgently make contact with at least one or two more people, as the old maxim says "a problem shared is a problem halved.

Heather Semple

David and Anne guiding the tree into position.

Ice Age Tree Planted at the Royal Botanic Gardens at Kew

On 28th February 2002, Anne Mawdsley and David Wilkie together with local MP Jenny Tonge, assisted with the planting of the tallest tree to be planted at Kew Gardens in the last 50 years. A 20-year-old, 30-foot Ginkgo biloba tree travelled over 600 miles from Hamburg to be planted at Kew Gardens to mark the Raynaud's & Scleroderma Association's 20th Anniversary.

Tony Kirkham, Head of the Arboretum and Horticultural Services at Kew, spent weeks researching the very best quality ginkgo tree and eventually tracked it down to a nursery in Hamburg. The tree weighed 2.5 tons, so it was a very challenging planting for Kew, because a 60 ton crane was needed to position the tree in a hole big enough to park a 4x4. Earth anchors stabilized the tree in the difficult location - a totally enclosed courtyard in the White Peaks area - and the real challenge was positioning the tree without damage. This new arrival joins the UK's oldest ginkgo tree, which was planted at Kew Gardens in 1761.

Health Perception Ltd, very kindly sponsored this planting, in partnership with Kew Gardens. We hope that by planting this tree, we will be able to bring the work of our charity to ever more prominent attention. A plaque giving details of the ginkgo tree together with our Association's name is by the tree.

We were delighted to be joined at this planting by Patron Roger Jefcoate, Trustee Alan Golding, Swedish Proton Motor Sport driver Mats Andersson and British co-driver Claire Mole and several members of the Association.

Later this year we have been invited by HRH Prince Charles to plant a ginkgo tree at Highgrove House.

From left to right, Roger Jefcoate, Nina Ingold, David Wilkie, Jean Cameron-Day (front centre). Anne Mawdsley, Alan Golding & Joyce Patterson, who joined us at Kew for the tree planting.

Six Million Pounds raised 1982-2002!

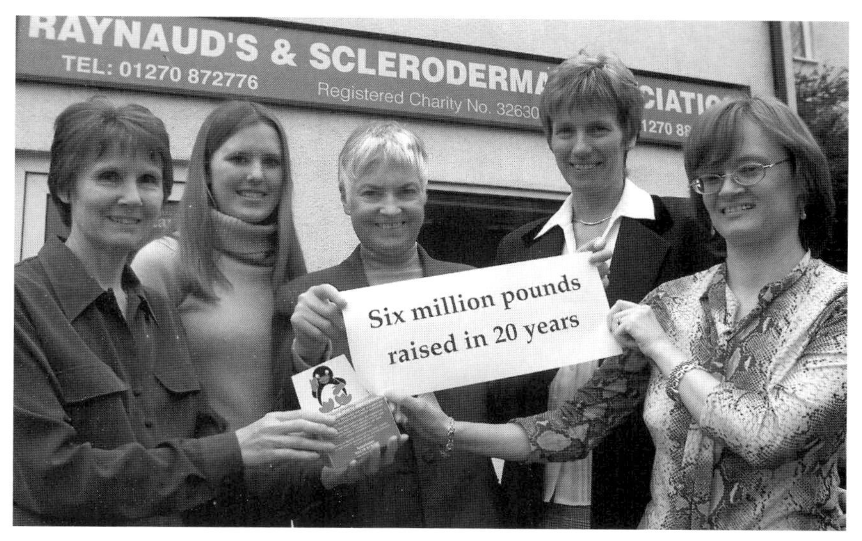

In our 20th Anniversary year we are delighted to announce that since 1982, we have raised a total of 6 million pounds for research and welfare projects. Photo of staff at Head Office in Alsager by courtesy of Chronicle Newspapers. From left to right: Pat Poulson, Fiona Trotter, Anne Mawdsley, Jan Scott and Karen Littley.

This is not the end of the story but more a new beginning. There are still many goals to be reached and many mysteries to be solved. However, with the development of new drugs, new ideas and extensive medical interest worldwide, there is every indication that this journey of discovery will lead to a better future for people with Raynaud's and scleroderma.

I would like to say a very big thank you to everyone who has supported the Association.

Anne H Mawdsley MBE

20th Anniversary Floral Display

This floral display was created by Congleton Borough Council Parks Department to commemorate the 20th Anniversary of the Raynaud's & Scleroderma Association.

For further information about the work of the Association contact:

Raynaud's & Scleroderma Association

112 Crewe Road, Alsager, Cheshire ST7 2JA

Telephone: 01270 872776

Email: webmaster@raynauds.demon.co.uk

Website: http://www.raynauds.demon.co.uk

If you would like to make a donation towards funding research into Raynaud's and scleroderma, please make cheques payable to: 'Raynaud's & Scleroderma Association' and send to the address above.

All donations are warmly welcomed

Registered Charity No. 326306